James L. Throne

THERMO FORMING

James L. Throne

THERMO FORMING

With 148 Figures and 110 Tables

Hanser Publishers, Munich Vienna New York

Distributed in the United States of America by
Macmillan Publishing Company, Inc., New York
and in Canada by
Collier Macmillan Canada, Ldt., Toronto

Distributed in USA by
Scientific and Technical Books
Macmillan Publishing Company, Inc.
866 Third Avenue, New York, N.Y. 10022

Distributed in Canada by
Collier Macmillan Canada Distribution Center,
539 Collier Macmillan Drive, Cambridge, Ontario

Distributed in all other countries by
Carl Hanser Verlag
Kolbergerstr. 22
D-8000 München 80

The use of general descriptive names, trademarks, etc, in this publication, even if the former are not especially identified, is not to be taken as a sign that such names, as understood by the Trade Marks and Merchandise Marks Act, may accordingly be used freely by anyone.

While the advice and information in this book are believed to be true and accurate at the date of going to press, neither the authors nor the editors nor the publisher can accept any legal responsibility for any errors or omissions that may be made. The publisher makes no warranty, express or implied, with respect to the material contained herein.

CIP-Kurztitelaufnahme der Deutschen Bibliothek

Throne, James L.: Thermoforming/James L. Throne. – Munich;
Vienna; New York:
Hanser; New York:
Macmillan, 1986.
  ISBN 3-446-14699-7 (Hanser)
  ISBN 0-02-947610-0 (Macmillan)

ISBN 3-446-14699-7 Carl Hanser Verlag München Wien
ISBN 0-02-947610-0 Macmillan Publishing Company, Inc., New York
Library of Congress Catalog Card Number 86-062090

Printed in Germany by Druckerei Appl, Wemding

Foreword

The Society of Plastics Engineers (SPE) is particularly pleased to sponsor this new technical volume entitled "Thermoforming." The book fills a void in the literature providing one of the first, if not the first, technical exposition concerning a method of plastics processing which has grown at a rate far faster than the plastics industry itself. Its contents will be of extreme interest to the knowledgeable engineer as well as to the individual seeking a deeper understanding of the process.

The expertise of the volume's author, Dr. James L. Throne, is well recognized within SPE. As one of the very few SPE Fellows, he has been a technical leader within the Society for many years. His contributions include roles as Technical Program Chairman for the 1983 Annual Technical Conference, former Chairman of the Technical Volumes Committee and most recently a member of the prestigious New Technology Committee. It was his fundamental technical competence that qualified him for selection in all three instances.

SPE, through its Technical Volumes Committee, has long sponsored books on various aspects of plastics and polymers. Its involvement has ranged from identification of needed volumes to recruitment of authors. An ever-present ingredient has been review of the final manuscript to insure accuracy of the technical content.

This technical competence pervades all SPE activities, not only in publication of books but also in other areas such as technical conferences and educational programs. In addition, the Society publishes five periodicals - *Plastics Engineering, Polymer Engineering and Science, Polymer Processing and Rheology, Journal of Vinyl Technology* and *Polymer Composites* - as well as conference proceedings and other selected publications, all of which are subject to similar rigorous technical review procedures.

The resource of some 25,000 practicing plastics engineers has made SPE the largest organization of its type in plastics worldwide. Further information is available from the Society at 14 Fairfield Drive, Brookfield Center, Connecticut 06805, U.S.A.

Robert D. Forger
Executive Director
Society of Plastics Engineers

Technical Volumes Committee
Thomas W. Haas, Chairman
Virginia Commonwealth University

Preface

Thermoforming is one of the oldest methods of processing plastic materials. It begins with a sheet of material. The sheet is somehow softened, stretched against a solid form and allowed to stiffen. The desired object is then trimmed from the shaped sheet. Thermoforming is one of the gentlest ways of processing plastics. It is a major element in the packaging industry and is used extensively to make design prototypes of products to be produced by other processes.

The thermoforming industry has prospered despite two major shortcomings. Most other thermoplastic processes such as extrusion, blow molding and injection molding, begin with plastic resin in powder or pellet form. Thermoforming begins with extruded plastic sheet. Thermoforming must therefore bear the cost of this *additional* processing step and the attendant loss in material physical properties. In addition, only a portion of the sheet is used to form the desired product. The rest of the sheet positions the forming portion in the mold and must be trimmed away. Economics dictate that this trim, also called web or edge trim, must be recovered, reground and *recycled* into sheet. Again, the process must bear the cost of this additional processing step and further deterioration in material physical properties.

These handicaps have been largely overcome by strict control of sheet quality and by ingenious mold design to minimize the amount of recycled material. Since economics so strongly influence process choice, a major portion of the chapter on economics is devoted to consideration of these limitations. The effect of reprocessing on physical properties is considered in the chapter on polymer material properties.

Thermoforming remains a relatively minor plastic process. The current engineering information about the thermoforming process is quite uneven. Substantial technical information is available on heating and stretching, but very little on mold and part design, for example. Certain aspects of the process have strongly developed artisan know-how with little substantial engineering support.

Source books on thermoforming are few. Höger's 1971 monograph, *Warmformen von Kunststoffen*, Hanser, was never translated into English and is now dated. It was the inspiration for this book, however. Bruins' 1971 edited book, *Basic Principles of Thermoforming*, Gordon and Breach, is an uneven collection of papers, many of which are quite descriptive. Other information is scattered in company pamphlets, encyclopedias, student theses, textbooks, symposia, and isolated technical papers.

This book represents a cohesive approach to thermoforming. The process can be rather neatly divided into several separate but connected sections. Each section can be analyzed in depth without major concern of process variable interaction. When the sheet is being heated it is not being stretched, and when it is being stretched it is not (necessarily) being cooled. And so on.

The book has eight chapters. It is neither a textbook nor an encyclopedia. It is a monograph or overview of thermoforming today.

> Chapter 1, "What is Thermoforming?", reviews the basic building blocks of thermoforming and introduces some of the terminology used throughout the book. It includes a brief history, the nature of the US markets served, and the nature of the process machinery. The appendix contains a list of abbreviations for the plastics discussed throughout the book.

> Chapter 2, "Polymer Materials", focusses on the chemical and mechanical nature of typical plastics that are formed from sheet into parts. As noted, it also includes

information on material physical property loss upon recycle. The chapter draws heavily on the material the author used in his section in M. Bakker, Ed., *Encyclopedia of Packaging Technology*, John Wiley, 1986.

Chapter 3, "Heating the Sheet", reviews the three basic ways of heating sheet – conduction, convection and radiation. Since infrared radiation is the most popular and efficient means of heating sheet, fundamental aspects are discussed. The interaction between the sheet and the heating source is detailed. The chapter includes a discussion of why certain heating methods should be used on certain applications and with certain plastics. Material in this chapter is at times quite technical.

Chapter 4, "Stretching the Sheet", is concerned with fundamentals of biaxial deformation. The nature of a plastic sheet under load can be considered as a rubbery solid, a highly viscous liquid, or something in between. Local part wall thickness can depend upon the way in which a plastic stretches under load. The material in this chapter is quite technical as well but provides a fundamental understanding for the rules of part design (Chapter 7).

Chapter 5, "Cooling and Trimming the Sheet", considers the interaction between the stretched sheet and the cool mold (and ancillary cooling sources). The roles of free surface cooling and heat removal from the mold are considered. Trimming is considered in terms of the nature of the forces needed to cleanly separate a finished part from its trim. This section includes milling and drilling guidelines as well.

Chapter 6, "Mold Materials", considers mold construction materials and techniques. Since so many materials can be used as molds in thermoforming, the differences in mold longevity and maintenance and repairability are important. Venting guidelines are also given.

Chapter 7, "Part Design", begins with a clear set of definitions on draw ratio. Then wall thickness calculations are given, beginning with simple geometries and ending with the newest techniques being developed to calculate local thickness values for the most complex formed shapes.

Chapter 8, "The Economics of Thermoforming", focusses on production costs for both rollfed and cut sheet operations. It also includes some guidelines and standards for incoming product quality control. Economics always include costs for extrusion and recycling.

Practical examples are used throughout to illustrate specific concepts. Most terms used in these examples have two sets of units – European metric and US customary [in brackets]. As with most engineering disciplines, pure units are impractical in many cases and mixed units are common. For example, resin density is given in (g/cm^3), even in US units. Radiant heater watt density is frequently given in (W/in^2) or (W/cm^2). Neither of these are "pure". The multiplier "M" is "10^6" in engineering terms but "10^3" in weights, number of units and monetary terms. The equations are unnumbered since they are always cited in context. A conversion table for traditional terms is given as Appendix A. A list of symbols and the first location of each in the text is given as Appendix B. Author and Subject indices are also supplied.

Certain caveats are necessary. The text material focusses on today's state-of-the-art on the primary processing schemes. Thus, engineers seeking the latest information on pressure forming, the heating of foam sheet or forming crystallizing PET will be disappointed. Tradition has separated rollfed, thin-gage formers from cut sheet, heavy-gage formers. It appears that this division is due in part to a common lack of understanding of the general interaction of the sheet with its process environs. Both processing types begin with sheet, heat it until it is rubbery, draw it against a solid cool form, hold it until set and trim away the final part. In the main therefore the book does not distinguish between these two groups of thermoformers.

Some of the gathered materials are guidelines and processing rules-of-thumb. These are usually presented without relating them to underlying causes or reasons. These will help the technician trying to debug his system. They will not substantially aid those trying to solve fundamental engineering problems. There are no apologies for this.

Some of the material is quite technical. In particular, in the last part of Chapter 3, sheet heating is approached from the fundamental understanding of radiant energy interchange. Sheet stretching is biaxial extension, akin to laboratory methods used to understand fundamental properties of polymeric materials. The material in the last part of Chapter 4, therefore, is fundamental and can be quite difficult to assimilate. The casual reader can skim the material without losing orientation.

The chapters have been designed to progress from the simplest concepts to detailed descriptions of fundamental principles when available. Parts designers will focus on the contents of Chapter 7, process engineers on Chapter 3 to 5, mold designers on Chapter 6, plant managers on Chapters 1 and 8 and so on. But all chapters are directly relevant and so the reader should at least review all material for general content.

Thermoforming is not an easy process. It just looks easy. In fact it is becoming technically challenging as newer process variations, newer materials, tighter sheet and part tolerances, more critical applications and more sophisticated controls are developed. The material in this book is not easy. But it is necessary to the long-range development of the process. The book breaks no new ground. It develops no new process or product. It reveals no new markets. It presents no new ideas on profitability. It is hoped that this book puts in one place the information that will be needed to intelligently develop the tools for thermoforming of tomorrow.

Dr. Richard C. Progelhof, Professor, New Jersey Institute of Technology, Newark NJ, critically reviewed all chapters and made invaluable suggestions on the reorganization and introduction of material in Chapter 3 and 4. Marilyn Bakker, Editor, *Encyclopedia of Packaging Technology*, provided the author with an extensive review and an early editing copy of his chapter in the encyclopedia. Those materials form the basis for Chapter 2. Many of the suggestions of John Grundy, President, Profile Plastics, Northbrook IL to improve the readability of Chapter 7 have been incorporated. The reviewer made several excellent recommendations on ways to improve material presentation, particularly in Chapters 3 and 4. Dr. H. R. Osmers, a fellow PhD Chemical Engineer-teacher-consultant, reviewed the materials with his characteristic sharp-pencil thoroughness, pointing out several technical weaknesses and fuzzy areas. Hopefully, the author has made all the necessary corrections and additions. Fred Pollak, Custom Automated Machinery, Elgin IL, reviewed Chapter 1 materials and answered many questions on machine design. William McConnell, Consultant, Arlington TX, provided many insights and encouragements and made available valuable written materials on thermoforming. Glenn Beall, President, Glenn Beall/Engineering, Gurnee IL, provided an early draft copy of his monograph on pressure forming. Dr. Dean Harper, University of Louisville kindly made available student theses on finite element analysis for thermoforming.

This effort could not have been completed without the moral and financial support of my wife, Jean. The book is dedicated to the memory of my parents.

James L. Throne, PhD   November 1985

TABLE OF CONTENTS

Chapter 6   MOLD DESIGN

Chapter 7   PART DESIGN

Chapter 8   THE ECONOMICS OF THERMOFORMING

1 WHAT IS THERMOFORMING?

Introduction

Thermoforming is a generic term encompassing many techniques for producing useful plastic articles from flat sheet. In its simplest concept, thermoforming is simply the manual draping of a temporarily softened sheet over a simple mold shape. Its most advanced form can involve automatic high-speed, indexing of a sheet of very accurately known temperature into a pneumatically actuated forming and in-situ trimming station, with integral web regrind and automatic parts counting, packaging and shipping.

Thermoforming is one of a family of processes that deal with the pressing or squeezing of pliable plastic into final shape. A century ago, celluloid (camphor-solvated cellulose nitrate) was the only maleable synthetic plastic (1). It was cut or rolled into sheet and was then made pliable with steam. When soft it could be squeezed into shape in matched dies or rolled into tubes and inflated against metal walls to produce hollow parts. It could also be draped over wooden forms. Thus, the earliest processing of synthetic plastics, restricted to one material and limited processing conditions, included common types of modern thermoforming.

Thermoforming always begins with a contiguous sheet of rubbery plastic. This sheet has been processed from resin pellets or powder by casting (PMMA), calendering (PVC), rolling (PE, PP), extruding (ABS), compression molding (CA), or similar plastics processing techniques*. Thermoforming is differentiated from injection or extrusion blow molding or the Hayssen Monoblow process (2). In these processes the initial resin state is fluid rather than solid. Compression molding begins with discrete plastic pieces (powder or pellets) and so is also not a variant of thermoforming. Nontraditional thermoforming processes include the Dow Scrapless Thermoforming Process (STP) where the extruded sheet is cut into squares that are heated and forged into shapes (3) and the Allied process where glass-reinforced PA-6 (nylon 6) sheet is heated to temperatures above the nylon melt temperature, then forged at relatively high pressures (0.1 to 1 MPa [150 to 1500 psi]) (4). Other nontraditional processes are discussed at the end of the chapter.

History

Keratin, as a component in tortoiseshell, was probably the first material to be thermoformed (1, 5). Keratin, also found in animal horn and hoof, can be softened by immersing it in boiling oil or water. The sheet is then manually draped over a form and held until cool. Natural cellulose, primary element in treebark, was shaped in a similar fashion by Native Americans.

Although others experimented with natural and extracted cellulosics in the 1800's, J. W. Hyatt is credited with first recognizing the full *commercial potential* of camphor-solvated cellulose nitrate, which he called celluloid. Most nineteenth century synthetic plastic products were produced of celluloid (or products of similar recipe) simply by drape forming. Sharps

---

* Throughout the text, plastics are referred to in abbreviations. Thus PMMA = poly(methyl) methacrylate, and so on. A list of the common abbreviations is given as Appendix 1.I to this chapter.]

piano keys, formed over captive wooden blocks, are an example. A chronology of the early days in plastics as they pertain to thermoforming is given in Table 1.1.

TABLE 1.1 CHRONOLOGY ON THERMOFORMING (Adapted from (1, 5))

Period	Event
Prehistory (Egypt)	Heating Tortoise Shell (Keratin) in Hot Oil, Then Shaping (Food Containers)
Prehistory (Micronesia)	Heating Tortoise Shell (Keratin) in Hot Water, Then Shaping (Bowls)
Prehistory (Americas)	Heating Treebark (natural cellulose) in Hot Water, Then Shaping (Bowls, Boats)
1845	Extrusion Process Commericalized for Plastics
1850's	Gutta-Percha Replaces Ivory for Billiard Balls
1856	First Moldable Plastic (Fibrous Cellulosic Pulp and Gum Shellac) – Peck
1862	Cellulose Nitrate Solvated with Camphor (Parkesine) – Alexander Parkes
1868	Celluloid, Molding Grade Pyroxylin – John Wesley Hyatt
1870's	Hydraulic Planer for Cutting Thin Sheets – Charles Burroughs Co., NJ
1870's	Celluloid Tubes Steam-Heated, Placed in Form, Inflated (Blow Molding)
1910	"Sharps" Piano Keys Drape-Formed Over Captive Wooden Core
1930	Bottle Formed From Two Thermoformed Halves – Fernplas Corp.
1930's	Relief Maps for US Coast & Geodetic Survey
1938	Blister Pack of Cellulose Acetate (CA)
1938	Rollfed Automatic Thermoformer – Clauss B. Strauch Co.
1938	Cigarette Tips, Ice-Cube Trays Automatically Thermoformed
1942	Cast PMMA (Acrylic) Thermoformed for Fighter/Bomber Windows, Windshields
1948	Cast PMMA (Acrylic) Thermoformed for Bathtubs (Troman Bros., England)
1954	Skin-Packaged Products – Hardware Manufacturers Association, Chicago
1970	ABS Automobile Body – Borg-Warner

Modern thermoforming began about 50 years ago with major developments in two important areas. Research in thermoplastic resin chemistry led to commercialization of sheet grade FPVC, PMMA, CA, and PS. And continuous forming was achieved with the invention of the screw extruder and the rollfed sheet thermoformer. These breakthroughs allowed a wide variety of prewar domestic products to be developed. And this in turn prepared formers for war product developments such as airplane canopies and war survey relief maps. The packaging industry adopted thermoforming as a basic process in the late 1940's to such an extent that the thermoformed package is considered as the most significant packaging development of the 1950's decade (6).

In the 1970's, demand for convenience food containers, ovenable portion servings, and more ductile disposable drink cups spurred development of foam PS, CPET and PP pressure forming processes. And engineers developed ways of forming reinforced plastic sheets for the automotive industry. And ahead lies further opportunities to replace welded steel in food cans, glass in jars, and aluminum in beverage cans, and hand layup of thermoset composites, and so on. The prospects for advanced thermoforming systems are discussed later in the chapter.

Markets

The packaging area accounts for more than 75% of thermoforming applications in the US (7, 8). A "best estimate" of the entire US consumption of thermoformed shapes in 1983-1984 is about 773 MMkg [1730 MM lb]*. About 575 MMkg [1288 MM lb] or about 74% is thermoformed into disposables (9). An estimate of the amounts of resin consumed in thermoforming in the US from 1969 to 1983-1984 is given in Table 1.2. The data were constructed from several sources (8-10). In 1969 the industry was projected to grow during the 1970's at 8.5 to 9% per year, with an estimate of 527 MMkg [1180 MM lb] consumed by 1978 (Figure 1.1). About 550 MMkg [1230 MM lb] was consumed in 1978. Continuing this extrapolation, consumption in 1984 was estimated to be 780 MMkg [1750 MM lb] to 830 MMkg [1860 MM lb]. This again compares well with the best-estimate of actual 1983-1984 consumption of 773 MMkg [1732 MM lb]. As seen, more than 60% of the applications used PS

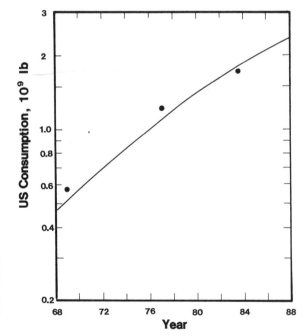

Figure 1.1 Projected and Estimated Amounts of Plastic Thermoformed (US) (7-10). Solid line: Projected (8). Circles: Best Estimate. Ordinate: US Consumption, in 10^9 lb (or 0.446 MM Metric Tons). Abscissa: Year.

* 1 T = 1000 kg = Mkg. "M" = 1000 in weights, number of items and dollars. "M" = 1,000,000 in physical property units.

TABLE 1.2 US RESIN CONVERTED VIA THERMOFORMING
(Compiled from (8-10))

Material	Amount Thermoformed, MT (MM kg)				Annual Growth, % (69-84)
	1962	1969	1977	1983-1984	
ABS	NA	40	70	127	8
PMMA	NA	21	36	38	4
Cellulosics	8	5	8	3 (?)	− 3
LDPE	NA	0.7	0.4	0.6	0
HDPE	NA	7	10	26	9
PP	NA	1	3	13	20
PS	69	166	392	480	7
PVC	4	13	24	45	9
Other*	1	NA	NA	40	–
Total	82	254	544	773	8

* = K-Resin, PAN, TPE, XT   NA = Not Available (Not Included)

in one form or another. This market continues to grow at about 7% per year. As expected (7), PP is very rapidly becoming an important thermoforming resin as seen in Table 1.2. And cellulosics continue to lose market share to PP, PVC and PS. In 1984, 7 MMkg [16 MM lb] thermoplastic polyesters were thermoformed. Only a very small fraction (less than 1%) was crystallized PET (CPET). Recently however, thermoformable CPET has been developed that can be used as disposable food serving and heating trays and dishes. These are acceptable for both microwave and conventional oven heating. Owing to this development the consumption of polyesters in thermoforming is expected to double in five years.

It has been estimated that about 50% of all sheet stock is converted by thermoforming (8). As seen in Table 1.3, very little LDPE sheet is converted by thermoforming (5%) whereas nearly ⅔ of all PS sheet (65%) is thermoformed. The amount of resin converted into sheet on the other hand varies from about half of all PMMA materials to less than 1% of all LDPE materials (Table 1.3). These percentages have held relatively constant since the 1960's.

Similarly, major markets have remained relatively obvious for nearly two decades. Major new packaging markets have continued to be in disposables as illustrated by the development of PP and CPET food packages and the commercial realization of convenience food foam carryout containers. The applications have also broadened to include packaging of

TABLE 1.3 APPROXIMATE CONVERSION OF THERMOPLASTIC RESIN TO THERMOFORMED PRODUCTS (Adapted from (7, 8))

Material	Amount of Resin Converted to Sheet	Amount of Sheet Thermoformed	Total Amount of Resin Formed into Parts
ABS	25%	60%	15%
PMMA	50	30	15
Cellulosics	25	50	12.5
HDPE	2	30	0.6
LDPE	0.25	5	0.01
PP	1	25	0.25
PS	30	65	19.5
PVC	5	20	1.0

heavier items (power tools) and medical items (critical care emergency packages). Nearly all packaging applications rely on rollfed thin-gage sheetstock. Some major markets are listed in Table 1.4 (8).

TABLE 1.4 EXAMPLES OF APPLICATIONS FOR THERMOFORMED PARTS

Packaging and Related Items
    Blister Packs, Point-of-Purchase
    Bubble Packs, Slip Sleeve, Vacuum Carded
    Electronics, Audio/Video Cassette Holders
    Tools, Hand, Power
    Cosmetics, Cases, Packages
    Foams, Meat, Poultry Trays
    Unit Serving, Foodstuffs
    Convenience, Carryout, Cook-in-Box
    Convertible-Oven Food Serving
    Wide-Mouth Jars
    Vending Machine Hot Cup
    Egg Cartons, Wine Bottle Protectors
    Produce Separators (Apples, Grapefruit)
    Portion, Unit Dose Drugs
    Form-Fill-Seal (Jelly, Crackers)

Vehicular
    Automotive Door Innerliners
    Automotive Utility Shelves, Liners
    Snow-Mobile Shrouds, Windshields
    Motorcycle Windshields, Scooter Shrouds, Mudguards
    All-Terrain Vehicle Exterior Components
    Golf Cart Shrouds, Seats, Trays
    Tractor Shrouds, Door Fascia
    Camper Hardtops, Interior Components (Doors, etc.)
    Truck Cab Door Fascia, Instrument Cluster Fascia
    Recreational Vehicle Interior Components, Window Blisters

Industrial
    Tote Bins
    Pallets
    Parts Trays, Transport Trays
    Equipment Cases

Building Products
    Shutters, Window Fascia
    Skylights, Translucent Domes
    Exterior Lighting Shrouds
    Storage Modules, Bath, Kitchen, Pantry
    Bath and Shower Surrounds (GR-UPE backed)
    Soaking Tubs (GR-UPE Backed)
    Retrofit Shower Components, Shower Trays

Others
    Exterior Signs
    Advertising Signs, Lighted Indoor Signs
    Swimming and Wading Pools
    Trays, Baskets, Hampers, Carrying Cases
    Luggage
    Boat Hulls, Surf-Boards (with PUR Foams)
    Animal Containers
    Prototype Concepts for Other Plastic Processes

In heavy-gage discrete sheet forming, the market traditionally has focussed on economic production of a few, large pieces. As a result, applications in major applicances (refrigerator door liners), recreation (swimming and wading pools), vehicles (snow mobiles, all-terrain vehicles, automotive inner-door panels, truck and tractor cab kick panels), home products (tub and shower stalls, backed with GR-UPE, luggage shells) and display items (advertising, exterior signs, point-of-purchase). The recent rediscovery of pressure forming of sheet against a female mold offers an entre into the economically important market of business machine housings (11).

Most of the fully developed, mature thermoforming markets have been with amorphous resins such as PVC, PS, ABS, and PMMA. These materials can be processed quite successfully over rather wide temperature ranges. Amorphous materials are usually quite forgiving in this respect. Crystalline and reinforced amorphous materials, on the other hand, have very narrow forming windows, usually require higher forming pressures, and usually cannot be consistently formed on conventional thermoforming equipment. Only recently has the industry begun to apply fundamental processing principles to the development of machinery capable of holding accurate sheet temperatures and forming pressures.

Several newer techniques are discussed briefly at the end of this chapter.

Some Definitions

The technology of thermoforming is rapidly changing. Old ideas about process limitations are being challenged daily. However, there are certain guidelines about the thermoforming process that are relatively generic.

Thermoforming offers processing advantages over competitive processes such as blow molding, injection blow molding, rotational molding, and injection molding. Relatively low forming pressures are needed and so mold costs are low and parts of relatively large size can be economically fabricated. Parts with very small thickness-to-area ratio can be fabricated. For thin-wall parts, fabrication time is extremely short, making the process very economical for very many parts. Since the molds see relatively low forces, molds can be made of relatively inexpensive materials and mold fabrication time is very short. Thus lead time is very short. Thermoforming is the method most usually selected for prototype and display parts to be made by other processes.

Typical thermoforming processing steps are clamping, heating, shaping, cooling and trimming (12). Thermoform sheet is loosely categorized as *thin-gage* (sheet thickness less than 0.25 mm [0.010 in]) and *thick-gage* (sheet thickness greater than 0.25 mm [0.010 in]). Thick-gage sheet can be further divided into medium-weight sheet (0.25 mm [0.010 in] to 1.5 mm [0.060 in]) and heavy-gage sheet (greater than 1.5 mm [0.060 in]). Thin-gage sheet is usually supplied to the former in rolls. Heavy-gage sheet is supplied as cut sheet, stacked and palletized. The majority of packaging applications (blister, form/fill/seal, foam sheet, biaxially oriented) use thin-gage sheet. Thermoforming presses that use roll sheet stock are called *rollfed* or *continuous sheet formers* (Figure 1.2 (13)). Heavy-gage sheet is supplied to the thermoforming presses as discrete cut sheets. These presses are called *cut sheet formers*. There are two basic styles of cut sheet formers. *Shuttle formers* heat and form one sheet at a time (Figure 1.2 (14)). *Rotary presses* accept a cut sheet at one station, heat in a second, and form in a third. A fourth station may be provided for in-press trimming (Figure 1.4 (15)).

If the sheet is rollfed, clamping is by chain-fed pins that pierce the sheet 25 mm [1 in] or so in from each edge. For high-temperature forming operations (CPET, PP), the rails are

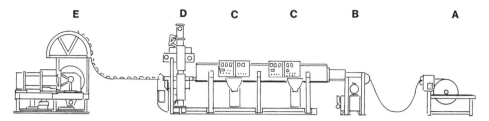

Figure 1.2 Schematic – Battenfeld Gloenco Rollfed Sheet + Thermoforming Line (13). A: Rollfed Sheet Take-off Station. B: Pin Chain Engagement. C: Heater Zone. D: Forming Station. E: In-Line Separate Mechanical Toggle-Clamp Trim Station.

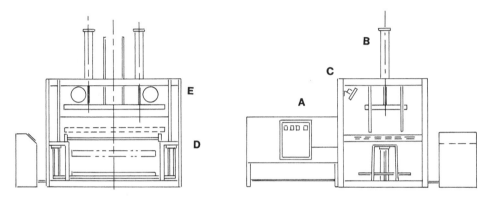

Figure 1.3 Single Station Cut Sheet Shuttle Press – Drypoll (14). A: Heater Zone. B: Pneumatic/Hydraulic Plug Assist. C: Auxiliary Free Surface Cooling Station. D: Forming Table. E: Vacuum Tanks. (Drawing used by permission of Drypoll.)

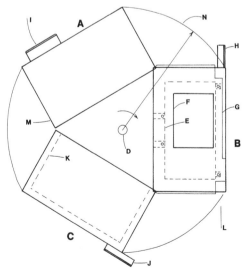

Figure 1.4 Rotary Station Cut Sheet Forming Press – Custom Automated Machinery (15). A: Heating Station. B: Forming Station. C: Load/Unload Station. D: Drive Center. E: Platen. F: Motor Well. G: Pit. H: Platen Control Panel. I: Oven Control Panel. J: Clamp Control Panel. K: Rotating Center Structure. L: Vacuum Service. M: Air Service. N: Safety Guard. (Drawing by permission of Fred Pollack, President, Custom Automated Machinery, Inc.)

shielded from the sheet heating source or are actively cooled. The edge material is trimmed, reground and reprocessed into new sheet. Cut sheet clamping frames are usually held closed with mechanical spring-loaded toggle clamps.

There are three basic ways of heating the sheet. *Contact heating*, where a heated plate is placed against the sheet, is used only in one specialized thermoforming area, trapped sheet forming (Figure 1.5). Heavy-gage cut sheets are frequently heated in *forced convection hot air* ovens. Thin-gage rollfed sheet is usually heated by passing the sheet between banks of *infrared radiant heaters*. Combinations of radiant and convection heating are used, as well (Chapter 4). Most of the plastics thermoformed today (PS, PVC, ABS) are formable at relatively low temperatures (120 to 230 C [250 to 450 F]). Heater temperatures are selected on the basis of optimizing the amount of energy transferred to the sheet per unit time.

There are three basic types of mold configurations. Sheet is usually formed over a *male mold* and into a *female mold* (Figure 1.6). In some cases, the sheet is formed between male and female molds. This is called *matched mold* or die forming. At times, the sheet is prestretched prior to forming by expanding it with air pressure. This is called *billow*, pillow, or bubble forming. A sheet can be stretched prior to forming with a mechanical assist known as a *plug*.

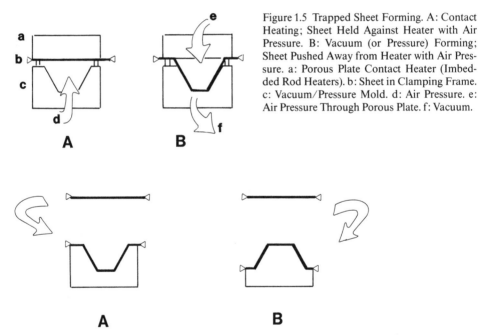

Figure 1.5 Trapped Sheet Forming. A: Contact Heating; Sheet Held Against Heater with Air Pressure. B: Vacuum (or Pressure) Forming; Sheet Pushed Away from Heater with Air Pressure. a: Porous Plate Contact Heater (Imbedded Rod Heaters). b: Sheet in Clamping Frame. c: Vacuum/Pressure Mold. d: Air Pressure. e: Air Pressure Through Porous Plate. f: Vacuum.

Figure 1.6 Definitions of Mold Configurations. A: Female Mold (or Negative Forming). B: Male Mold (or Positive Forming).

In the earliest days of thermoforming, the rubbery sheet was manually stretched or draped over a male mold. *Drape forming* requires no forming pressure and no difference in pressure across the sheet. *Matched die forming* also requires no difference in pressure across the sheet, although the pressure required to force the die halves into the sheet can be 0.1 to 10 MPa [15 to 150 psi]. *Vacuum forming* uses a pressure differential across the sheet of up to

0.1 MPA [15 psi] or one atmosphere. Typically, the applied vacuum is on the order of 0.05 to 0.09 MPa [7.3 to 14 psi]. Historically, steam pressure was used to force celluloid against mold surfaces (16). Recently, this *pressure forming* technology has been rediscovered. Air rather than steam supplies the pressure (11). Although forming pressures to 3.45 MPa [500 psi] can be used, the typical pressure forming range is 0.14 to 0.56 MPa [20 to 80 psi] with 1.4 MPa [200 psi] considered the practical upper limit. Pressure forming can be combined with vacuum forming to gain additional differential pressure. Pressure forming is best suited to heavy-gage sheet forming into female molds. Of course, higher forming pressures require more substantial mold construction. This increases the mold cost and lead time.

Thin-gage sheet can be *trimmed* in the mold or in a separate in-line hydromechanical trimming device (See Figure 1.2). Heavy-gage sheet is usually removed from the clamp and trimmed with routers or saws. Robots are being used to automate heavy-gage sheet trimming.

Although heavy-gage sheet is rarely rolled, the demand for large numbers of large, heavy-wall parts (refrigerator doorliners, vehicle interior components) has led to development of *in-line heavy-gage sheet thermoforming* (13). The sheet extruder is placed in-line with the thermoformer, thus bypassing all the problems associated with handling cut sheet materials (Figure 1.7).

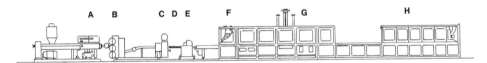

Figure 1.7 In-line Heavy-Gage Sheet Forming System – Shelly (13). A: Extruder. B: Down-Roll Stack and Cooling Table. C: Edge Trim. D: Hold-Down Table. E: Edge Clamp Engagement. F: Sheet Heating Zone. G: Forming Station. H: In-line Trimming Station.

Historically, thermoforming rules-of-thumb have been based on the "depth-of-draw" of a given material into a given mold configuration. The *depth-of-draw* concept has been loosely understood among formers as the ratio of the depth a sheet could be drawn into a female mold to the minimum dimension at the rim, and was frequently given the notation h:d. Unfortunately, this definition can be misinterpreted, is vague for noncylindrical shapes, and does not truly describe the stretching process. Other definitions based on areal and linear

Methods of Forming

As noted, in its simplest form, thermoforming is the stretching of a rubbery sheet into a final shape. As the sheet is stretched against the mold surface, it stops drawing. As a result, the final part has thick walls where the sheet touched the mold first and thin walls where it touched last (Figure 1.8). In many applications, particularly with thin-gage sheet forming, the extent of sheet stretching is small and so the thick-to-thin wall ratio is relatively small as well. The package integrity and durability are therefore uncompromised. Typical applications are in packaging areas such as blister and bubble packs and form/fill/seal packages (17). If a high degree of stretching is needed or heavy-gage sheet must be used, simple stretching techniques cannot be used. The methods of forming can then be divided into *one-*

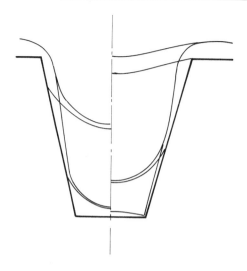

Figure 1.8 Wall Thickness Variation During Draw-Down in Simple Female Vacuum Forming.

step forming (drape forming), *multiple-step* forming (plug-assist forming) and *other* variations (diaphragm forming).

One-Step Forming. There are five types of one-step forming.

In *drape forming* (Figure 1.9), the heated clamped sheet is either lowered onto the male mold or the male mold is raised into the sheet. The sheet in contact with the mold does not stretch. As the mold penetrates and stretches the sheet, the air trapped between the sheet and the mold is evacuated. Either vacuum or air pressure is used to produce the differential pressure to force the sheet against the male mold. In drape forming, the formed part has a thick bottom and thin sidewalls. The part is thinnest at the rim.

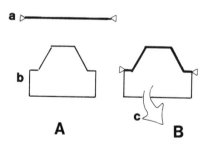

Figure 1.9 Drape Forming. A: Preheated Sheet Prior to Forming. B: Formed Sheet onto Male Mold. a: Preheated, Clamped Sheet. b: Male Mold with Vacuum Holes. c: Vacuum.

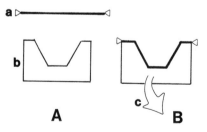

Figure 1.10 Vacuum Forming. A: Preheated Sheet Prior to Forming. B: Formed Sheet into Female Mold. a: Preheated, Clamped Sheet. b: Female Mold with Vacuum Holes. c: Vacuum.

In *vacuum forming* (Figure 1.10), the clamped heated rubbery sheet is sealed against the rim of a female mold. Vacuum is then applied. This differential pressure draws the sheet against the mold surface. As noted before, the formed part has a thick rim and is thinnest in the bottom corners. This is also called cavity forming (18).

Pressure forming (Figure 1.11) is similar to vacuum forming except that positive air pressure forms the differential to push the sheet into the mold corners. Since air pressure to 1.4 MPa [200 psi] might be used, a pressure box must be provided over the free surface of the sheet. Pressure forming is used for difficult-to-form rollfed thin-gage materials such as PP and for production of highly detailed heavy-gage parts (11).

In *free blowing* (Figure 1.12), the clamped heated rubbery sheet is stretched with air into a free-form shape. The amount of air pressure is controlled with a photocell that senses the height of the expanding bubble. Since the air is slightly cooler than the sheet, the sheet cools into the free-form shape. This technique was pioneered for aircraft gun enclosures. Since the sheet does not touch a solid surface during forming, it remains mar-free. Except near the clamping area, the bubble wall thickness is quite uniform. Freely blown bubbles are also used extensively with rollfed thin-gage sheet for blister packs.

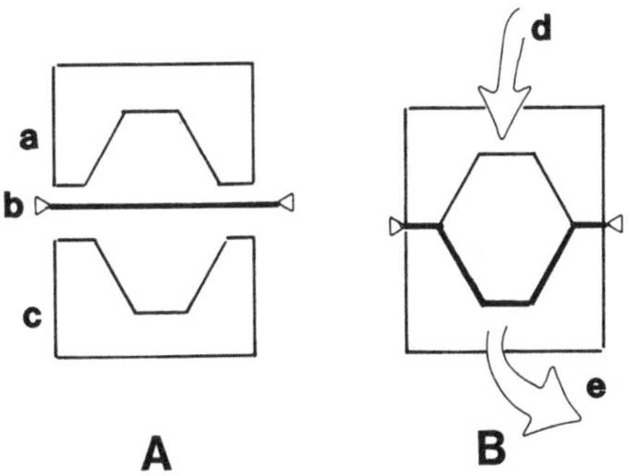

Figure 1.11 Pressure Forming. A: Preheated Sheet Prior to Forming. B: Formed Sheet into Female Mold. a: Pressure Box. b: Preheated, Clamped Sheet. c: Female Mold with Vacuum/ Vent Holes. d: Applied Air Pressure. e: Venting or Vacuum.

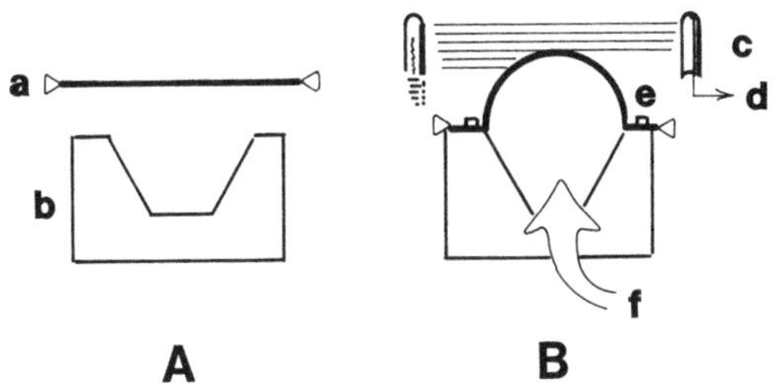

Figure 1.12 Free Blowing. A: Preheated Sheet Prior to Forming. B: Free-Blown Sheet; Bubble Height Determined by Photocell Monitor. a: Preheated, Clamped Sheet. b: Pressure Box. c: Proportional Photocell Monitor. d: Signal to Air Pressure. e: Hold-Down Ring. f: Air Pressure.

Matched die molding (Figure 1.13) is a common way of forming shapes from relatively stiff polymers, such as PS foam. The clamped heated rubbery sheet is positioned between two mold halves. As the mold halves close, vacuum can be applied to the female half of the mold to assist with forming. Part wall thickness depends upon the mating tolerances of the two mold halves. Appreciable material movement is possible if applied forces are relatively large. Usually however, applied pressures are no more than 1 MPa [150 psi] and usually about 0.34 MPa [50 psi].

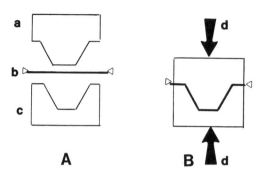

Figure 1.13 Matched Die Forming. A: Pre-heated Sheet Prior to Forming. B: Sheet Formed by Simultaneous Motion of Two Mold Halves. a: Male Mold Half. b: Pre-heated, Clamped Sheet. c: Female Mold Half. d: Applied Force.

Multiple-Step Forming. In thin-gage thermoforming, cycle times are very short and shapes are relatively simple. As a result, forming is usually restricted to one of the one-step techniques described above. In heavy-gage forming, quite complex and quite deep parts are sometimes required. More importantly, wall thickness uniformity becomes a significant design parameter. As a result, forming frequently has more than one step. The first step is usually a form of sheet stretching, such as *plug assist* or *billowing*. The prestretched sheet is then pressed against the mold surface. Some examples of multiple-step forming follow.

> *Billow drape forming* (Figure 1.14) begins with a clamped heated rubbery sheet that is expanded into a bubble with air pressure. Typical air pressures for inflation are 0.014 to 0.055 MPa [2 to 8 psi gage]. A male mold is then inserted into the bubble, air pressure is bled off and vacuum is applied if needed. The resulting part has a much more uniform wall thickness than that from straight drape forming. If the sheet is prestretched by drawing it into a large rectangular box with vacuum, the technique is called *vacuum snap-back forming* (Figure 1.15). To form very deep female parts, the sheet can be prestretched by blowing it away from the female cavity with air pressure, then pulling it against the female mold wall with applied vacuum (Figure 1.16). This is called *billow vacuum forming.*

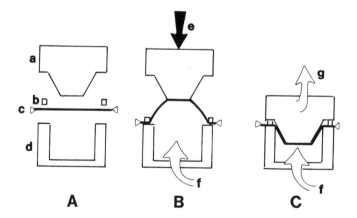

Figure 1.14 Billow Drape Forming. A: Preheated Sheet Prior to Forming. B: Billow Formed, Male Mold Moving Against Blown Bubble. C: Part Formed Against Male Mold by Vacuum/Air Pressure. a: Male Mold, with Vacuum Holes. b: Hold-Down Ring. c: Clamped, Preheated Sheet. d: Pressure Box. e: Male Mold Moving. f: Applied Air Pressure. g: Vacuum.

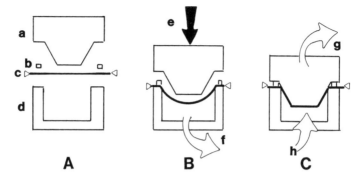

Figure 1.15 Vacuum Snap-Back Forming. A: Preheated Sheet Prior to Forming. B: Vacuum-Drawn Bubble, Male Mold Moving into Bubble Cavity. C: Vacuum/Pressure Applied to Force Sheet Against Male Mold. a: Male Mold with Vacuum Holes. b: Hold-Down Ring. c: Preheated, Clamped sheet. d: Pressure/Vacuum Box. e: Male Mold Moving. f: Partial Vacuum to Prestretch Sheet. g: Vacuum. h: Air Pressure.

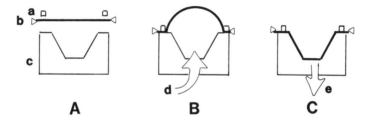

Figure 1.16 Billow Vacuum Forming. A: Preheated Sheet Prior to Forming. B: Sheet Prestretched with Air Pressure. C: Sheet Vacuum Formed into Female Cavity. a: Hold-Down Ring. b: Preheated, Clamped Sheet. c: Female Mold with Pressure/Vacuum Holes. d: Applied Pressure. e: Vacuum.

Sheet is frequently prestretched with a mechanically driven plug. *Plug-assist vacuum forming* is the simplest example of its use (Figure 1.17). The sheet is prestretched by pressing the plug into it and down into the female mold cavity. Vacuum is then applied to pull the sheet against the mold surface. If the sheet is forced against the female mold surface with air pressure applied through the plug, the technique is known as *plug assist pressure forming* (Figure 1.18).

Billow forming and plug assist forming have been combined in several ways. Once a bubble has been blown, the plug penetrates it to stretch it into the female mold cavity (Figure 1.19). At this point, air pressure can be applied through the plug to force the sheet against the female mold. This is called *reverse draw with plug assist* (Figure 1.20). If vacuum is applied, the sheet is drawn from the plug to the female mold surface. This is called *vacuum reverse draw with plug assist.* If the plug is replaced with a male mold and either vacuum applied through the mold or pressure applied from the female pressure box, the technique is called *pressure bubble immersion forming* (Figure 1.21).

All these variations have been devised to prestretch the sheet prior to forming in order to achieve more uniform wall thickness and deeper draws.

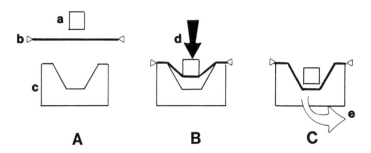

Figure 1.17 Plug-Assist Vacuum Forming. A: Preheated Sheet Prior to Forming. B: Sheet Stretched with Moving Plug. C: Sheet Vacuum Formed into Female Cavity. a: Plug. b: Preheated, Clamped Sheet. c: Female Mold with Vacuum Holes. d: Moving Plug. e: Vacuum.

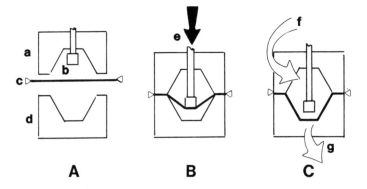

Figure 1.18 Plug-Assist Pressure Forming. A: Preheated Sheet Prior to Forming. B: Sheet Stretched with Mechanical Plug Advance. C: Sheet Air-Pressure Formed into Female Mold. a: Pressure Box. b: Plug. c: Preheated, Clamped Sheet. d: Female Mold with Vent Holes. e: Moving Plug. f: Applied Air Pressure. g: Venting Air (or Vacuum).

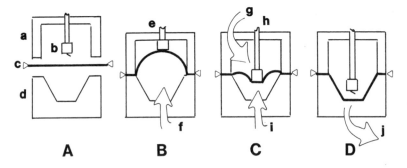

Figure 1.19 Pressure Reverse Draw with Plug-Assist. A: Preheated Sheet Prior to Forming. B: Sheet Prestretched into Bubble with Applied Air Pressure. C: Plug Moves into Sheet while Air Pressure Still On. D: Sheet Vacuum Formed into Female Mold. a: Pressure Box. b: Plug. c: Preheated, Clamped Sheet. d: Female Mold with Air Pressure/Vacuum Holes. e: Plug Begins to Move When Billow Touches it. f: Applied Air Pressure. g: Air Pressure. h: Plug Moving into Billow. i: Continuing Air Pressure. j: Vacuum.

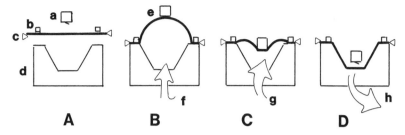

Figure 1.20 Vacuum Reverse Draw with Plug-Assist. A: Preheated Sheet Prior to Forming. B: Formation of Bubble. C: Plug Moves into Billow, Air Pressure Continues. D: Vacuum Applied, Pulling Sheet into Female Mold. a: Plug. b: Hold-Down Ring. c: Preheated, Clamped Sheet. d: Female Mold with Air Pressure/Vacuum Holes. e: Plug Motion activated when Bubble Touches it. f: Applied Air Pressure. g: Continuing Air Pressure as Plug Advances. h: Vacuum.

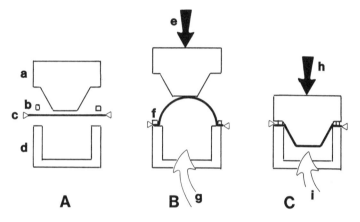

Figure 1.21 Pressure Bubble Immersion Forming. A: Preheated Sheet Prior to Forming. B: Male Mold Moving Against Blown Bubble. C: Air Pressure Forces Sheet Against Male Mold. a: Male Mold. b: Hold-Down Ring. c: Preheated, Clamped Sheet. d: Pressure Box. e: Male Mold Moving Against Bubble. f: Sheet Clamped Against Internal Bubble Pressure. g: Air Pressure. h: Male Mold Seals Off Against Hold-Down Ring. i: Pressure Continues.

Other Variations. In order to form certain types of plastics, techniques other than those given above have been devised.

One is *trapped sheet forming* (Figure 1.5), for highly oriented (OPS) or temperature sensitive sheet (PP, PE). The clamped sheet is held against a heated porous plate until it reaches forming temperature. Pressure is then applied through the plate, forcing the sheet against the female mold. Alternately, vacuum can be applied, drawing the sheet away from the heater and against the mold.

In *slip forming*, the heated rubbery sheet is initially not tightly clamped. As the differential pressure is applied, the sheet is drawn over the rim and into the cavity. At a predetermined time, the sliding is stopped by increased clamping force (Figure 1.22). This technique parallels deep-draw metal forming practice.

Splitty plastics such as PET and PA (nylon) can be formed without bursting by *diaphram forming* (Figure 1.23). A warm thick-walled neoprene bladder or diaphram is placed against the clamped heated rubbery plastic sheet and inflated either with air or a liquid such as hydraulic fluid or hot water. The inflating bladder stretches the plastic sheet into a female mold. Very uniform wall thicknesses and relatively deep draws can be obtained for plastics that cannot be formed in other ways.

Twin-sheet thermoforming has been a technically viable process for many years (Figure 1.24). Two sheets are kept separate while heating, then brought together in a double female mold arrangment. A blow pipe is provided between the sheets and once the sheets are clamped together, air pressure inflates them against their respective molds. Twin-sheet forming produces a relatively flat hollow part that can be filled with PUR foam for additional stiffness. For large, heavy-gage parts, the technique competes with blow molding. In rollfed thermoforming, twin-sheet forming is used a different way (Figure 1.25). In packaging, packages that provide oxygen barrier to the product are desired. The most effective barrier materials developed so far are laminates of essentially incompatible plastics (EVOH, PP, PA, PET, PVDC and so on). The web and trim scrap from coextruded laminates of some of these materials cannot be used. As a result, a variation on the twin-sheet thermoforming process has been developed wherein single-layer sheets are fed from individual rolls through sandwich heaters and brought together at the forming station. Once the multi-layer formed product has been trimmed, the individual layers are stripped from the resulting web. Each material scrap is therefore clean and can be recycled to produce new sheet. The diverse layers of material in the formed product are only contact-adhered and so can be delaminated through misuse.

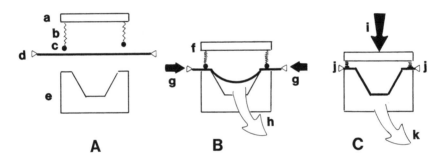

Figure 1.22 Slip Forming. A: Preheated Sheet Prior to Forming. B: Applied Vacuum Draws Excess Sheet Over Rim. C: Spring-Loaded Hold-Down Plate Stops Sheet Travel, Vacuum Continues to Draw Sheet. a: Hold-Down Plate. b: Springs. c: Low-Friction Pads. d: Preheated, Clamped Sheet. e: Female Mold with Vacuum Holes. f: Hold-Down Plate Allows Sheet Slippage. g: Sheet Sliding into Female Mold Cavity. h: Vacuum. i: Hold-Down Plate Stops Sheet Slippage. j: Sheet Clamps Also Stop Sheet Slippage. k: Vacuum Continues.

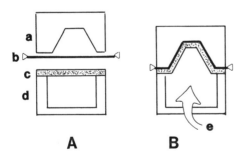

Figure 1.23 Diaphram Forming. A: Preheated Sheet Prior to Forming. B: Diaphram Stretching Sheet into Female Mold. a: Female Mold with Vent Holes. b: Preheated, Clamped Sheet. c: Thick, High-Temperature Flexible Diaphram (Neoprene). d: Pressure Box. e: Applied Air Pressure.

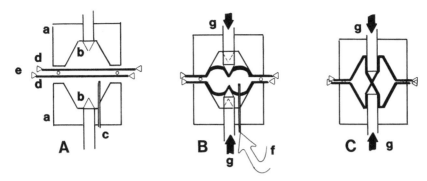

Figure 1.24 Twin-Sheet Cut Sheet Thermoforming. A: Preheated Sheets Prior to Forming. B: Sheets Blown Against Respective Female Molds with Air Pressure, through Blow Pipe that Pierces Sheet Surface. C: (Optional) Plug-Assist Forming for Ribs, Reinforcing Members. a: Female Mold with Vent Holes. b: (Optional) Plug. c: Blow Pipe. d: Preheated, Clamped Sheet. e: Removable Sheet Separator. f: Air Pressure Applied Through Blow Pipe. g: Plugs Mechanically Moved Together to Form Rib.

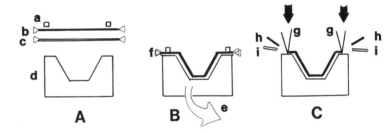

Figure 1.25 Twin-Sheet Rollfed Thermoforming. A: Preheated, Separated Rollfed Thin-Gage Sheet Prior to Forming. B: Vacuum Forming into Female Mold. C: In-Situ Trimming, Separating of Trim for Recycle. a: Hold-Down Ring. b: Preheated, Clamped Sheet of Material A. c: Preheated, Clamped Sheet of Material B. d: Female Mold with Vacuum Holes. e: Applied Vacuum. f: Hold-Down in Place. g: In-Situ Trimming Knives. h: Trim Scrap of Material A. i: Trim Scrap of Material B.

If the applied forces increase, thermoforming begins to mimic metal forming techniques. At pressures of 1.73 MPa [250 psi] or more, the process is similar to tin metal embossing. At pressures of 6.9 MPa [1000 psi], the process resembles coining. And at pressures of 13.8 MPa [2000 psi], the process is more like forging (19). It has been adequately demonstrated that useful products can be fabricated with high-speed *impact forming* (Dow STP process).

The incentive to achieve more uniform part wall thickness even in very deep draw parts has spurred development of these multiple-step procedures. However, the more sophisticated these procedures become, the more difficult it is to adapt them to high-speed forming. And yet many new packaging applications, for example, are seeking just such designs. Thermoforming process innovation remains a lively art.

Modern Thermoforming Machinery

From a machinery and equipment viewpoint, the thermoforming process can be analyzed as (19):

> Heating source
>
> Forming station, including machine frame, forming table with drive system and ejection system
>
> Vacuum and air pressure system
>
> Sheet stretching frame and transporting mechanism
>
> Electrical/Electronics for automatic system
>
> Additional equipment (sheet, web/trim handling, trimming)

Heating Sources. The various heating methods are detailed in Chapter 3. Sheet temperature should be held to within ± 5 C [± 10 F]. During transfer to the forming station, the temperature drop should not exceed 5 to 10 C [10 to 20 F]. Infrared heating is most popular today. The various heating techniques include (19):

> Simple nickel-chrome heating wires
> Metal resistance rods (hot rods)
> Ceramic radiators
> Gas-fired radiant plates
> Quartz heaters in rod or square plate form
> Heat lamps
> Quartz glass plates

Heater surface temperature is usually monitored with thermocouples or thermistors. Heating wires and resistance rods are inexpensive but oxidize rapidly and so lose heating efficiency. Quartz heaters are quite efficient, do not deteriorate appreciably in performance but are quite expensive. Quartz is preferred for high-temperature and "shaped heating" needs (Chapter 3).

Sheet can also be heated by direct contact with a hot metal plate (contact heating), by placing it in a hot air oven (convection heating), or by passing it through a high-frequency electromagnetic field (RF or microwave heating). In the last case, the material must absorb the high-frequency energy. PVC is heated by radio-frequency energy in the flow-molding embossing process. Other materials must be doped with "lossy" substances, such as carbon black.

Sheet Transport. There are several ways of transporting rollfed sheet through the heater zone and into the forming station. The most common method uses pins mounted on a bicycle-chain style drive. These pins are spaced at about 25 mm [1 in]. They penetrate the sheet from below at the roll stand end of the machine and carry the web away to a windup stand or regrinder at the other end. Sheet clamps, similar to tenter clamps, are also used (19; pg. 140, 20). Clamps have the advantage that as the sheet heats, they can be individually retracted to keep the sagging sheet taut. These are far more expensive and more difficult to maintain than pin chains. Sheet transfer is accomplished with a single rotation jog-stop action. Linear indexing accuracy is within 0.25 mm [0.010 in].

Cut sheet is usually held in place with mechanical toggle clamps. Toggles that are simultaneously locked or opened with air pressure are common. Air support beneath the sheet can be used to minimize sagging during heating (19; pg. 126, 21). On shuttle presses, the clamp frame can be indexed by motor-driven rack-and-pinion rails or by push-pull action of pneumatic or hydraulic pistons. On very simple vacuum forming presses, the sheet remains fixed and the (top-only) heater is shuttled away prior to forming. On rotary presses, a carrousel is needed to carry the sheet from station to station. The linear indexing of this carrousel should be accurate to within 0.25 mm [0.010 in]. This requires a rotary drive motor accuracy and repeatability to within one arc min. This can be accomplished on very large carrousels with high-torque, low-rotation motors (1 RPM), limit switches and electronic brakes. Indexing can also be done by driving the rotary table with a pneumatic cylinder. Positive position lock-in is accomplished by dropping a tapered shot pin into a hardened bushing on the table. The pin is then pneumatically extracted prior to the next index sequence (21). Ideally, the rotation cycle should have smooth acceleration and deceleration.

Forming Platform. The forming station should include all elements necessary to prestretch the sheet to form the part, to cool it, and to eject it from the mold:

> Substantial tierods. For molds greater than 300 mm [12 in] in length or 600 mm [24 in] in width and for all pressure forming applications, four tierods are recommended.
>
> Easy mold removal/maintenance.
>
> Easily adjustable mold daylight.
>
> Adequate headroom for plug assist equipment.
>
> Proper manifolding for mold temperature control.
>
> Adequate provision for prestretching/billowing.
>
> Free surface cooling; fans, blowers, chilled air jets, fogging nozzles (Chapter 5 on Mold Cooling).
>
> Vacuum/air pressure access lines.
>
> Mold venting area.
>
> Stripping or ejection system (although this can be integral to the mold).
>
> Substantial, reinforced frame to carry heavy molds, ancillary equipment.
>
> In-mold trim anvil, knives and mechanical drive system.
>
> Cut-off part takaway system.

The drive system that raises and lowers the table is the key to forming station performance. Depending on the application, the drive unit can be as inexpensive as a simple air cylinder or as complex as the hydromechanical clamps used on injection molding machines. Table 1.5 (19) rates some of the drives used in thermoforming presses. Many high-speed presses use electrically-driven toggle clamps and cams. For high-speed pressure forming (PP), double toggle clamps are used. Some straight hydraulic clamps are being used in high pressure applications. Most vacuum forming drive systems are designed to close and clamp at maximum pressures of 0.15 to 0.30 MPa [20 to 40 psi]. For pressure forming, the drive system must work against the forming air pressure. Safety factors of 3 to 4 are recommended. Thus, if 2 MPa [30 psi] air pressure is used in forming, the drive system should be designed to remain closed against 6 to 8 MPa [90 to 120 psi]. For a typical mold forming area of 500×250 mm [20×10 in], the drive system clamping load is 32 to 107 Mkg-f [9 to 12 tons]. Platens and tierods must be designed to accommodate the higher bending forces. For forming pressures in excess of 0.7 MPa [100 psi], forming station designs should appear similar to those used in thermoplastic structural foam injection molding.

TABLE 1.5 COMPARISON OF FORMING TABLE DRIVE UNITS
(From (21), Table 8, by permission of Hanser Verlag)   0 = Low/Poor   3 = Moderate/Average
5 = High/Excellent

Characteristic	Pneumatic Air Cylinder	Geared Motor-Cogwheel	Hydraulic	Pneumatic Driven Toggle	Eccentric Motor (Cams)	Motor-Driven Spindle
Uniformity	0	5	4	0	3	5
Stroke Limit Control	1	5	5	3	3	5
Timing Control	2	5	4	1	2	4
Repeatability	0	5	4	0	3	5
Speed Control	3/4	0/2/5	5	1	0	2
Forming Force	3	3	5	0	1	5
Clamping Force	3	3	5	5	5	4
Stability (Tracking)	0/3	3/4	0/3	4	4	5
Energy Consumption	0	5	1	0	3	2
Trouble-free Nature	3	5	0	2	4	3
Maintenance	4	5	0	2	3	3
Noise Level	0	5	3	0	4	1
Construction Quality	1	3	1	5	5	5
Cost	5/2	4/1	0	3	1	1
Preblowing Capacity	5	5	5	0	0	0
Total	30/31	61/64	42/45	26	41	50

Vacuum System. Even the least expensive vacuum former must have adequate means of rapidly drawing the sheet against the mold surface. The key to efficient vacuum draw-down lies in an unencumbered, adequately sized line between the vacuum surge tank and the mold cavity. Proper vacuum system design requires a vacuum pump capable of drawing down to 710 to 735 mm Hg vacuum (25 to 50 torr) [28 to 29 in Hg or 0.5 to 1 psi absolute] in the vacuum tank prior to the forming cycle. The path between the surge tank and the cavity between the hot sheet and the mold should have as few elbows as possible. Long pipes, flow constrictors, quick-disconnects and restrictive valves should be eliminated. Fast-acting rotary ball valves are recommended (22).

A good estimate of the time required to evacuate a mold cavity can be obtained as follows (23). The pump-down time θ to evacuate a vessel of volume V is given as:

$$\theta = (V/S_0) \ln [(p_1 - p_0)/(p_2 - p_0)]$$

p_1 is the initial vessel pressure (absolute), p_0 is the vacuum tank pressure, and p_2 is the final vessel pressure. S_0 is the evacuation speed. The evacuation speed of the vacuum pump is given as S_p. Then:

$$1/S_0 = 1/S_p + 1/C$$

where C is the cumulative conductance of the system between the pump and mold cavity (vacuum tank, connecting piping, valves, and so on). This can be written as:

$$1/C = 1/C_1 + 1/C_2 + 1/C_3 + \ldots + 1/C_n$$

for n resistances in series. For any element, the conductance is related to flow resistance by:

$$C = q'/\Delta P$$

$q' = w/\rho =$ volume flow rate, $Pa \cdot m^3/s$ $[(lb_f/ft^2)(ft^3/s)]$. ΔP is pressure drop, w is mass flow rate and ρ is gas density $(kg/m^3 \cdot Pa)$ $[(lb/ft^3)(lb_f/ft^2)]$. For a round pipe:

$$C_p = F' \, (\pi D^3/8\,L) \; \sqrt[2]{(RT/M)}$$

D is pipe diameter, L is pipe length, R is the universal gas constant, M is gas molecular weight, T is gas temperature and $F' = 1$ for typical vacuum lines. L can include equivalent resistances for constriction, elbows, valves and so on (24). Typically, $L = L_e = nD$, where n represents these constrictions in equivalent pipe diameters. For RT air, $T = 25$ C [77 F], $C_p = 10.67(D^3/L) = 10.67(D^2/n)$ (m^3/s) $[= 377(D^3/L)$ $(ft^3/s)]$. If the vacuum tank capacitance is C_t, then $1/C = 1/C_t + 1/C_p$ and $1/S_0 = 1/S_p + 1/C_t + 1/C_p$.

Usually the resistance between the vacuum tank and the mold cavity should not exceed the vacuum tank resistance, or $1/C_p \leqslant 1/C_t$. And this combined resistance should not exceed the pump resistance, $1/S_p$, or $1/S_p \leqslant (1/C_t + 1/C_p)$. Manufacturers' specifications usually list vacuum pump capacity, S_p, in ℓ/min [CFM]. If $S_p = 0.0283$ $m^3/s = 100$ $m^3/h = 1700$ ℓ/min [1 $ft^3/s = 60$ CFM], and the recommended guidelines are met, $1/S_0 = 2/S_p = 70.58$ (s/m^3) [$= 2$ s/ft^3]. As an example, let $V = 0.1$ m^3 [3.5 ft^3]. If $p_1 = 760$ mm Hg, $p_0 = 20$ mm Hg and $p_1 = 50$ mm Hg (710 mm Hg vacuum), the draw-down time θ is:

$$\theta = (0.1\,m^3/0.01417\,m^3/s) \ln [(760-20)/(50-20)] = 22.6 \text{ s}$$

If the vacuum tank and piping resistance are negligible, $S_0 = S_p$ and $\theta = 11.3$ s. This is the most rapid evacuation rate for this pump capacity. If the pump resistance $1/S_p$ is known and the guidelines followed, the diameter of the lines connecting the pump to the vacuum tank to the mold cavity can be calculated. $(1/S_p) = 1/C_t + 1/C_p = 2/C_p = 2/[10.67(D^3/L_e)]$. Thus $D = 0.572$ $(S_p L_e)^{1/3} = 0.433$ $(S_p n)^{1/2}$. If $L_e = 1$ m and $S_p = 0.0283$ (m^3/s) for example, $D = 17.4$ cm [6.9 in]. Short, large diameter pipes are required in vacuum lines in order to minimize pressure losses.

The time θ_r to recover the vacuum tank pressure to p_0 value can be calculated with the same equation. The vacuum tank volume is substituted as V and the final tank pressure at the end of draw-down is p_1, the initial pressure. p_0 is the vacuum pump pressure and p_2 is the desired vacuum tank final pressure. If $p_0 = 10$ mm Hg, $p_1 = 100$ mm Hg and $p_2 = 20$ mm Hg, $V = 0.1$ m^3 and $S_0 = 0.0283$ (m^3/s), $\theta = 7.8$ s. The total cycle time, $\theta_t = \theta + \theta_r$. For most cases, $\theta_r \leqslant \theta$, and so the total cycle time is assumed to equal twice the draw-down time (19; pg. 136). Vacuum pumps are either single or double stage. Two stage vacuum pumps can draw pressures down to 10 mm Hg, but the evacuation capacity is half that for single stage pumps. Typical pump capacities are given in Table 1.6 (19; pg. 135).

TABLE 1.6 TYPICAL VACUUM PUMP SPECIFICATIONS (From Hoger (21), Table 10)

Pump Specifications			Theoretical Vacuum Capacity				
No of Cylinders	Diameter (mm)	Stroke Length (mm)	Single Stage (m^3/min)	Two Stage (m^3/min)	Pump Speed (RPM)	Power Required kW	Exit Pipe Dia (mm)
1	76	70	0.255	–	800	0.56	19
2	76	70	0.510	0.255	800	0.74	25
2	102	70	0.906	0.453	800	1.48	32
2	127	80	1.70	0.850	750	2.2/3.7	38
2	140	102	2.80	1.40	900	3.7	52
3	140	102	4.22	2.80	900	5.6	52

Pressure System. Pneumatic action (air cylinders) usually requires working air pressures of 0.6 MPa [90 psi]. Air consumption depends upon the size of the press and the type of forming being used. Typically maximum airflow range for both rollfed and cut sheet presses is 1000 to 7000 ℓ/min = 1 to 7 m³/min [35 to 250 CFM]. Air is usually delivered at 0.7 to 1.4 MPa [100 to 200 psi]. Air should be very dry (dew point at -40 C [-40 F]) and absolutely oil-free, particularly if it is used as instrument air or for prestretching or pressure forming. Prestretching air is delivered to the mold cavity at very low pressures of 0.0035 to 0.035 MPa [0.5 to 5 psi] and at a very carefully controlled flow rate ($\pm 0.1\%$). Pressure forming air is delivered to the pressure box at 0.14 to 0.55 MPa [20 to 80 psi], also at carefully controlled flow rates.

Pressure forming air should be carefully exhausted from the pressure box prior to mold opening. A two-tank system can be used to handle spent air. Air from tank 1 is used to form the part, then exhausted to tank 2 where it is recompressed and used again. This spent air is then exhausted to tank 1 which in the meantime has been emptied by exhaustion to the atmosphere. Alternately, spent air in tank 2 can be flowed through jet nozzles or vortex tubes to cool the free surface of the part once the mold is opened.

Process Control. Process repeatability has always been of concern to thermoformers. The earliest rollfed press was equipped with automatic cycle timers (Table 1.1). Accurate measurement and control of sheet temperature (surface and average), mold temperature, prestretching pressure, preinflation level, rate of stretching by plug assist or by inflation, forming pressure and sheet registry are desired. Control of the rates of change of sheet temperature, bubble inflation, plug assist position, and draw-down is now sought. For example, repeatability of the crystalline level of CPET depends upon accurate control of the rate of heating crystallizing sheet prior to forming (24). Newer, more accurate processing techniques are replacing less reliable ones. For example, microprocessor-driven servo motors are replacing cam-operated sequencing wheels. Newer presses include programmable mold height, daylight adjustment, multi-step, programmable mold closing speeds, programmable rollfed chain width spacing, and programmable forming station sequencing (including prestretching, post-forming sequences). Sheet gage and pattern registry monitors can now be added.

Safety is an ongoing concern. Higher heater temperatures are being used to increase throughput and to heat sheet more efficiently (Chapter 4). An emergency line shutdown should not only shut off heaters but shield the stationary sheet from the heaters. Heaters are now designed to automatically swing away or shift horizontally whenever the sheet stops moving. This reduces the chances of fire. Pressure boxes are pneumatic pressure vessels and so must have appropriate safety ratings and overpressure relief diaphrams. Pressure forming stations should have pressure interlocks that prevent opening when internal air pressure exceeds a fixed (relatively low) level.

In many cases, increased production efficiency and substantially reduced labor costs more than offset the substantial costs of these process controls.

Trimming and Cut Parts Handling. Cut sheet trimming has been traditionally done at an off-line station. Trimming can be done by pneumatic or hydromechanical steel-rule dies, routers, saws and/or punches (Chapter 5). Semi-automatic microprocessor-controlled trimming sequences are used for many parts. Robots can be used as well. Manual trimming is reserved for few, large or prototype parts.

In-line trimming stations are commonly used in rollfed forming operations. In-situ trimming requires that the forming table be equipped with a separate pneumatic or mechanical press that drives the cutting knives through the formed sheet and into the mold. The cut-out parts can then be transported with the web out of the forming station to another table. There the parts are mechanically separated from the web and collected for packaging. The web goes on to a wind-up station. The cut-out parts can also be separated from the web immediately after cutting. Typically, as the knives are extracted, an integral vacuum-assist table lifts the cut parts from the web. The table usually swings out of the forming station area to deposit the cut parts and returns prior to forming table sequencing. In-situ places an added burden on the design of the forming station and can make maintenance difficult. Newer in-situ trimming tables include automatic knife sharpening.

The separate in-line trim press is an alternative to in-situ trimming. Typically, the press is a cam-action mechanical toggle-clamp platen press with steel-rule die cutters. If the trim press is integral with the former, the sheet with the formed parts intact is guided through the press bed by the integral chain drive. If the unit is separate, proper sheet indexing must be provided. If the formed material shrinks appreciably immediately after forming, care must be taken in indexing to ensure pattern repeatability. Integral trim presses are much easier to align and register than separate units. They are recommended for rollfed forming of CPET and PP.

Advanced Techniques

As seen in Table 1.2, PS represents more than 60% of the materials formed in the US today. Newer processes such as SPPF (solid phase pressure forming) for PP (25) and CPET (26) represent only a very small fraction of the total market today. A great deal of sophistication is needed to form these newer materials. This results in advanced monitoring techniques, improved control systems, vastly improved heating and forming techniques and new trimming and recycle philosophies. These advanced techniques are now becoming available to formers of the more common plastics. The result is improved quality, uniformity of product, and more economical processes.

In addition, the new developments require a better understanding of the basic process of thermoforming. For example, until the development of CPET forming, all thermoforming was characterized as beginning and ending with polymer in state "A". With CPET, an amorphous sheet of highly-nucleated PET is heated very rapidly. The sheet begins to crystallize and continues to do so as it is drawn onto a heated mold (24, 27-29). The initial PET sheet is essentially amorphous or has 0% crystallinity. The sheet at the time of first touching the hot mold is about 8 to 10% crystalline. The formed and trimmed PET tray is about 30 to 35% crystalline and capable of withstanding 200 C [400 F] for up to 1 h. PET has essentially been transformed from a material with "A" properties to one with "B" properties.

Today PS foam is achieving success in meat trays, apple separators, picnic trays, and so on. Yet foams are extremely difficult to form into deep shapes (30). Part of the reason is that the internal cell gas pressure offers substantial resistance to the forming pressure. Most foam sheet is therefore match die molded. One very simple solution to minimizing the internal pressure uses steam as the heating medium. Steam diffuses very rapidly through PS, plasticizing it and sweeping air from the cells. Very deep draws can be achieved at steam temperatures of 105 C [220 F] or so. The technique has yet to be commercialized.

Nearly all materials thermoformed today are unfilled and unreinforced. The exceptions are glass-reinforced PP (GR-PP) and glass- or graphite-reinforced PA for automotive applications (4, 31). These sheet materials are heated to above the melt temperature of the polymer and then forged. Relatively high temperatures and pressures are needed to move and separate the stiff, brittle reinforcing fibers. Less brittle, less stiff, more ductile organic fibers should provide reinforcing for relatively low-temperature plastics without requiring atypical thermoforming conditions. Fibers such as PET, PA-66 (nylon) and highly oriented HDPE are becoming available. These should be considered in combination with current developments in pressure forming. Self-reinforcing fibers are just now becoming commercial. Thus there is a real possibility of forming sheet with in situ reinforcement.

As noted, there are three current methods of heating plastic sheet – conduction, convection and infrared radiation. The last is a form of electromagnetic radiation. Radio frequency heating and microwave heating are also methods of electromagnetic heating. Most common plastics are transparent to these methods of heating and so must be doped with absorbers. Absorbers are typically polar in nature, with pendant $-OH$, $-COOH$, or $-NH_2$ groups. Hydrated inorganics such as hydrated magnesium hydroxide can be used to 20% (wt) to provide olefins (PE, PP) with some absorptancy. Carbon black to 10% (wt) can also be used where color is not a factor. Embossing is done today by heating FPVC sheet in an RF field and applying pressure to it when hot.

Serendipity can also yield new techniques. It was found that softened inorganic silica glass sheet could not be pierced with a cold rod if the rod was driven into the sheet at very high speeds (27). The technique was found to work with certain amorphous plastics such as PS and PET as well. This is because amorphous plastics are essentially organic glasses. If the rod is articulated to spread during penetration, a square-bottom container can be mechanically formed. The technique is then similar to wire-frame plug assist forming.

References

1. J. Harry DuBois, *Plastics History USA*, 1972, pg. 38–51.
2. Anon., "STP, Scrapless Forming Process", Dow Chemical Co., Midland MI, 1976.
3. A. H. Steinberg, "Stamped Reinforced Thermoplastic Sheet", Design Engng. Seminar, 33rd SPI RP/C Conference, Washington DC, Feb. 1978.
4. Anon., "Monoformer", Hayssen Mfg. Co., Sheyboygan WI, 1977.
5. W. McConnell, "The Oldest Infant", in P. F. Bruins, Ed., *Basic Principles of Thermoforming*, Gordon and Breach, 1971, pg. 3.
6. S. E. Farnham, *A Guide to Thermoformed Plastic Packaging*, Cahners Books, 1972, pg. 8.
7. J. L. Throne, "Thermoforming: Polymer Sheet Fabrication Engineering. Part 1. Solid Sheet Forming", Plas. Rubber: Proc., *4*, 1979, pg. 129.
8. E. S. Childs, "Thermoforming – Trends and Prospects", in P. F. Bruins, Ed., *Basic Principles of Thermoforming*, Gordon and Breach, 1971, pg. 37.
9. M. Bakker, 1 October 1985, personal communication.
10. Anon., "Thermoforming", Modern Plastics, *62*: 1 (1985), pg. 59.
11. G. L. Beall, "Designers' Guide to Pressure Forming", Plas. Design Forum, *10*: 5, 1985, pg. 42.
12. Anon., "Thermoforming Lustran ABS, Lustrex Polystyrene and Cadon Engineering Thermoplastics", Monsanto Bulletin # 6547, Undated, pg. 3.
13. R. Wood, "Inline Thermoforming Offers Efficiencies for Packaging and Large Components", Plast. Mach. Equip., *19*: 7, 1985, pg. 18.
14. Single Station Vacuum Thermoforming Machine, Drypoll Inc., P. O. Box 728, Flushing NY 11352, 1985.
15. Fred R. Pollak, President, Custom Automated Machinery, Inc., 1150 Davis Rd., Elgin IL 60120, personal communication.
16. G. P. Kovach, "Thermoforming", in *Encyclopedia of Polymer Science and Technology, 13*, 1969, pg. 832.
17. S. Anthony, Jr., "Blister-Sealing Machinery for Medical Device Packages", Med. Device &. Diagn. Ind., *7*: 11, 1985, pg. 30.
18. G. Gruenwald, "Introduction to Thermoforming", available from the author, 36 W 34th St., Erie PA 16508.

19. A. Höger, *Warmformen von Kunststoffen*, Hanser Verlag, 1971, Chapter 4, "Maschinen zum Warmformen".
20. Anon., "Plastic Sheet Thermoforming Machine Line", Senba Iron Works, Ltd., Osaka Japan, undated. Senba uses sheet clips rather than clamps.
21. Anon., "Kostur .. The Shape of Performance in Thermo Forming Production", Kostur Enterprises, Inc., Riviera Beach FL, 12 December 1983.
22. Wm. K. McConnell, Jr., Material Presented, Distributed at SPE Industrial Thermoforming Symposium & Workshop, 12-14 March 1985. Material Copyrighted by Author.
23. B. C. Sakiadis, "Fluid and Particle Mechanics", Section 5, in R. H. Perry, et al., Eds., *Perry's Chemical Engineers' Handbook*, 6th Ed., 1984, pp. 5-32 to 5-34.
24. J. L. Throne, "Thermoforming Crystallizing PET", SPE Tech. Papers, *27*, 1981, pg. 598.
25. Anon., "The Shell Process for Pressure Forming PP in the Solid Phase, Stage 0", Royal Dutch/Shell, Netherlands, 1975.
26. J. L. Throne, "Thermoforming: Polymer Sheet Fabrication Engineering. Part II: Foam and Crystallizable Sheet Forming", Plast. Rubber: Proc., *4*, 1979, pg. 143 +, esp. pg. 148.
27. J. L. Throne, "Thermoforming – A Look Forward", SPE Tech. Papers, *29*, 1983, pg. 464.
28. R. G. Dempsey, et al., to Amoco Chemicals Corp., USP 4, 127, 631, 28 November 1978.
29. R. J. Gartland, R. E. Fruzzetti, "Thermoformed Polyester Ovenable Trays", SPE Tech. Papers, *29*, 1983, pg. 475.
30. J. L. Throne, "Polystyrene Foam Sheet Expansion During Heating", SPE Tech. Papers, *31*, 1985, pg. 1328.
31. D. P. Hug, "Solid Phase Processes", Plastics World, *36*: 1, 1978, pg. 68.

Appendix 1.I

ABBREVIATIONS FOR POLYMERS REFERRED TO IN THE TEXT

Abbreviation	Definition
ABS	Poly(Acrylonitrile-Butadiene-Styrene).
BOPP	Biaxially oriented PP. Usually thin-gage. Also known as OPP.
CA	Cellulose Acetate. One of a family of cellulosics that includes CN, CAP, CAB.
CAB	Cellulose Acetate Butyrate. Sometimes called cellulose butyrate.
CAP	Cellulose Acetate Propionate. Also called cellulose propionate or just propionate.
CPET	Crystallized or Crystallizing PET. Reserved for high-heat products where PET crystallinity exceeds about 20%.
CN	Cellulose Nitrate.
EVOH	Ethylene Vinyl Alcohol. Used as barrier film in packaging applications.
FEP	Fluoroethylene Polymer. The extrusion, molding grade of PTFE.
FPVC	Flexible PVC. Also called plasticized PVC or soft PVC.
FRP	Glass-Fiber Reinforced Unsaturated Polyester. See also GR-UPE.
GR-UPE	Glass-Fiber Reinforced Unsaturated Polyester. Also known as FRP.
HDPE	High-Density Polyethylene (sp. gr. = 0.96). Also called low-pressure or hard polyethylene.
HIPS	High-Impact Polystyrene. Also called rubber-modified polystyrene.
LDPE	Low-Density Polyethylene (sp. gr. = 0.92). Also called high-pressure or soft polyethylene.
MIPS	Medium-Impact Polystyrene. Also called rubber-modified polystyrene.
OPP	Oriented PP, usually thin-gage.
OPS	Oriented PS, usually thin-gage.
PA	Polyamide. Generic, unless followed with numbers such as PA-6, for polycaprolactam. Also called "nylon".

PAI	Polyamide-imide. High-temperature amorphous polymer.
PAN	Polyacrylonitrile.
PA-6	Polycaprolactam Nylon-6.
PA-66	Poly(hexamethylene diamine/adipic acid). Nylon-66.
PC	Polycarbonate.
PE	Polyethylene. See also HPDE and LDPE.
PET	Polyethylene terephthalate Also called thermoplastic polyester, TPE, or polyester. Usually the amorphous type of PET.
PFEP	(Poly)fluoroethylene polymer. See also FEP.
PMMA	Poly(Methyl) Methacrylate. Also known as "Acrylic" although this term could include other types of acrylates as well.
POM	Polyoxymethylene. Also known as polyacetal or acetal. Can include the copolymer as well.
PP	Polypropylene.
PPO	(Poly)para-phenylene oxide. An intractable polymer unless mixed with other polymers such as PS, MIPS, or HIPS.
PPS	(Poly)phenylene Sulfide.
PS	Polystyrene. Usually refers to the generic family of styrenics, including crystal and impact grades. See also MIPS and HIPS.
PTFE	Polytetrafluoroethylene.
PUR	Thermoset Polyurethane.
PVAc	Polyvinyl acetate. Used as release agent in mold preparation.
PVB	Poly(Vinyl) Butyral.
PVC	Polyvinyl Chloride. See also RPVC and FPVC.
PVDC	Polyvinylidene chloride. Also known as polyvinyl dichloride. Used primarily as a barrier film in packaging applications.
PVF	Polyvinyl fluoride.
PVF2	Polyvinylidene fluoride. Used as barrier film in packaging applications.
PVOH	Polyvinyl Alcohol. Used as a mold parting agent.
RPVC	Rigid PVC. Also called unplasticized PVC.
TPE	Thermoplastic Polyester. PET.
TPE	Thermoplastic Elastomer. Not normally thermoformed.
UHMWPE	Ultrahigh Molecular Weight Polyethylene.
XPE	Crosslinked Polyethylene.

2 POLYMERIC MATERIALS

Introduction

It has been said that if a polymer can be produced as a sheet, it can be thermoformed into a product (1, 2). Polymers are high molecular weight organic molecules that are produced by combining very pure carbon-based simple molecules under heat, pressure and catalyst systems. There are more than twenty major classes of polymers available today and many subclasses, obtained by combining polymers with polymers, polymers with fillers and reinforcements, and polymers with additives and processing aids. In order to achieve thermoformed parts having commercially interesting combinations of physical properties, it is necessary to understand the way in which basic polymer architecture affects material properties.

Network Nature of Polymers

There are two general catagories of polymers – thermoplastics and thermosets. Commercially, the most important thermosetting polymers are intrinsically crosslinked resins such as epoxies, phenolics, and reacted unsaturated polyester resins. The polymers are formed from relatively simple chemically unsaturated molecules that are usually liquids at the reaction conditions. The unsaturation is seen as isolated, regularly-spaced double bonds regularly spaced along the carbon-carbon backbone, as $-R-C=C-R-$. The formation of three-dimensional ties is accomplished by opening the double bonds, $-C=C-$, with chemical aids and sometimes heat and pressure. At some point during the formation of this three-dimensional network, the material usually becomes infusible and takes a permanent shape. Thermosets usually cannot be reused or returned to their original forms.

More than 80% of all the polymers used in the world today are thermoplastics. These polymers are characterized by exceptionally long two-dimensional, near-linear organic molecules, usually having saturated (single covalent bond) carbon-carbon backbones, as $-C-C-$. In their final form, thermoplastics are thermally and chemically stable at processing conditions. This means that they can be softened or melted, formed into useful articles, then resoftened or remelted and reused. Thermoforming economics depend upon the thermal stability and resulting recyclability of polymers, and so nearly all commercially thermoformable polymers are thermoplastics.

The toughness of thermosets is due to the rigid three-dimensional network of relatively small building blocks. The toughness of thermoplastics is mainly due to the entanglements of the very long two-dimensional molecules. For example, if the molecule ethylene, $(CH_2=CH_2)$, were scaled in dimension 100 million times, each $-CH_2-$ unit would be about 10 mm [⅜ in] long. The single ethylene unit in a polyethylene backbone $(-CH_2-CH_2-)$ is called a repeat unit. An olefin grease or oil, having 100 repeat units, would be about 2 m [6 ft] long, if the chains could be fully extended. Low density polyethylene (LDPE) would have about 1000 repeat units and would be about 20 m [65 ft] long. Ultrahigh molecular weight polyethylene, a nearly intractable resin used for friction-and-wear applications, has about 100,000 repeat units and the chains would be about 2 km [1.2 miles] in length. On the other hand, the chain lengths between tie points for thermosets are about

10 to 20 repeat units in length. On the same scale, phenol-formaldehyde would have chain lengths (between tie points) of about 25 mm [1 in] with molecular diameters of nearly 25 mm [1 in]. Other comparisons are made in Table 2.1 (3).

TABLE 2.1 COMPARATIVE SIZES OF POLYMER MOLECULES
(Fully Extended Chains – Scaled 100,000,000:1)

Material	End-to-End Distance, Å	Degree of Polymerization	Model Length $-CH_2-$ groups ∅ 3/8" diameter
Phenolic	40.1	8	8.5 inches
Melamine	35.4	5	7.5 inches
Alkyd – Unsaturated Polyester Resin	94.4	19	20 inches
Epoxy Adhesive	15.9	1	3.3 inches
Epoxy Resin – Medium MW	110.9	6.5	24 inches
Epoxy Resin – High MW	580.6	34	10 feet
Olefin Grease	200	67	50 inches
Polyethylene, Low-Density	2000	670	42 feet
Polyethylene, UHMW	91,000	30,000	0.4 miles

Some thermoplastic polymers such as polyethylene can be further toughened by crosslinking, with either irradiation or peroxide chemicals. Crosslinking is accomplished by removal of a small molecule such as hydrogen from the primary carbon-carbon backbone. Active sites on adjacent chains then react to form a tie point or crosslink. The number of tie points per thousand repeat units is usually quite small. Typically, crosslinked high-density polyethylene (HDPE) has about 0.5 to 1 tie points per thousand carbons. Low-density polyethylene (LDPE) has about 5 to 10 per thousand. These few tie points serve only to partially immobilize the polymer above its traditional melting point. Thus, instead of becoming fluids above their melting points, crosslinked thermoplastics remain very soft, thermoformable solids (Figure 2.1). As might be expected, LDPE with its greater frequency of tie points is considerably more difficult to stretch-form than HDPE. The reprocessing (regrinding and reextrusion) of crosslinked thermoplastics usually results in mechanical destruction of some tie points or backbone carbon-carbon bonds.

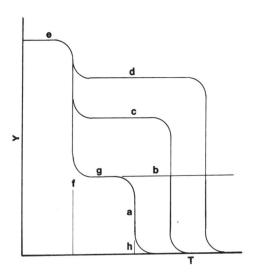

Figure 2.1 Schematic of Temperature-Dependent Young's Modulus. a: Amorphous. b: Crosslinked. c: Low Crystallinity. d: High Crystallinity. e: Glassy Polymer. f: Glass Transition. g: Rubbery Plateau. h: Liquid Flow Temperature. T: Temperature. Y: Young's Modulus (log Scale).

TABLE 2.2 CHEMICAL STRUCTURE OF VINYL-TYPE THERMOPLASTICS

$$\begin{array}{cc} R_1 & R_3 \\ -C - C - \\ R_2 & R_4 \end{array}$$

Common Name	R_1	R_2	R_3	R_4	Subspecies	Glass Transition Temperature, °C	Crystaline Melt Temperature, °C
Polyethylene	H	H	H	H	LDPE (branched) HDPE (linear)	− 70 −110	112 134 (137)*
Polypropylene	H	H	H	CH$_3$	Atactic Syndiotactic	− 15 5	A 165 (170)*
Polybutene	H	H	H	CH$_2$CH$_3$	(isobutylene)	− 70	A
Polybutadiene (divinyl)	H	H	H	HC=CH$_2$		− 55	A
Polyvinyl chloride (PVC)	H	H	H	Cl		90	A (212)*
Polyvinyl fluoride (PVF)	H	H	H	F		− 20	A
Polyvinyl dichloride (PVDC)	H	H	Cl	Cl		− 17	A
Polyvinylidene fluoride (PVF$_2$)	H	H	F	F		− 35	A
Polytetrafluoroethylene (PTFE)	F	F	F	F		125	326
Polystyrene (PS)	H	H	H	C$_6$H$_5$ (Ø)		94	A (240)**
Polyvinyl Alcohol (PVOH)	H	H	H	OH		85	A
Polyvinyl Acetate (PVAc)	H	H	H	OOCCH		30	A
Polymethylmethacrylate (PMMA)	H	H	CH	COOCH		100	A
Polyacrylonitrile	H	H	H	CN		104	275***(327)*

A = Commerically amorphus polymer
Ø = benzyl ring, as ⊚

* = Melting temperature of pure crystal polymer
** = Isotactic melting point
*** = as a highly oriented fiber

Thermoforming requires biaxial stretching of polymer sheet. Although certain thermosetting polymers such as rubber soften above their glass transition temperatures, the tight three-dimensional network of most rigid thermosetting polymers restricts the gross deformation necessary in thermoforming. Recently however, partially crosslinked polyurethane has been simultaneously drawn, formed, and heat-catalyzed to produce fully crosslinked thermoset shapes (4). Once these molecules are immobilized, very little additional shaping can take place. Additional thermal energy input or regrind then leads to polymer degradation.

Addition and Condensation Polymerization

Thermoplastic polymers are produced in either of two ways. Addition polymers are formed by continuous extension of a preexisting polymer chain by attachment of a monomer con-

TABLE 2.3 CHEMICAL STRUCTURE OF TYPICAL CONDENSATION THERMOPLASTICS

Common Name	Chemical Repeat Unit	Glass Transition Temperature, °C	Crystalline Melt Temperature, °C
Polyethylene Terephthalate (PET)	$-(CH_2)_2-O-\overset{\overset{O}{\|\|}}{C}-\varnothing-\overset{\overset{O}{\|\|}}{C}-O-$	70	260 (267)*
Nylon 66	$-\underset{H}{N}-(CH_2)_6-\underset{H}{N}-\overset{\overset{O}{\|\|}}{C}-(CH_2)4-\overset{\overset{O}{\|\|}}{C}-$	48	240 (265)*
Nylon 6	$-\underset{H}{N}-(CH_2)_6-\overset{\overset{O}{\|\|}}{C}-$	50	210
Polycarbonate	$-\varnothing-\underset{CH_3}{\overset{CH_3}{C}}-\varnothing-O-\overset{\overset{O}{\|\|}}{C}-O-$	150	A
Polyacetal (Polyoxymethylene)	$-\underset{H}{\overset{H}{C}}-O-$	− 60	180
Cellulose **	Cellulose (R = OH)	40	?***
	Cellulose Nitrate (R = NH₃)	53	?
	Cellulose Triacetate (R = OOCCH₃)	70, 100 (?)	280 (?) (305)*
	Cellulose Tributyrate (R = OOCC₃H₇)	120	180 (?) (185)*

A   = Commercially amorphous polymer
*   = Melting temperature of pure crystal polymer
**   = Natural polymer
∅   = benzyl ring, as ⊚
*** = infusible, degrades before melting

taining a reactive double bond. The largest group of addition polymers are called, generically, VINYL polymers. Table 2.2 (5, 6) summarizes the chemical structure of many common addition polymers, including many common thermoformable polymers such as PVC, PP, HDPE, and polystyrene. Condensation polymers are produced by reacting one or two (or more) saturated comonomers with active end groups (amine, hydroxyl, carboxyl). The reaction usually results in evolution of a small by-product molecule such as water. This molecule must be removed continuously to continue the reaction. PET thermoplastic polyester, nylon, polymethyl methacrylate (PMMA), and polycarbonate are examples of condensation polymers. These and others are summarized in Table 2.3.

Aliphatic and Aromatic Polymers

Polyethylene and polypropylene are simple (nearly) linear polymers consisting of $-C-C-$ building blocks, with no backbone double-bond unsaturation. These are aliphatic thermoplastics. Polystyrene has an unsaturated benzyl pendant group on every other backbone carbon, and is the simplest form of an aromatic polymer. Higher order aromatic polymers such as PET or polycarbonate have backbone double bonds on regular intervals. Polymer properties such as stiffness and thermal stability are strong functions of the degree of aromaticity.

Molecular Weight and Molecular Weight Distribution

The molecular weight of a given polymer molecule is obtained by multiplying the molecular weight of the repeat unit by the number of repeat units, then adding in the molecular weights of the end groups. For example, the molecular weight of the ethylene repeat unit $(-CH_2-CH_2-)$ is 28. For HDPE of 10,000 repeat units, the molecular weight is 280,030. In all commercial polymers, there is a distribution of polymer chain lengths (Figure 2.2). The *Number-Average* polymer chain length is obtained by calculating the total weight of all polymer chains and dividing by the total number of chains:

$$M_n = w/n = \sum N_i M_i / \sum M_i$$

The *Weight-Average* molecular weight is obtained by multiplying the weight of a chain of a given length by the number of these chains, then dividing by the total weight of chains:

$$M_w = nw/w = \sum N_i (N_i M_i) / \sum N_i M_i$$

The ratio of weight average to number average molecular weight is known as the *Dispersity Index*:

$$DI = M_w / M_n$$

It generally represents the shape of the chain length distribution curve. These three terms help to define the molecular characteristics of the polymer. Molecular weight distributions cannot be measured directly. Dilute solution viscosity measurements yield indirect information, as do end group analyses, turbidity and osmotic pressure measurements, and calculations based on infrared analyses. Thus, whenever the phrase *Molecular Weight Distribution* is used, it must be carefully defined.

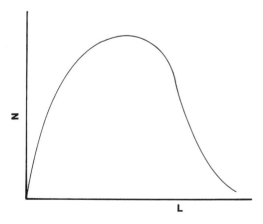

Figure 2.2 Molecular Weight Distribution of Typical Polymer. N: Number of Chains of a Given Length. L: Chain Length.

Molecular Weight and Properties

A polymer that has a low molecular weight is easier to extrude into sheet than one with a very high molecular weight, but high molecular weight yields improved hot strength during forming and improved finished part properties. As an example, consider HDPE, in Figure 2.3 (7). At low MW (1,000), it is a waxy solid at room temperature and an oily liquid at temperatures less than 100 C [212 F]. At a molecular weight of 100,000, it is a tough ductile plastic at room temperature and a highly elastic liquid above its 110 C [230 F] melting point. At MW of 1,000,000 (UHMWPE), it is an extremely tough crystalline solid at room temperature, with such a high degree of order that it barely flows even at temperatures far above its 134 C [273 F] melting point. PMMA at MW of 300 is a viscous liquid at room temperature. It is commonly used as a cell casting syrup. At MW = 30,000, PMMA at room temperature is a glassy, brittle transparent solid. When heated to temperatures of 100 to 150 C [180 to 270 F] above its softening point (known as the glass transition temperature, Tg = 105 C [220 F]), it becomes a rubbery contiguous formable sheet. Increasing the temperature further causes excessive chain mobility, manifested as sheet sag.

For some polymers, the molecular weight distribution can be significantly altered during polymerization or afterward in special depolymerization steps. Typically, broad MWD polymers have very shear-sensitive viscosities over wide temperature ranges and so are much easier to process than narrow MWD polymers. Broad MWD polymers are used in extrusion coating, laminating and heat sealing where high melt strength over a wide processing temperature range is sought. On the other hand, certain narrow MWD polymers can be highly oriented and so yield very tough film and thin-gage sheet. Narrow MWD polymers usually have better mechanical properties than broad MWD polymers. It is difficult to generalize here however, since other factors such as extent of chain entanglements, pendant group size and frequency, molecular level energy interactions such as van der Waals and hydrogen bonding forces, and side-chain branching can act to override the effect of molecular weight for any given homologous class of polymers.

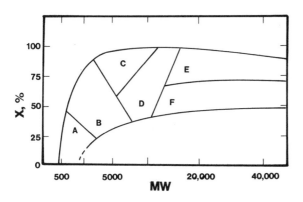

Figure 2.3 Relationship Between Polyethylene Molecular Weight (MW), Crystallinity (X), and Polymer Nature (5). A: Grease, Liquid. B: Soft Wax. C: Brittle Wax. D: Tough Wax. E: Hard Plastic. F: Soft Plastic. (Redrawn figure used by permission of copyright owner.)

Morphology and Properties

Polymer processing in general is concerned with the economic transition between the solid and fluid or semi-fluid states of the polymers. It is easy to identify the liquidus phase of nonpolymeric crystalline substances (metals, ceramics) by an abrupt first-order thermodynamic transition from a rigid substance to a waterlike fluid with a measurable absorption of energy (called the latent heat of fusion). Crystalline materials in the solid state have regular, ordered atomic structures that sharply diffract X-rays in known, repeatable fashions. It is difficult to envision long-chain, highly entangled polymers as having the high degree of order needed to form crystalline domains. Yet certain polymers such as nylon, polyethylene, PET, and PP crystallize readily when cooled from the melt. Although single polymer crystals have been formed in laboratories, polycrystalline structures are formed in commercial applications. Crystallite formation is a kinetic or rate-dependent process. Noncrystalline or amorphous polymers have molecular structures that are unordered. Disorder can be caused by the bulk or stiffness of the polymer chain due to side-chain branching frequency and size, large pendant groups, steric hindrance or by a ladder-type backbone structure, or by rapid quenching of a potentially crystalline polymer from the melt state. Most crystallite regions in commercial crystallizable polymers are mixtures of spherulitic (sphere-like) and dendritic (tree-like) crystals in amorphous regions. The extent of crystallinity (and to some extent the size of the crystallites) of any polymer strongly affects the sharpness of its X-ray pattern, its melting point, and nearly all commonly measured physical properties. For a crystallizable polymer, high molecular weight, narrow MWD, and backbone linearity yield high crystallinity levels. Small amounts of nucleants such as pigments, organic promoters, catalyst residue, or fillers enhance the rate of crystallization. High shear processing and rapid cooling inhibit crystallization. Annealing and orientation enhance it.

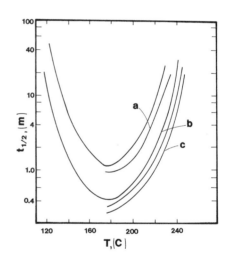

Figure 2.4 Half-Time for Crystallizing PET (8). $t_{1/2}$: Half-Time (m)(log Scale). T: Temperature (C). a: 1.0 IV PET (High MW). b: 0.65 IV PET (Low MW). c: 0.65 IV PET with Talc Nucleant.

Crystallization is a rate-dependent process. The isothermal time to reach 50% of the ultimate crystallized fractional volume change is known as the crystallization half-time. The temperature-dependent semi-logarithmic half-time curves are characteristically cup-shaped, as seen for PET in Figure 2.4 (8). These curves are classically fit with the Avrami equation:

$$-\ln \varphi = Kt^n$$

where φ is the fraction of uncrystallized material, given as:

$$\varphi = 1 - \Delta\eta/\Delta\eta_\infty$$

Here $\Delta\eta$ is the volumetric change as determined by dilatometric methods. K and n are empirical coefficients. K is polymer specific and a strong function of temperature and possibly nucleator concentration (if any). n, the Avrami constant, is a measure of the nature of the crystallite formation. For moderate processing conditions, $n = 3$ for constant nucleation of spherical crystallites or sporatic plate-like growth (9). It can be seen from this equation (or from Figure 2.4), that slow cooling enhances crystallization and quench cooling inhibits it. Reheating amorphous sheet of a crystalline polymer such as PET to temperatures where appreciable crystallization can take place can lead to unwanted haze. It can also lead to a method for fabricating crystalline structures from initially amorphous sheet (10).

X-ray patterns for polymers with crystalline levels below about 30% are difficult to interpret. Amorphous polymers have no X-ray diffraction patterns, no melting points, and thus no latent heats of fusion. Thus, when an amorphous polymer is heated, the temperature range over which it changes from a rubbery solid to a flowable fluid can be as broad as 50 to 70 C [80 to 125 F]. Polystyrene and plasticized PVC are amorphous polymers. The temperature at which a polymer changes from a brittle, glass-like material to a rubbery one is the glass-transition temperature, Tg. This is a second-order thermodynamic temperature where substantial chain segment mobility takes place along the backbone. Under stress, permanent chain motion and intermolecular deformation is possible. Since polymers have broad distributions of molecular chain lengths, the glass transition temperature is in reality a temperature range of a few degrees. Nevertheless a single value is usually given for a specific polymer. The glass transition temperature is the absolute lowest temperature at which the polymer can be formed. As processing temperatures increase above Tg, amorphous polymers become increasingly easier to process. Crystalline thermoplastic polymers and thermosetting polymers have glass transition temperatures as well. For thermosets, chain mobility is restricted by the three-dimensional molecular network until the thermal degradation temperature is reached. In crystalline polymers, the crystallite order restricts amorphous phase chain mobility until the melting point is reached. This is seen in schematic in Figure 2.1. For crystalline polymers the ratio of melt temperature to glass transition temperature is 1.4 to 2.0 (in °K). For polymer homologs, increasing MW yields increasing crystallinity and melt temperature (11). Tg is relatively unaffected by MW (Figure 2.5). Glass transition temperatures for typical thermoformable polymers are given in Tables 2.2 and 2.3.

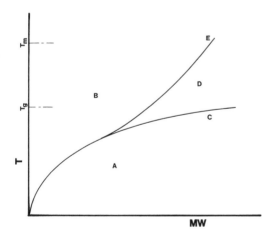

Figure 2.5 Effect of Molecular Weight on Transition Temperatures (5). A: Rigid Crystalline Polymer. B: Viscous Liquid. C: Glass Transition. D: Flexible Crystalline Polymer. E: Melting Point. T: Temperature. MW: Molecular Weight. Tg: Glass Transition Temperature. Tm: Melt Temperature. (Composite figure redrawn and used here by permission of copyright owner.)

Molecular Orientation

In order to obtain improved properties in some polymers, sheets are biaxially oriented during the extrusion process. Both crystalline and amorphous polymers can be oriented. For crystalline polymers, unique combinations of properties can be achieved by carefully matching levels of mechanical stress with heating and cooling rates. Crystallites thus formed can be formed from highly oriented molecules, yielding dramatic reductions in haze level and equally impressive increases in ultimate tensile strength (albeit at reduction in elongation at break). Thin-gage sheets of amorphous polymers such as PS and PMMA can be biaxially oriented as well, to yield substantially increased ultimate elongation and ductility in the heated sheet and in the final product (Table 2.4 (12)).

TABLE 2.4 BIAXIAL ORIENTATION PROPERTIES OF BRITTLE POLYMERS
(Adapted from (5); pg. 266)

Material	Tensile Strength MPa [1000 psi]	Elongation at Break, %	Impact Strength, J/m [ft-lb/in]
Polystyrene			
Unoriented	34.5–62 [5–9]	1– 3.6	13.3–27 [0.25–0.5]
Biaxially Oriented	48.3–83 [7–12]	8–18	>160 [>3]
PMMA			
Unoriented	51.7–70 [7.5–10]	5–10	215 [4]
Biaxially Oriented	55.2–75.8 [8–11]	25–50	800 [15]

Chain Mobility and Polymer Stiffness

The intrinsic strength of a polymer depends upon chain rigidity and ability of polymer-to-polymer intermolecular structure to withstand deformation or disentanglement under load. The ductility, hardness, resistance to impact and stiffness of a plastic product is related to the nature of the polymer molecular structure. Flexibility is a function of the degree of chain segment rotation about the $-C-C-$ backbone. If double bonds are included in the backbone, stiffness is increased. It is increased further if the occurence of double bonds is regular, such as $-C-C=C-C=C-$. Aromaticity in a pendant group adds stiffness as with PS and benzene ring inclusion in the backbone as with PC or PET further increases stiffness. If the backbone has only aromatic carbon-carbon bonds, as with polycyclic diphenyls, the polymer becomes quite stiff. Some of the stiffest polymers are the polyimides where backbone bonding occurs at four points on the aromatic ring (rather than two), thus forming a ladderlike structure. Decreasing chain mobility implies increasing difficulty in thermoforming the polymer sheet.

As noted with PS, its benzyl pendant group stiffens the polymer chain. This is due to the difficulty in fitting the bulky pendant groups side by side along the backbone and is called steric hindrance. Not all pendant groups cause stiffening, however. Long-chain branching on LDPE acts to separate main chains, increase free volume or molecule-level voids in the solid, thus reducing the bulk density of the polymer. The lowered density results in greater flexibility, lower tensile strength, lower Tg and Tm and lower levels of crystallinity. Polypropylene on the other hand has a methylene group on every other carbon, thus representing the limiting case on short side-chain branching. The steric hindrance forces the polymer chain into a helix, thus stiffening the backbone but at the same time creating even greater free volume. As a result, PP has very low density and relatively high Tg and Tm.

Although not pendant groups, per se, halogen atoms such as chlorine on PVC and fluorine on PTFE/FEP are much larger than, say, a hydrogen atom, thus causing substantial steric hindrance. More important is the highly electronegative state of halogen atoms. In very regular polymers, these tend to repel one another, thus stiffening the backbone into a rodlike configuration. All halogen-substituted polymers are quite difficult to process into sheet without plasticizers. Polymers that have very high hydrogen bonding levels, such as nylons or PMMA, also have increased stiffness. Secondary hydrogen bonds occur between main chain groups such as amines $(-H-N\ldots H-)$ and hydroxyls $(-H-O\ldots H-)$, in effect increasing the effective diameter of the chain segment and thus reducing its mobility.

Stress-Crack Resistance

Environmental stress-crack resistance (ESCR) is the ability of a strained polymer to withstand an agressive medium. Many thermoformed products must withstand environments such as detergents, oils and greases, and mild solvents. Solvent molecules tend to be quite small and so readily diffuse into the polymer, move between adjacent polymer chains and act to separate them. When the polymer-solvent attraction forces exceed the polymer-polymer intermolecular attraction forces, the polymer chains are separated by solvent, and the polymer is dissolved, swollen or crazed. Weak solvents can act on the polymer chain only when it is strained. Unfortunately, most product stress crack failures occur because the strained polymer failed in a weak solvent over a long period of time (Figure 2.6 (13)). Classic examples are rubber-impact-modified polystyrene shower stalls and refrigerator inner-door liners. Surface deglossing and microcrazing on PMMA and PVC can also be caused by exposure to very mildly aggressive environments (but more probably are due to migration and loss of small molecule plasticizers, erosion, acid rain, and UV-embrittlement probably due to surface crosslinking).

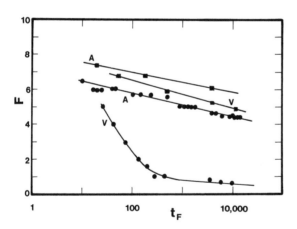

Figure 2.6 Effect of Environment on Flexural Creep Rupture (F) of Two Polymers (13). A: Air. V: Vegetable Oil. Solid Circles: HIPS. Solid Squares: ABS. F: Applied Flexural Stress ($\times 1000$ psi, $\times 6.9$ MPa). t_F: Time to Failure (min). (Figure used by permission of John Wiley & Sons.)

Gas Permeation

Gas transmission through polymers depends upon the extent of free volume in the formed part and upon the relative order of magnitude of polymer-polymer and polymer-gas molecule attraction forces. Gases that are chemically similar to the polymer repeat unit tend to migrate more readily. Cellulosics transmit water but polyolefins do not. Olefins tend to transmit fluorocarbon gases but styrenics do not. The permeation of a gas through a plastic is the product of its solubility in the plastic and its diffusivity through the plastic. Solubility is directly related to polymer-solvent affinity (14). The small molecule diffusion rate through amorphous or unordered polymer regions is many times higher than that through highly ordered crystalline regions. In partially crystalline materials such as olefins, an increasing degree of crystallinity leads to a decrease in permeability of all small molecules. Orienting any polymer substantially increases the small molecule diffusion path. Orienting a crystalline polymer leads to substantially reduced gas permeation and so materials such as PET and nylon become efficient gas barriers.

Copolymerization

Polymers made from a single set of monomers are called homopolymers. Frequently specific end uses or processing conditions dictate properties that cannot be attained by homopolymers. A common method of altering polymer properties is by co-reacting small amounts of reactive monomers with the primary polymer molecules. By controlling the nature of the polymerization, these copolymers can be added randomly along the polymer backbone (random copolymerization), added as pendant groups (branched or graft copolymerization), or added into the polymer backbone as long-chain homopolymer segments (block copolymerization). Random copolymerization results in broadening of melt and glass transition temperatures, reduced stiffness (or increased flexibility), reduction in melt viscosity and crystallinity and an increase in high temperature (rubbery) sheet strength and melt strength. Classic examples include ethylene into polypropylene to reduce Tg and increase thermoformability and sodium methacrylate into polyethylene to produce an ionomeric polymer with reduced crystallinity, improved transparency and toughness. Block copolymerization can provide main chain flexibility in otherwise brittle polymers, as with butadiene in polystyrene. The butadiene segments are not cosoluble with PS, and so form a separate but chemically linked phase. ABS (acrylonitrile-butadiene-styrene) is a terpolymer, with acrylonitrile polymer grafted to the block butadiene-styrene copolymer backbone. The acrylonitrile adds improved solvent resistance and high (forming) temperature toughness to impact-modified (otherwise brittle) PS.

Blends

If two polymers are cosoluble, such as PS and PPO (polyphenylene oxide) or polyvinyl acetate and PMMA, intensive shear melt mixing can yield a true thermodynamic single phase material. The resulting polymer properties are (nearly) identical to those that might be obtained through copolymerization. Note that physical blends of homologs such as polyethylenes or vinyls should yield true single phase blends, but may not. Insoluble blends yield macroscopic two-phase systems that can behave as if they were copolymers, as is the case of melt coblending butadiene rubber and polystyrene. However many insoluble blends yield valueless polymers.

Plasticizers

Plasticizers are small molecules of a chemical structure similar to the polymer in which they are dissolved. Their role is to separate the main chains, thus reducing polymer-polymer intermolecular forces and allowing the polymer chains to move past one another during shearing. Plasticized polymers have lower processing viscosities, stiffness, glass transition, melt and continuous use temperatures and greater flexibility, toughness, tear strength, and ultimate elongation at break. These effects are controlled to a great degree by the thermodynamic compatability of polymer and plasticizer, and plasticizer concentration and glass transition temperature. The glass transition temperature is also broadened by the plasticizer, with the greatest broadening occurring when the plasticizer is a poor solvent for the polymer. PVC is the most important polymer that is thermoformed as plasticized sheet. PVC is nearly intractable in an unplasticized state. When dioctyl phthalate is added to 40 (vol%), Tg is reduced from 105 C [220 F] to 5 C [40 F] and the transition region is increased from less than 10 C [18 F] to 30 C [50 F]. In order to ensure long-term property retention, plasticizers must have very low vapor pressure at room temperature and must be non-migrating.

Additives

Plasticizers are one very specific category of additives. Many chemicals are added to polymers in order to change specific undesirable characteristics. Surfactants and lubricants are aids used to improve processing quality and/or extruder production rate (throughput). Antioxidants are added to minimize polymer yellowing during processing and reprocessing. Tints are dyes added to change transparent plastic color from nonwhite to perceived "water-white". Organic dyes color transparent plastics but do not appreciably affect their longwave radiant energy absorption spectra (15). Organic and inorganic pigments color opaque plastics. The dosage level is usually less than 2 (wt%). Titanium dioxide is an opacifier in low doses, as is carbon black. Carbon black is also used extensively as an ultraviolet light absorber, particularly in vinyls and polyolefins. To produce foam sheet, chemical and physical blowing agents are added to the polymer during extrusion. Chemical blowing agents are very fine powders of ultrapure thermodynamically unstable chemicals, such as azodicarbonamide, $(H_2N-CO-N=N-CO-NH_2)$ that decomposes to produce nitrogen. Sodium bicarbonate/citric acid decomposes to produce CO_2 and H_2O vapor and has been used extensively to produce PS foam sheet. Frequently, hydrocarbons such as pentane and butane and fluorocarbons such as refrigerent ll and l2 are added to PS and polyethylene to produce low-density closed cell foams for cushioning applications.

Fillers

Common inorganic fillers such as talc, calcium carbonate and clay increase sheet stiffness and processing temperature by interfering with polymer chain segment mobility. Some increase in stiffness can be beneficial. For example, 20 (wt%) talc in PP broadens the thermoforming processing window enough to allow forming on conventional equipment. Although fillers reduce overall resin costs, they restrict bulk chain straightening and flexing under load. This causes reduced ultimate elongation, tensile strength, impact strength and fatigue strength. Milled glass fibers, to 30 (wt%), provide exceptional strength improvement, but processing is restricted to pressure forming. Even further improvement in polymer stiffness is obtained by adding inorganic reinforcing elements such as glass fibers, mica, or graphite fibers. Unfortunately, these elements so stiffen the polymer sheet that matched-die forming above the polymer melt temperature with (near) compression molding pressures is required. Nevertheless, commercial parts are fabricated of glass-reinforced PP, PET and nylon and graphite-reinforced polyimide.

Laminates

Certain end use applications need mechanical properties that no single polymer can provide. Polymers are therefore laminated, coated or coextruded into multilayer sheet. Examples include the UV (or chemical) barrier of PMMA on ABS, solid impact PS "cap sheets" on PS foam for stiffness, and the thermoformable PET-EVOH-PET thin-gage sheet used to produce preforms for high barrier stretch-blow-molded containers. The control of multilayer thickness is of great concern to the sheet extruder. Mismatched viscosities can lead to interlayer thickness variation. Temperatures must be matched to ensure good interlayer bonding. Plasticizer and additive concentrations must be nonmigratory and must be carefully monitored to prevent "blooming" at interfaces. Biaxial orientation during thermoforming will reveal poor interlayer adhesion. Orientation must also be carefully monitored to minimize formation of microvoids in inherently weak inner layers. Multilayer structures must be carefully heated to prevent innerlayer interface overheating and delamination from mismatched thermal expansion coefficients.

Stress-Strain Behavior of Plastics

Thermoforming is a deformation process on a polymer in its rubbery solid state above Tg (but below its crystalline melting temperature). Technically, a (nearly) uniform force is applied to a two-dimensional membrane to biaxially stretch it. The amount of force required and the extent of stretching are directly related to the stress-strain behavior of the polymer at process conditions. Below Tg, all polymers are brittle in that the stress-strain curve is linear and quite steep until fracture at a very low strain level (Figure 2.7 (16)). In general, tensile modulus values of all unfilled (neat) amorphous polymers below Tg are about 0.345 GPa [500,000 psi] (17). Within 20 C [40 F] above Tg, tensile modulus values have dropped 3 to 4 decades, to 35 to 350 MPa [50 to 500 psi]. Ultimate tensile strengths also drop rapidly to values in this range.

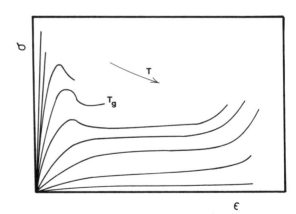

Figure 2.7 Stress-Strain Schematic for Amorphous Polymers. σ: Stress. ε: Strain (or Elongation for Tensile Stress). T: Temperature. Tg: Glass Transition Temperature.

As the isothermal temperature increases above Tg, amorphous polymers become increasingly ductile, as seen by yielding at a modest strain level. The applied stress is then sustained over ever-increasing strain levels. There is strong indication that the minimum forming temperature is where the abrupt yield point vanishes. In crystalline polymers, the rubbery region is compromised to a great degree by the crystalline structure (Figure 2.1). At high levels of crystallinity as with UHMWPE and PTFE, the modulus of the polymer above the glass transition temperature is only slightly less than that below the glass transition temperature, and so extraordinary measures are required to form the material in this solid region. An increasing level of crystallinity then has the effect of compressing the temperature effect on the stress-strain curves, as seen in Figure 2.8. Further, for homologous crystalline polymer species, yield strength and ultimate tensile strength at a given temperature increase with increasing crystallinity (Figure 2.1).

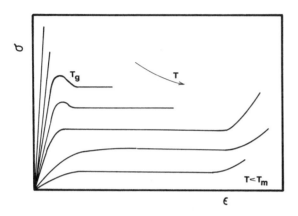

Figure 2.8 Stress-Strain Schematic for Crystalline Polymers. σ: Stress. ε: Strain (or Elongation for Tensile Stress). T: Temperature. Tg: Glass Transition Temperature. Tm: Melt Temperature.

It is apparent that there is a direct relation between the stress-strain behavior of a given polymer and process of thermoforming it in sheet form. As expected, the normal forming temperature for any polymer is closely related to Tg (and Tm for crystalline polymers). Forming temperature ranges for many materials are given in Table 2.5 (18). Typically, for amorphous materials, the lower forming temperature is about 20–30 C [40–55 F] above Tg and the normal forming temperature is about 70–100 C [125–180 F] above Tg. The "set temperature" is the temperature at which a part can be removed from a mold without distortion. It is approximately the polymer heat distortion temperature at 0.455 MPa [66 psi], which in turn is about 10–20 C [20–40 F] below Tg. High mold temperatures yield improved part surface quality. Mold temperatures should be about 0–10 C [0–20 F] below material set temperature (or HDT) and so about 10–30 C [20–55 F] below Tg. The crystalline polymer forming temperature range is usually quite narrow and the recommended forming temperature is often within a few degrees of the polymer melt temperature. Highly crystalline polymers such as PP retain a very high degree of order and hence stiffness up to an abrupt melting point and so may have normal processing windows as narrow as 2 to 5 C [5 to 10 F]. A more thorough analysis of the interaction of temperature-dependent stress-strain behavior, applied stress and extent of drawing is given in Chapter 4.

Thermal Properties

Heat capacity (or specific heat) and thermal conductivity are two important polymer physical properties that are used extensively in thermoforming. Heat capacity (at constant pressure), c_p, is a thermodynamic property, defined as the isobaric change in polymer enthalpy with temperature. Heat capacity values for many polymers can be obtained from enthalpic

TABLE 2.5 CHARACTERISTIC TEMPERATURES OF CERTAIN THERMOPLASTICS

Material	Type	Glass Transition Temperature T_g, C [F]	Melt Temperature T_m, C [F]	Heat Distortion Temperature @ 66 psi, C [F]	Recommended Mold Temperature # C [F]	Polymer Set Temperature # C [F]	Lower Forming Temperature # C [F]	Normal Forming Temperature # C [F]	Upper Processing Temperature # C [F]
ABS	A	88–120 [190–248]		77–113 [170–235]	82 [180]	85 [185]	127 [260]	146 [295]	182 [360]
Acrylonitrile	C	95 [203]	135 [275]	78 [172]	–	85 [185]	127 [260]	149 [300]	182 [360]
Acetate	C	70,100 [158, 212]	230 [445]	52–93 [125–200]	88 [190]	71 [160]	127 [260]	154 [310]	182 [360]
PMMA	A	100 [212]	–	74–113 [165–235]	–	85 [185]	149 [300]	177 [350]	193 [380]
Acrylic/PVC	A	105 [221]		81 [177]		79 [175]	163 [325]	188 [370]	204 [400]
Butyrate	C	120 [248]	140 [284]	54–108 [130–227]	–	79 [175]	127 [260]	146 [295]	182 [360]
PC	A	150 [300]		138 [280]	127 [260]	138 [280]	168 [335]	191 [375]	204 [400]
PET	C	70 [158]	255 [490]	49 [120]	–	77 [170]	121 [250]	149 [300]	166 [330]
Polyethersulfone	A	230 [445]		216 [420]	–	204 [400]	274 [525]	316 [600]	371 [700]
20% GR PES	A	225 [437]		216 [420]	–	210 [410]	279 [535]	343 [650]	382 [720]
HDPE	C	–110 [–166]	134 [273]	79–91 [175–196]	71 [160]	82 [180]	127 [260]	146 [295]	182 [360]
Propionate	C	–		64–121 [147–250]	–	88 [190]	127 [260]	146 [295]	182 [360]
PP	C	5 [41]	168 [334]	107–121 [225–250]	–	88 [190]	143 [290]	154–163 [310–325]	166 [330]
40% GR PP	C	–	168 [334]	166 [330]	–	91 [195]	132 [270]	204 [400]	232 [450]
P-Sulfone	A	190 [374]		181 [358]	163 [325]	163 [325]	191 [375]	246 [475]	302 [575]
P-Styrene	A	94 [200]		68–96 [155–204]	82 [180]	85 [185]	127 [260]	149 [300]	182 [360]
PTFE/FEP	C	–	275 [527]	70 [158]	–	149 [300]	232 [450]	288 [550]	327 [620]
Rigid PVC	A	90 [194]		57–82 [135–180]	60 [140]	66 [150]	104 [220]	138 [280]	154 [310]
Mod. PPO	A	104–110 [219–230]		110 [230]	–	99 [210]	163 [325]	188 [375]	204 [400]

A = Amorphous. C = Crystalline
# Mold and material temperatures courtesy of W. K. McConnell (18), by permission of copyright owner.

tables (19). Crystalline polymer heat capacity values are usually quite temperature-dependent approaching melt temperature and exhibit discontinuities at the melt points (Figure 2.9 (20, 21)). As a result, it is difficult to give specific values for heat capacity. Heat capacity values for amorphous polymers, on the other hand, are only slightly temperature-dependent (Table 2.6). The temperature dependency for amorphous material heat capacity values decreases slightly at temperatures above the Tg. Very accurate techniques for predicting heat capacities of simple organic molecules have been extended to polymers by assuming that energy is transmitted by translation of molecules or molecular segments, that each segment acts as a liquid harmonic oscillator and that the polymer is characterized as a semicrystalline solid (22). The total molecular energy is the sum of its components – translational, external rotational, internal rotational, vibrational, and electronic. From established tables of molecular energy contributions for each of the elemental segments of the polymer (repeat units, end groups, pendant groups, and the like), relatively accurate but tedious calculations yield reasonable predictions of polymer heat capacity. Experimentally, the entire temperature-dependent heat capacity curve for any polymer can be obtained in a few minutes with only a few grams of polymer using standard differential scanning calorimetry (DSC). Basically a known weight of polymer is heated at a constant rate and its time-dependent temperature compared with a standard of constant heat capacity. Characteristically within normal thermoforming heating ranges, neat amorphous materials have heat capacity values of about 0.5 cal/g C [0.5 Btu/lb F] and crystalline materials have (average) values of about 0.9.

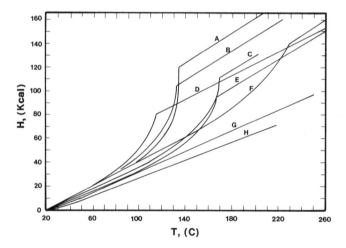

Figure 2.9 Temperature-Dependent Enthalpies for Several Polymers (20). H: Enthalpy, (kcal). T: Temperature (C). A: HDPE (0.96 sp. gr.). B: MDPE (0.945). C: POM (Acetal). D: LDPE (0.92), PMMA. E: PP. F: PA-6 (Nylon 6). G: PS, MIPS, ABS. H: FPVC, PVC. (Figure used by permission of Paul Kiefel GmbH.)

Thermal Conductivity

Energy transmission through polymer solids and quiescent liquids is by molecular interaction, rather than the electron transfer characteristic of metals. Thus thermal conduction, a measure of the efficiency of energy transfer, is governed by the same energy elements that contribute to heat capacity. Theoretical predictions are based on a linear relationship between thermal conductivity, heat capacity and liquid sonic velocity. The accuracy of prediction is excellent for simple organic molecules. For polymers, processing effects on intermolecular free volume and molecular order in partially crystalline polymers cause the calculated results to deviate substantially from carefully measured experimental values. Further, energy tends to be preferentially transmitted along the molecule backbone rather than between molecular chains. Thus, the nature of the crystalline order and the type of

TABLE 2.6 HEAT CAPACITIES OF CERTAIN THERMOPLASTICS IN CAL/G C [OR BTU/LB F]

Material	Type	Cp from Enthalpy Data (19) $(T_g < T < T_m)$	Cp from Graph (20) $(50 < T < 90$ C$)$	Cp from DSC Experiments	$\Delta Cp/\Delta T$ (per 100 C)
PS	A	0.68	0.45	0.50 @ 225C	0.043
ABS	A	–	0.45	0.54 @ 225	0.074
PMMA	A	0.56	–	0.56 @ 225	0.048
PC	A	–	–	0.50 @ 225	0.033
PVC	A	0.65	0.39	– @	–
PP	C	0.78	0.47	0.96 @ 125	0.132
HDPE	C	0.58	0.61	0.88 @ 80	0.597
EP-copoly	C	0.80	–	– @	–
PTFE	C	0.25	–	– @	–
PA-6	C	–	0.50	0.87 @ 180	0.502
PA-66	C	0.74	–	– @	–
PET	C	–	0.45*	– @	0.09*
Mod PPO	A	–	(0.50)	– @	–

* (24)

pendant groups can influence the values. Thermal conductivity is one of the most difficult transport properties to measure (25). As a result, very few accurate values of thermal conductivity are available for polymers. Fortunately, thermal conductivity is not strongly temperature-dependent and homologous series of polymers (olefins, styrenics, vinyls) tend to have similar values (Table 2.7). Typically, thermal conductivity values for amorphous polymers such as PS, PMMA and PVC, tend to be in the range of 3 to 4×10^{-4} cal/g· cm· C [0.073 to 0.097 Btu/ft· hr· F]. Owing to the high degree of order, values for crystalline polymers tend to be about twice the amorphous values, at 6 to 10. The exception is PP, where the effect of crystalline order is obviated by the high free volume caused by steric hindrance.

Thermal Diffusivity

Although thermal conductivity is a measure of the extent of energy transmission, through solids, thermal diffusivity is a measure of the rate at which energy is transmitted:

$$\alpha = k/\rho \, c_p$$

$$(cm^2/s) = (cal/g \text{ cm s } C)/(g/cm^3)\,(cal/g \text{ C})$$

$$[ft^2/hr] = [Btu/ft \text{ hr F}]/[lb/ft^3]\,[Btu/lb \text{ F}]$$

This combination of physical properties arises naturally from considerations of transient heat conduction. Values for all polymers are typically 5 to 10×10^{-4} cm^2/s [2 to 4×10^{-3} ft^2/h], with olefins showing the greatest range in values. In contrast, metals have values that are hundreds of times larger (Table 2.7).

Thermal Expansion Coefficient

As polymers heat, chain mobility increases and molecules tend to move away from one another, increasing free volume. Factors that inhibit chain mobility tend to minimize thermal

TABLE 2.7 THERMAL PROPERTIES OF CERTAIN THERMOPLASTICS

Resin	Density g/cm³ [lb/ft³]	Thermal Conductivity 10⁻⁴ cal/s cm C [Btu/ft hr F]	Heat Capacity cal/g C [Btu/lb F]	Thermal Diffusivity 10⁻⁴ cm²/s [10⁻³ ft²/hr]	Thermal Expansion Coefficient 10⁻⁶/C [10⁻⁶/F]
ABS	1.05 [65.5]	2–3 [0.048–0.073]	0.5	3.8– 5.7 [1.47–2.21]	60–130 [33–72]
PS	1.05 [65.5]	3 [0.073]	0.5	5.7 [2.2]	50– 83 [28–46]
PMMA	1.20 [74.9]	4–6 [0.097–0.145]	0.56	6– 8.9 [2.3–3.45]	50– 90 [28–50]
PC	1.20 [74.9]	4.7 [0.114]	0.5	7.8 [3.0]	68 [38]
PVC	1.35 [84.2]	3.5–5 [0.085–0.121]	0.6	4.3– 6.2 [1.67–2.4]	50–100 [28–56]
PP	0.9 [56.2]	2.8 [0.068]	0.9	3.5 [1.36]	81–100 [45–56]
HDPE	0.96 [59.9]	11–12 [0.266–0.290]	0.9	12.7–13.9 [4.9–5.4]	59–110 [33–61]
EP-copoly	0.94 [58.7]	10 [0.242]	0.8	13.3 [5.15]	70–110 [39–61]
PTFE/FEP	2.2 [137.3]	6 [0.145]	0.3	9.1 [3.53]	(70–140) [39–78]
PA [nylon]-6	1.12 [69.8]	5.8 [0.140]	0.8	6.5 [2.52]	80– 83 [44–46]
PA[nylon]-66	1.13 [70.5]	5.8 [0.140]	0.75	6.8 [2.64]	80 [44]
PET	1.35 [84.2]	3.3–3.6 [0.080–0.087]	0.45	5.4– 5.9 [2.1–2.29]	65 [36]
Mod. PPO	1.07 [66.8]	3.8 [0.092]	0.5	7.1 [2.75]	38–68 [21–38]
Aluminum	2.68 [167.2]	3000 [72.5]	0.23	4900 [1900]	19 [10.6]
Copper/Bronze	8.8 [549]	4500 [109]	0.09	5700 [2200]	18 [10]
Nickel	8.9 [555]	2200 [53.2]	0.112	2200 [853]	13 [7.2]
Steel	7.9 [493]	880 [21.3]	0.11	1000 [388]	11 [6.1]
Maple	0.45 [28.1]	3 [0.073]	0.25	27 [10.5]	60 [33]
Plaster	0.9–1.1 [56–69]	7.2 [0.174]	0.26	25–30 [9.7–11.6]	10 [5.6]
Al-Epoxy	1.7 [106]	20–40 [0.484–0.967]	0.3	39 [15.1]	45 [25]
Zinc Alloy	6.7 [418]	2500 [60.4]	0.10	3700 [1430]	27 [15]

expansion. Thermal expansion is reduced with increasing crystallinity, orientation, steric hindrance, hydrogen bonding, crosslinking, rigid fillers, molecular polarity (such as with PVC). It is enhanced with plasticizers, lubricants, processing aids, solvents and dissolved gases. Flexible polymers tend to have thermal expansion coefficient values of about 100×10^{-6} mm/mm C [in/in C] and rigid ones have values of about 50×10^{-6} (Table 2.7). In contrast, metals have values of 10 to 20×10^{-6}.

Infrared Spectra of Polymers

Certain polymeric molecular elements and chain segment motions are sympathetic to specific energy levels. The presence of these elements is detected by measuring the intensity and wavelength location of absorbed infrared electromagnetic radiation. For reference, the visible light radiation wavelength range is 0.38 μm to 0.71 μm (or 14,100 to 26,300 wave numbers, in cm^{-1}). Ultraviolet (UV) radiation wavelengths are below 0.38 μm and infrared (IR) radiation wavelengths are above 0.71 μm. As discussed in detail in Chapter 3, thermoformer radiant heaters emit energy in the infrared region, with the peak wavelength depending upon the radiant heater temperature. The efficiency of absorption of that radiation by semitransparent polymers depends upon matching the radiant source peak wavelength to the primary absorption wavelengths of the polymer. Each functional group on the polymer molecule may have more than one absorption wavelength. For example, the simple $-C-H$ unit stretching band is 3 to 3.7 μm, the bending band is 6.7 to 7.7 μm and the rocking band is 11 to 17 μm. The combination of functional group absorption bands is called the IR spectrum. Polymers yield unique IR spectra. Since the intensity of an absorption band is directly related to the concentration of the functional group absorbing the radiation, IR can be used for quantitative analysis. Absolute measures of copolymer and blend concentrations, amounts of organic admixtures such as processing aids, dyes, plasticizers and solvents can be obtained. Further, the nature of the polymerization can be ascertained by measuring end group concentration. And the extent of thermal and oxidative degradation can be determined by subtracting the IR spectrum of virgin polymer from that of the processed one, then measuring the intensity of the $-C=O$ stretching band (5.4 to 6.1 μm) and/or that of the $-C=C$ stretching band (5.9 to 6.4 μm). Characteristic IR-absorption bands are given in Table 2.8.

TABLE 2.8 CHARACTERISTIC IR ABSORPTION BANDS

Specific Vibrational Mode	Wavelength Range μm	Wavenumber Range cm^{-1}
$-OH$ Stretch	2.7 – 3.3	3030–3700
$-NH$ Stretch	2.7 – 3.3	3030–3700
$-CH$ Stretch	3.0 – 3.7	2700–3300
$-C=X$ Stretch	4.2 – 4.78	2090–2380
$-C=O$ Stretch	5.4 – 6.1	1640–1850
$-C=N$ Stretch	5.9 – 6.4	1560–1695
$-C=C$ Stretch	5.9 – 6.4	1560–1695
$-NH$ Bend	6.1 – 6.75	1480–1640
$-CH$ Bend	6.75– 7.7	1300–1480
$-OH$ Bend	6.85– 8.3	1205–1460
$-C-O$ Stretch	7.7 –11.1	910–1300
$-C-N$ Stretch	7.7 –11.1	910–1300
$-C-C$ Stretch	8.3 –12.5	800–1200
$-CH$ Rock	11.1 –16.7	600– 900
$-NH$ Rock	11.1 –14.2	700– 900

The IR spectra for a few common transparent or translucent thermoformable polymers are given in Figures 2.10 to 2.15. The strong absorption band at 3.2 to 3.6 μm is $-C-H$ stretching, and should be found in all $-C-C-$ polymers. In PVC, the absorption band at about 8.1 μm is apparently due to $-C-Cl$ stretching. In cellulose acetate, the band at about 2.8 to 3.0 μm is due to $-O-H$ stretching (shown in Table 2.8 as having a range of 2.7 to 3.3 μm). In PC, the $-C=O$ stretching is seen as being 5.4 to 6.1 μm.

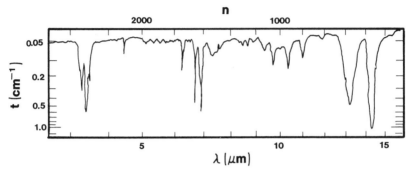

Figure 2.10 IR Transmission Spectrum for PS (18). λ: Wavelength (μm). t: Transmission Coefficient (cm^{-1}). n: Wavenumber (cm). (Figures 2.10 through 2.15 used by permission of copyright owner.)

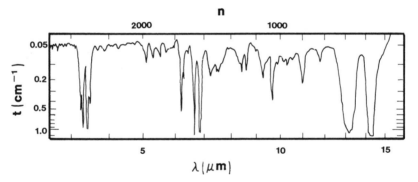

Figure 2.11 IR Transmission Spectrum for ABS (18). λ: Wavelength (μm). t: Transmission Coefficient (cm^{-1}). n: Wavenumber (cm).

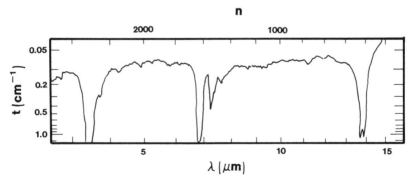

Figure 2.12 IR Transmission Spectrum for PE (18). λ: Wavelength (μm). t: Transmission Coefficient (cm^{-1}). n: Wavenumber (cm).

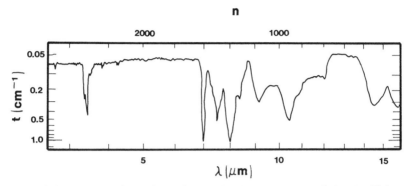

Figure 2.13 IR Transmission Spectrum for PVC (18). λ: Wavelength (μm). t: Transmission Coefficient (cm^{-1}). n: Wavenumber (cm).

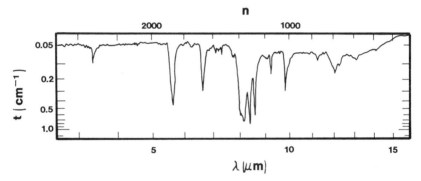

Figure 2.14 IR Transmission Spectrum for PC (18). λ: Wavelength (μm). t: Transmission Coefficient (cm^{-1}). n: Wavenumber (cm).

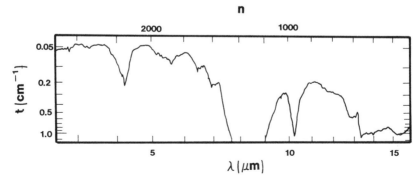

Figure 2.15 IR Transmission Spectrum for PTFE/FEP (18). λ: Wavelength (μm). t: Transmission Coefficient (cm^{-1}). n: Wavenumber (cm).

In certain polymers, such as polyamides (nylons), polyethylenes and PET, orientation and crystallinity are revealed in specific IR absorption bands. For example, the crystalline portion of nylon 66 absorbs at 10.7 μm and 11.7 μm, whereas the amorphous material absorbs at 8.8 μm (23). Thus the extent of crystallinity can be determined simply by comparing the intensities of these two bands.

The strong IR absorption bands for common thermoplastics are given in Table 2.9. The infrared spectra are unaffected by sheet thickness (except for very thin films where some surface orientation may distort the absolute values of IR spectra). Opacifiers such as pigments reduce the extent of transmission but do not change the shape of the spectra. Tints and organic dyes usually affect the spectra only in the visible portions of the curves (Figure 2.16).

TABLE 2.9 CHARACTERISTIC POLYMER IR ABSORPTION BANDS
(in Wavelength, μm) (Values in parens represent Weak Absorption Bands)

Polymer	Primary	Secondary
HDPE	3.2–3.9	(7.0–8.0)
LDPE	3.2–3.9	6.7–7.1, 7.0–8.0
PP	3.2–3.6	6.6–7.0, 7.1–7.3,
		(8.4–8.7), (9.8–10.1)
PS	3.2–3.6	6.4–7.3
ABS	2.8–3.2	6.5–7.5
PVC	3.2–3.6	(1.65–1.8), 2.2–2.5,
		7.1–9.0
PMMA	1.4–2.2	1.1–1.25
PA(nylon)-6	2.8–4.2	1.9–2.8, (4.2–5.2)
Cellulose	2.8–3.6	5.2–6.0
Acetate		
PC	3.2–3.6	5.5–6.2, 6.6–7.7

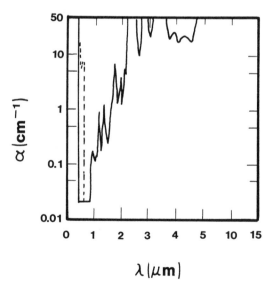

Figure 2.16 IR Absorption Spectrum for Clear and Dyed PMMA. λ: Wavelength (μm). α: Absorption Coefficient (cm^{-1}). Solid Line: Clear PMMA. Dotted Line: Red Dyed PMMA.

TABLE 2.10 EFFECT OF REGRIND MATERIAL ON RT PET MECHANICAL PROPERTIES (±STD. DEV.)

Property	Run 1 *(Virgin)*	Run 2 *(50% Virgin)*	Run 3 *(50% Virgin)*
Intrinsic Viscosity	0.83	0.68	0.68
Secant Modulus, psi (MD)	259,000 (±7,500)	244,000 (±6000)	245,000 (±6,000)
(TD)	237,500 (±13,500)	207,000 (±9800)	236,000 (±16,700)
Percent Elongation, Yield (MD)	10.0 (±2.9)	10.0 (±0.7)	9.8 (±0.8)
(TD)	10.2 (±1.1)	10.0 (±0.7)	9.7 (±1.2)
Percent Elongation, Break (MD)	650 (±17)	575 (±28)	600 (±160)
(TD)	670 (±27)	670 (±59)	270 (±35)
Tensile Strength, psi, Yield (MD)	5000 (±390)	4900 (±200)	5100 (±270)
(TD)	4600 (±150)	4600 (±230)	4600 (±540)
Tensile Strength, psi, Break (MD)	8300 (±610)	7900 (±1900)	7000 (±2300)
(TD)	7800 (±390)	7100 (±580)	4700 (±1080)
Spencer Impact, gms	2800 (±650)*	2300 (±1030)	2400 (±910)

* 2 of 5 specimens did not break at 6400 gms.

Material Property Deterioration upon Regrind

A large portion of the thermoformed sheet is web or trim. The efficient recovery and reuse of trim is essential to the economic viability of the process. For rollfed sheet, rectangular shapes yield up to 25% trim. For small, round shapes, up to 50% trim is expected. In cut sheet thermoforming, sheetstock of standard dimension may be more economical than sheet cut to special size. But the use of standard dimension sheetstock may lead to high percentages of trim. Even if the trim can be totally recycled (and material property deterioration is minimized), the cost of regrinding, drying if necessary, and reextruding must be carefully considered in the process economics. Chapter 8 considers this in some detail.

The action of heat and shear in grinding, extrusion and to some extent, thermoforming, can thermomechanically degrade most polymers. The typical mechanical effect is chain breaking. This leads to loss in ultimate tensile strength, elongation at break, toughness (area under the stress-strain curve), and impact strength. With some polymers such as PP and other olefins, oxidative degradation can occur, resulting in yellowing and odor. Polymers with extensive plasticizer packages can become brittle owing to deterioration or loss of effectiveness of the packages. FPVC is the classic example. Polymers with fire retardants are particularly sensitive to the high time-temperature environments common in multiple recyclings. Regrinds of moisture-sensitive polymers must be carefully dried to minimize dehydrolysis. Condensation polymers, such as PET, PA and PC, are classic candidates.

Usually, thermomechanical deterioration is not catastrophic. Small changes in observed physical properties usually do not cause dramatic changes in processing conditions. And final part performance is not substantially lowered. Nevertheless, the mechanical properties of polymeric material that has been reground and recycled many times should be lower than those of the virgin polymer. Theoretically, in a closed loop process, a small amount of material is reground and reprocessed many, many times. The arithmetic for determining the extent of mechanical property loss upon recycling is given as Appendix 2.I. As noted, if the *after-processing* mechanical property is X times that before processing, and Y is the fraction of material recycled, then the polymer mechanical property *after* N passes (Mp_N) is related to the virgin polymer mechanical property (Mo) by:

$$Mp_N = \left[1 - (1 - X) [1 - (XY)^{N-1}]/[1 - XY]\right] Mo$$

If the polymer has been recycled an infinite number of times (Mp_∞), the relationship is:

$$Mp_\infty = [1 - (1 - X)/(1 - XY)] Mo$$

As an example, let the polymer tensile strength after one recycle be 90% of that of the virgin polymer ($X = 0.9$) and let recycled material account for 50% of each pass. After 3 passes ($N = 3$), the net tensile strength of the polymer is 83.5% of that of the virgin material. After 8 recycle passes, the net value is 81.9%, and after an infinite number of passes, the value asymptotically reaches 81.8%. The arithmetic predicts that after 3 or 4 passes, the mechanical properties of mixed regrind-virgin sheet are within 2 to 3% of those after an infinite number of passes.

To illustrate, CPET was dried, extruded, reground, dried, and mixed 50:50 with dried virgin, and reextruded. The effect of reprocessing on mechanical properties is shown in Table 2.10. Note the loss in intrinsic viscosity (deterioration in molecular weight) and an indication of loss in elongation at break, ultimate tensile strength and Spencer impact. These property value losses are small and therefore not considered detrimental to the final part performance.

References

1. J. Frados, Ed., *Plastics Engineering Handbook*, 4th ed., Van Nostrand Reinhold Co., 1976, pg. 274.
2. J. L. Throne, "Polymer Properties", in M. Bakker, Ed., *Encyclopedia of Packaging Technology*, John Wiley & Sons, Inc., 1986.
3. H. R. Simonds, *Source Book of the New Plastics*, Vol. II, Van Nostrand Reinhold Co., 1961, pg. 21.
4. J. L. Throne, "Thermoforming - A Look Forward", SPE Tech. Papers, *29*, 1983, pg. 464.
5. R. D. Deanin, *Polymer Structure, Properties, and Applications*, Cahners Books, 1972, pg. 154.
6. J. L. Throne, *Plastics Process Engineering*, Marcel Dekker, 1979, pg. 65.
7. T. Alfrey and E. F. Gurnee, *Organic Polymers*, Prentice-Hall, 1967, pg. 51.
8. J. L. Throne, "Thermoforming Crystallizing PET", SPE Tech. Papers, *27*, 1981, pg. 598. (This paper contains an error in theory. Please write the author for corrections.)
9. L. B. Morgan, Phil. Trans. Roy. Soc., *A247*, 1954, pg. 21.
10. R. E. Dempsey, et al., USP 4, 127, 631, to Amoco Chemicals Corp., 28 Nov 1978.
11. J. A. Brydson, *Plastics Materials*, Iliffe, 1966, pg. 34.
12. L. E. Nielsen, *Mechanical Properties of Polymers*, Reinhold, 1962, pg. 244.
13. J. B. Howard, "Fracture - Long Term Testing", in N. M. Bikales, Ed., *Mechanical Properties of Polymers*, Wiley-Interscience, 1971, pg. 73.
14. R. L. Baldwin and K. E. Van Holde, Fortschr. Hochpolym. Forsch., *1*, 1960, pg. 451. See also J. L. Throne, *Plastics Process Engineering*, Marcel Dekker, 1979, pg. 765.
15. F. Brinken and H. Potente, "Some Considerations of Thermodynamics in Thermoforming", SPE Tech. Papers, *29*, 1983, pg. 467.
16. J. L. Throne, "Polystyrene Foam Sheet Expansion During Heating", SPE Tech. Papers, *31*, 1985, pg. 1328.
17. J. A. Brydson, *Plastics Materials*, Iliffe, 1966, pg. 58.
18. Material adapted from W. K. McConnell, Jr., Handout material, "Thermoforming Technology for Industrial Applications", SPE Seminar, 12-14 March 1985, Arlington TX. Used by permission of copyright owner.
19. J. L. Throne, *Plastics Process Engineering*, Marcel Dekker, Inc., 1979, pp. 714-735. Taken from an extensive series of tables published by R. G. Griskey in Modern Plastics, 1966-1967. Note that Table 14.3-7 for PP is incorrect. See: R. G. Griskey and N. Waldman, Mod. Plast., *43*: 3, 1966, pg. 121, for correct values.
20. H. Voigt, "Lehrgang fur Thermoformung", Paul Kiefel GmbH, undated.

21. Z. Tadmor and C. G. Gogos, *Principles of Polymer Processing*, John Wiley & Sons, 1979, pp. 697–703.
22. B. C. Sakiadis and J. Coates, AIChE J., *2*, 1956, pg. 88. See also J. L. Throne, *Plastics Process Engineering*, Marcel Dekker, Inc., 1979, pg. 737.
23. Ivo Kossler, "Infrared-Absorption Spectroscopy", in N. M. Bikales, Ed., *Characterization of Polymers*, Wiley-Interscience, 1971, pg. 125.
24. H. R. Osmers, Material presented at SPE Seminar, "Thermoforming Technology for Industrial Applications", 12–14 March 1985, Arlington TX.
25. R. C. Progelhof, J. L. Throne, and R. R. Ruetsch, "Methods for Predicting the Thermal Conductivity of Composite Systems: A Review", Polym. Eng. Sci., *16*, 1976, pg. 615.

APPENDIX 2.I

MECHANICAL PROPERTY LOSS IN REGRIND

The following assumptions are made:

1. *After* each processing step, the mechanical property is X times that of the material *before* processing.
2. For each unit of material processed, Y units are regrind.
3. $0 < X < 1; 0 < Y < 1$.
4. A composite mechanical property is obtainable from the properties of the virgin and regrind via the law of mixtures.

The following definitions hold:

1. Mo is the mechanical property of the virgin resin.
2. Mr is the mechanical property of the regrind.
3. Mm is the mechanical property of the mixture.
4. Mp is the mechanical property of the processed material.

For the first cycle, there is no regrind. Thus:

$$Mp_1 = XMm_1 = XMo$$

For the second cycle:

$$Mp_2 = XMm_2$$

but,

$$Mm_2 = YMr_1 + (1 - Y)Mo$$

and,

$$Mr_1 = Mp_1$$

therefore:

$$Mp_2 = X[YX + (1 - Y)]Mo$$

For the third cycle:

$$Mp_3 = XMm_3$$

but,

$$Mm_3 = YMr_2 + (1 - Y) Mo$$

and,

$$Mr_2 = Mp_2$$

therefore,

$$Mp_3 = [X^3Y^2 + X^2Y(1-Y) + X(1-Y)]Mo$$

For the Nth cycle:

$$Mp_N = \left[(X-1) \sum_{i=0}^{N-1} (XY)^i + 1 \right] Mo$$

but,

$$\sum_{i=1}^{n} ar^i = ar + ar^2 + ar^3 + \ldots + ar^n = a \left(\frac{1-r^n}{1-r} \right)$$

therefore, for the Nth cycle:

$$Mp_N = \left[1 - (1-X) \left(\frac{1-(XY)^{N-1}}{1-(XY)} \right) \right] Mo$$

For an infinite number of cycles:

$$\text{Since } (XY) < 1, \lim_{N \to \infty} (XY)^{N-1} = 0$$

and,

$$Mp_\infty = \left[1 - \left(\frac{1-X}{1-XY} \right) \right] Mo$$

Example for $X = 0.9$, $Y = 0.5$:

After   1 Cycle: $Mp_1/Mo = 0.9$
After   2 Cycles: $Mp_2/Mo = 0.855$
After   3 Cycles: $Mp_3/Mo = 0.835$
After   8 Cycles: $Mp_8/Mo = 0.8185$
After 20 Cycles: $Mp_{20}/Mo = 0.8182$
Infinite Cycles: $Mp_\infty/Mo = 0.8182$

Thus, after 3 cycles, in this example, accuracy is within 2% of the limit, which is well below experimental error.

3 HEATING THE SHEET

Introduction

As noted in Chapter 1, the thermoforming process can be neatly segmented into four steps: heating the sheet, stretching it, cooling it on the mold surface, and trimming the part from its surroundings. During the forming and trimming steps, the sheet dimensions are changing but the sheet is essentially at constant temperature. During the heating and cooling steps, the sheet dimensions are essentially constant, but the sheet temperature is changing. Thus the heat transfer process and the mechanical deformation process can be treated separately.

This chapter is concerned with the ways in which sheet can be heated to the stretching temperature. Chapter 4 focusses on the technical details of sheet stretching. Chapter 5 considers the process of cooling the sheet and the trimming step. The reader should note that the material in these chapters is quite technical. However, the newer thermoforming technologies mandate a thorough understanding of the basic concepts underlying the general process. And many of the troubleshooting solutions to processing problems are apparent once these concepts are understood. Rollfed formers have used infrared heating for years owing to its efficiency in heating thin-gage sheet. Heavy-gage cut sheet formers have used forced convection air ovens for heating, in order to minimize sheet surface degradation. There are technical reasons behind these decisions but there are certain instances where these are not necessarily the optimum choices. In another example, pattern heating is used extensively to produce more uniform part wall thicknesses and so parts designers should be aware of some of the details of this technique. Again, what is important is an adequate understanding of the interaction between the plastic sheet, initially at room temperature but being heated to a proper forming temperature, and its heating medium.

This material in this chapter begins with a review of the basic types of heating methods. Then thin-gage heating, particularly infrared heating, and forced convection air heating of thick-gage material are considered in detail. Equilibration time is discussed. This is the time it takes for the sheet to achieve a uniform temperature across its cross-section, once the heating source is removed. And finally guidelines for determining heating cycle times for both thin-gage and thick-gage sheet are presented.

Energy Absorption by Sheet

Thermoforming is an energy intensive plastics process. Economics require the most efficient use of energy. The amount of energy needed to heat a unit mass of sheet from room temperature (RT) to the forming condition (T_f) is obtained with an energy balance:

$$Q = \int_{RT}^{T_f} c_p(T)\, dT \qquad (cal/g) = (cal/g\ C)(C)$$
$$[Btu/lb] = [Btu/lb\ F][F]$$

$c_p(T)$ is the temperature-dependent heat capacity. The forming temperature here is assumed to be the average sheet temperature:

$$T_f = (1/L) \int_0^L T(x) \, dx$$

$T(x)$ is the temperature at position x across the sheet half-thickness, $0 < x < L$. If the temperature dependency of heat capacity is unknown, an average value will give a reasonable estimate. If the heat capacity of a specific polymer is unknown, a value of a homologous polymer can be used as a first approximation. A better method uses the change in enthalpy between room temperature and the forming temperature:

$$Q = H(T_f) - H(RT)$$

H is the enthalpy at a given temperature, (cal/g)[Btu/lb]. Figure 3.1 provides enthalpy values for several thermoformable polymers (1). The energies needed to heat typical polymers to forming temperatures are given in Table 3.1. Some of these values are based on assumed values for heat capacity and others are approximate.

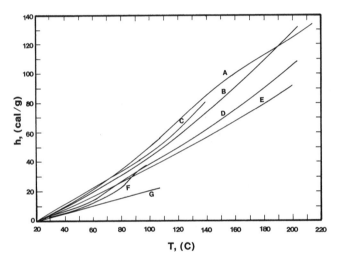

Figure 3.1 Enthalpy of Selected Polymers (Adapted from (1)). T: Temperature, C · h: Enthalpy, cal/g. A: TPE (Olefin). B: LDPE, PP. C: PMMA. D: PS. E: PA-66 (nylon). F: RPVC. G: PTFE.

TABLE 3.1 THIN-GAGE HEATING EFFICIENCIES
$T_\infty = 760\,C$ $Q/A = 40\,kW/m^2$

Material	Normal Form. Temp T_f, C	ΔH cal/g (T_f-20)	ρ sp. gr. g/cm³	c_p (avg) cal/g C*	Heating Rate, s/mm	Energy Absorbed kW/m²	Efficiency, %	Maximum Effective Heat Transfer Coefficient, h kW/m² C	[Btu/ft² h F]
LDPE	129	71.7	0.92	0.498	25	11.5	27.6	0.0182	3.21
PMMA	177	104.1	1.2	0.559	27	19.44	48.6	0.0333	5.87
PVC	138	55.9	1.4	0.265	21	15.88	39.7	0.0255	4.50
PS	146	65.0	1.05	0.341	13–15	19.03–21.97	47.6–54.9	0.0310–0.0358	5.46–6.30
PTFE**	288	66.9	1.2	0.342	13	25.86	64.7	0.0548	9.65
PA-66***	***224	105.0	1.2	0.419	27	19.84	49.6	0.0370	6.52

  * Used only in "Effective h" calculations
 ** PTFE/FEP from Figure 3.2
*** PA-6 from Figure 3.2

There are many ways of heating sheet to the forming temperature. No heating process is 100% efficient. All heating systems must therefore input more specific energy than the amount indicated in Table 3.1 for any given plastic. Economics dictate a balance between the efficiency of net energy interchange and the net rate of heating to the forming conditions. Where the heating rate controls the cycle time, process optimization usually calls for lowered energy efficiencies. Sheet thickness dictates, to a large degree, the type of heating that is most effective. Thin sheets can be heated quite efficiently with radiant heaters whereas thick sheets are best heated in forced convection air ovens.

Heat Transfer Modes

There are three ways of exchanging energy between objects of different temperatures: conduction, convection and radiation. *Conduction* is solid phase energy transfer on an atomic or molecular level. Owing to high vibrational and rotational mobility of electrons and regular crystallographic structure, metals achieve high levels of conduction energy transfer. Organic materials, on the other hand, have relatively immobile atomic structures and so are poor thermal (and electrical) conductors. Polymers have even less molecular mobility and, in addition, have high free volumes, allowing chain segments to move without contacting other segments. Polymers are therefore very poor thermal (and electrical) conductors. This was noted in Chapter 2.

Classically, thermoformable sheet is considered as a two-dimensional planar surface with lateral dimensions far greater than its thickness dimension. In all analyses that follow, the sheet is assumed to be planar to incident energy. One-dimensional *steady-state heat conduction* across the sheet thickness is given as:

$$Q/A = -k \, \Delta T / \Delta x$$

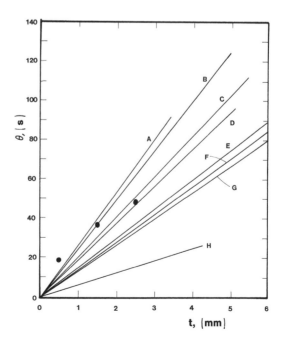

Figure 3.2 Two-Side Quartz Heating of Sheet. θ: Heating Time, s. t: Sheet Thickness, mm. Heat Flux: 40 kW/m² [12,700 Btu/ft²·h]. Mean Wavelength: 2.8 μm. Heater Temperature: 760 C [1400 F]. A: PMMA. B: HDPE. C: RPVC. D: CAB. E: ABS, PVC-Copolymer. F: FPVC. G: HIPS. H: Foam PS. Circles: PE from Rowe (26). His Heater Temperature: 510 C [950 F]. Mean Wavelength: 3.7 μm. Heat Flux: 43 kW/m² [13,700 Btu/ft²·h].

Q/A is the heat flux, k the material thermal conductivity. ΔT the temperature difference, and Δx the sheet thickness (Figure 3.2). $\Delta T/\Delta x$ is the thermal gradient across the sheet thickness. The dimensions of these terms are:

k	cal/cm s C	[Btu/ft h F]
Δx	cm	[ft]
ΔT	C	[F]
Q/A	cal/cm^{2}s or kW/m^2	[Btu/ft^2 h]

Consider the importance of material thermal conductivity in conduction heat transfer. If a 0.3 cm [0.01 ft] *PS* sheet, with a thermal conductivity of 5.8×10^{-4} cal/cm $\cdot$ s $\cdot$ C [0.14 Btu/ft $\cdot$ h $\cdot$ F] is exposed to a thermal heat flux of 0.21 cal/cm$^2 \cdot$ s (8.8 kW/m^2) [2800 Btu/ft$^2 \cdot$ h], the steady state temperature difference will be 111 C [200 F]. Note that at a given energy transfer, the thermal driving force ($\Delta T/\Delta x$) is inversely proportional to thermal conductivity. For an *aluminum* sheet of the same thickness with a thermal conductivity of 5.8×10^{-1} cal/cm $\cdot$ s $\cdot$ C [140 Btu/ft $\cdot$ h $\cdot$ F], the temperature difference would only be 0.11 C [0.2 F] at the same heat flux.

For thick-gage sheet, conduction of energy between the sheet surface and its interior controls the heating rate. The *rate* at which energy transfer occurs is called *transient one-dimensional heat conduction*. The time-dependent net energy increase or decrease equals the change in heat flux within the plastic sheet (2, 3):

$$\text{Net enthalpy change per unit time} = \frac{\partial H}{\partial \theta} = \rho c_p \frac{\partial T}{\partial \theta} = \frac{\partial}{\partial x}\left(k\frac{\partial T}{\partial x}\right) = \frac{\partial}{\partial x}(\frac{Q}{A})$$

The polymer temperature now is a function of time and position across the sheet thickness, $T(\theta, x)$. Three boundary conditions are needed to solve this equation. The initial temperature $T(0, x)$ throughout the sheet is needed. If the sheet is heated uniformly from both sides, a symmetry condition is used. That is, the heat flux across the centerline of the sheet (at $x = 0$) is set to zero:

$$\frac{\partial T}{\partial x}(\theta, 0) = 0$$

The condition at the sheet surface in contact with the heating environment is also required. The simplest (conduction) assumes a known sheet surface temperature: $T(\theta, L) = T_1(\theta)$. Another (known heat flux) assumes that the net heat flux at the surface is a function of a thermal driving force:

$$\frac{Q}{A} = -k\frac{\partial T}{\partial x}(\theta, L) = f(T, T_\infty)$$

T_∞ is an environmental temperature. In many practical situations, $f(T, T_\infty)$ is linear in temperature:

$$-k\frac{\partial T}{\partial x}(\theta, L) = h(T - T_\infty)$$

The proportionality term (h) is a convection heat transfer coefficient. When the energy source is a fluid, energy is transferred between the bulk moving fluid and the solid surface

TABLE 3.2 RANGE IN VALUES FOR CONVECTION HEAT TRANSFER COEFFICIENT (h)

Fluid	$h \, (\times 10^{-3} \, W/cm^2 \, s \, C)$	$[Btu/ft^2 \, h \, F]$
Quiescent Air	0.5- 1	0.8- 2
Air Moved with Fans	1 - 3	2 - 5
Air Moved with Blowers	3 - 10	5 - 20
Air and Water Mist	30 - 60	50 - 100
Fog	30 - 60	50 - 100
Water Spray	30 - 90	50 - 150
Oil in Pipes	30 - 180	50 - 300
Water in Pipes	60 - 600	100 - 1000
Steam in Pipes, Condensing	600 -3000	1000 -15000

across a thin near-stagnant fluid layer. The heat transfer coefficient is a measure of the resistance to heat transfer across this layer. As the bulk fluid motion increases, the resistance to heat transfer decreases (h increases in value). As seen (Table 3.2), air is a poor convective heat transfer medium and condensing steam is an excellent one.

For purely radiant heat transfer, the heat flux, $Q/A = f(T, T_\infty)$, is in general nonlinear with respect to temperature. As discussed below, the function $f(T, T_\infty)$ is generally written as:

$$Q/A = f(T, T_\infty) = G(T^4 - T_\infty^4)$$

where G includes geometry and radiation characteristics of the heating source and the sheet. T_∞ is the heating source temperature and both temperatures are in absolute degrees. Numerical solution of the one-dimensional transient heat conduction equation is difficult with the nonlinear radiant heat flux boundary condition. High radiant heater temperatures $(T_\infty \gg T)$ are frequently used in forming thin-gage rollfed sheet into products such as cookie trays, blister packs, and live plant containers. As a result, the nonlinear radiation condition can be approximated by a *pseudo-convection* condition:

$$Q/A = f(T, T_\infty) \doteq h_r (T - T_\infty)$$

where h_r is a *pseudo-convection* heat transfer coefficient, sometimes called the radiation heat transfer coefficient. As detailed below, h_r can be combined with a conventional convection heat transfer coefficient to produce a combined coefficient. In certain instances, for thin-gage rollfed sheet exposed to high radiant heater temperatures, the heat flux can be considered constant:

$$Q/A = f(T, T_\infty) \equiv f(T_\infty)$$

Constant heat flux is only one useful approximation for the heating of thin-gage sheet, however. In certain cases, the energy transfer *through* the sheet can be considered secondary to energy transfer *to* the sheet. This approximation allows the material to be analyzed using a very simple time-dependent heat balance. This *lumped-parameter* model is discussed later in this chapter.

Sheet can be heated to forming temperature by conduction and/or convection energy transfer. In *trapped sheet forming* (7), the sheet contacts a heated, porous blow plate only on one side (Figure 3.3). Thus energy is conducted through the sheet and convected to the environment on the free surface. Thick PMMA sheet is held vertically on rails in large forced air convection ovens prior to being *drape-formed* into aircraft canopies (8). Slow convection heating allows very thick sheets to thoroughly dry, anneal and stress relieve. This gentle treatment minimizes distortion, springback, and impact crazing. Convection/conduction applications are less prevalent than radiation energy transfer applications, however, and so will be treated later.

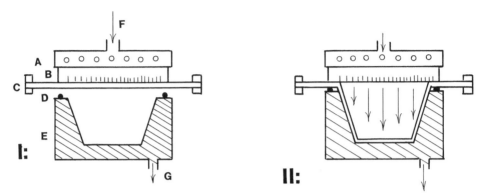

Figure 3.3 Trapped Sheet Thermoforming. A: Hot Plate. B: Porous or Slotted Blow Plate. C: Sheet Held in Clamps in Contact with Blow Plate. D: Urethane or Silicone Gasket. E: Mold. F: Blowing Air. G: Air Exhaust or Vacuum.

Radiation Heating

Radiation is electromagnetic energy transfer between a hot source and a cold sink *that it sees*. Radiation energy transfer does not depend upon the distance separating sink and source. It is the most energy efficient way of heating planar surfaces but misuse can lead to surface scorching or burn and very uneven temperature distribution across the sheet thickness. Most rollfed and many shuttle thermoformers now heat with radiant sources. Common heaters are Nichrome spiral wires, steel rod heaters, quartz tube heaters, ceramic plates with imbedded resistance wires and steel plates that reradiate combustion energy from gas flames.

Primary radiant heat transfer is correctly a net energy interchange between source and sink, since the cold sink also radiates energy (albeit weakly) toward the hot source (Figure 3.4). The primary energy impinging on any surface is either absorbed, reflected or transmitted. If incident radiation energy is either reflected or absorbed on the surface, the material is opaque. Other radiation characteristics of materials are in Table 3.3.

The thermal radiation wavelength range is normally from about 0.1 μm to 100 μm. The ultraviolet (UV) region is 0.1 μm to 0.38 μm and the visible light range is 0.38 μm to 0.7 μm. Near-infrared is 0.7 μm to about 3 μm and far-infrared is 3 μm to 20 μm or more. The important wavelength range for most radiant thermoforming processes is about 0.3 μm to about 20 μm. As reference, the sun at an effective surface temperature of 5500 C [10,000 F] emits more than 90% of its radiation in the wavelength range of 0.1 μm (UV) to 3 μm (near IR).

TABLE 3.3 RADIATION CHARACTERISTICS OF MATERIALS

Nature	Definition
Surface Reflection	
Diffuse	Incident radiation reflected evenly in hemsiphere
Specular	Incident radiation reflected preferentially in a given steradian segment of hemisphere
Opaque	Unreflected incident radiant energy absorbed on surface – no transmission
Transparent	All unreflected incident radiant energy transmitted through and out of material
Transparent with Internal Reflection (Light-Piping)	All unreflected incident radiant energy transmitted through material, partially reflected back from second surface (sometimes specular)
Translucent	Properly, semitransparend
Semi-Transparent	Nonreflected incident radiant energy partially absorbed volumetrically, partially transmitted through sheet
Black Body (Ideal)	All radiant energy totally absorbed at all wavelengths (No energy reflected, no energy transmitted)
	Also, a radiant source that emits the maximum amount of energy at all wavelengths
White Body (Ideal)	In contrast to a black body. No radiant energy absorbed at any wavelength. Can be either ideally transparent or perfectly reflecting
Grey Body (Ideal)	A fixed fraction of radiant energy absorbed, independent of wavelength

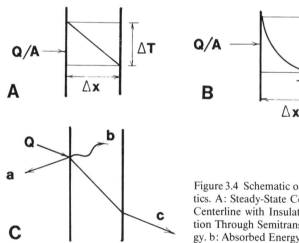

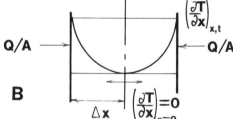

Figure 3.4 Schematic of Temperature Profiles Through Plastics. A: Steady-State Conduction. B: Transient Conduction, Centerline with Insulated Boundary Conditions. C: Radiation Through Semitransparent Materials. a: Reflected Energy. b: Absorbed Energy. c: Transmitted Energy.

Black Body Radiation

The *maximum* total energy emitted at all wavelengths by any source at a given absolute temperature T is that emitted by a *black body*:

$$E_b = \sigma T^4$$

T is the source temperature, in K $(=C+273)$ or R $[=F+460]$, σ is the Stefan-Boltzmann constant, $\sigma = 0.5674 \times 10^{-10}$ kW/m$^2 \cdot$ C^4 $[=0.1714 \times 10^{-8}$ Btu/ft$^2 \cdot$ h $\cdot$ R$^4]$, and E_b is the total emitted energy for all wavelengths (kW/m^2) [Btu/ft$^2 \cdot$ h]. All thermoforming radiant sources can be referenced to the amount of energy emitted by a black body source.

The wavelength-dependent radiant energy emitted by a black body at temperature T is given as:

$$E_{b,\lambda} = C_1 \lambda^{-5}/[\exp(C_2/\lambda T) - 1]$$

where λ is the wavelength, in μm, $C_1 = 3.743 \times 10^5$ kW $\cdot \mu$m^4/m^2 $[=1.187 \times 10^8$ Btu $\cdot \mu$m^4/ ft$^2 \cdot$ h] and $C_2 = 1.439 \times 10^4$ K $\cdot \mu$m $[=2.59 \times 10^4$ R $\cdot \mu$m]. The wavelength-dependent energy emitted by a black body source at temperature T is given in Figure 3.5. The wavelength at which the maximum energy is emitted is given as:

$$\lambda_{max} = a/T$$

where $a = 2897.6$ μm $\cdot$ K $[=5215.6$ μm $\cdot$ R]. The specific energy emitted at this wavelength is:

$$E_{b,\lambda,max} = C_3 T^5$$

$C_3 = 1.287 \times 10^{-14}$ kW/m$^2 \cdot$ K$^5 \cdot \mu$m $[=2.161 \times 10^{-13}$ Btu/ft$^2 \cdot$ h $\cdot$ R$^5 \cdot \mu$m]. The total amount of energy emitted by an 800 C [1472 F] black body is 75.3 kW/m^2 [23,880 Btu/ft$^2 \cdot$ h]. The specific energy output at 2.7 μm is 18.3 kW/m$^2 \cdot \mu$m [5.817 Btu/ft$^2 \cdot$ h $\cdot \mu$m]. Nearly 20% of the total emitted energy is within ± 0.5 μm of the peak value. Typical radiant heater temperatures range from 250 C to 1100 C [482 F to 2012 F]. The total energy emitted by a perfect source, the wavelength at maximum energy emission and the energy emitted at that wavelength are given in Table 3.4 for several temperatures in this range. Most plastics absorb radiant energy preferentially in specific wavelength ranges (Chapter 2 and Table 3.5). To maximize the energy absorbed by the plastic, thermoformer heater temperatures should be set to the temperatures corresponding to these wavelength ranges. The practical upper limit for

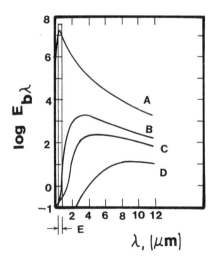

Figure 3.5 Monochromatic Black Body Radiation Intensity as a Function of Wavelength for Several Source Temperatures. Intensity, $E_{b,\lambda}$: Btu/ft$^2 \cdot$ h $\cdot \mu$m. A: Solar, 6500 C [10,000 F]. B: 538 C [1000 F]. C: 260 C [500 F]. D: 38 C [100 F].

TABLE 3.4 WAVELENGTH OF MAXIMUM ENERGY EMISSION BLACK BODY RADIATION

Temperature		Wavelength	Specific Energy* at Peak Wavelength	
F	C	μm	kW/m² μm	[Btu/ft² h μm]
400	204	6.06	0.32	102
500	260	5.43	0.55	176
600	316	4.92	0.91	289
700	371	4.50	1.43	454
800	427	4.14	2.16	686
900	482	3.84	3.16	1 005
1000	538	3.57	4.52	1 435
1100	593	3.34	6.28	2 000
1200	649	3.14	8.57	2 720
1300	704	2.96	11.5	3 650
1400	760	2.80	15.1	4 810
1500	816	2.66	19.7	6 250
1600	871	2.53	25.2	8 020
1700	927	2.41	32.0	10 200
1800	982	2.31	40.1	12 700
1900	1038	2.21	49.8	15 800
2000	1093	2.12	61.3	19 500

* $E_{b, \lambda, max} = C_3 T^5$
$C_3 = 1.287 \times 10^{-14}$ kW/m² K⁵ μm
$\quad = 2.161 \times 10^{-13}$ Btu/ft² R⁵ μm

TABLE 3.5 IDEAL RADIANT HEATER TEMPERATURE RANGES FOR SEVERAL THERMOFORMABLE PLASTICS

Plastics	Ideal Wavelength, μm	Temperature Range	
		C	F
LDPE	3.2 –3.9	470– 630	877–1170
HDPE	3.2 –3.7	510– 630	950–1170
PS	3.2 –3.7	510– 630	950–1170
	(6.4 –7.4)	120– 180	245– 355
PVC	1.65–1.8	1340–1480	2440–2700
	(2.2 –2.5)	885–1045	1625–1910
PMMA	1.4 –2.2	1045–1800	1910–3265
PA-66	1.9 –2.8	765–1250	1405–2285
	(3.4 –5)	310– 580	585–1075
Cellulose Acetate	2.2 –3.6	530–1045	990–1910
	(5.2 –6)	210– 285	440– 545

thermoformer heater temperature is about 900 C [1650 F]. Above that, special materials of construction are needed for the heaters, special reflectors are required, and the high energy level makes sheet temperature control very difficult.

The fraction of energy emitted by a black body source at a given temperature over a given wavelength range is obtained by subtracting values from Figure 3.6. An 800 C [1472 F] black body source emits about 42% of its energy between 2.0 and 4.0 μm. At 700 C [1292 F], it emits about 38%.

Grey Body – Emissivity

No practical material emits at black body energy levels. Many materials emit at 80 to 95% of the maximum level, however. A *grey body* is a material that emits energy at a fixed fraction (ε) of the black body level:

$$E_g = \varepsilon \, \sigma \, T^4$$

ε is emissivity, $0 < \varepsilon < 1$. If that fraction is wavelength-dependent, the total energy must be found by integration:

$$E_{g,\,tot} = \int_0^\infty \varepsilon(\lambda) \, \sigma T^4 \, d\lambda =$$

$$= \sigma T^4 \int_0^\infty e(\lambda) \, d\lambda$$

As an approximation, $e(\lambda)$ can be considered constant over specific ranges in wavelength. The individual energies in these range segments are then summed:

$$E_{g,\,tot} = \sigma T^4 / (\lambda_N - \lambda_1) \sum_{j=1}^{N-1} \varepsilon_j (\lambda_{j+1} - \lambda_j)$$

The individual black body energies are obtained from Figure 3.6.

Emissivities are usually wavelength-dependent for real surfaces (Figure 3.7). Values at given maximum-energy wavelengths and temperatures are frequently reported (Table 3.6 (9)). For many materials, only an average value is known. Polished or very smooth surfaces emit at much lower energy levels ($0 < \varepsilon < 0.3$ to 0.4) than pitted, oxidized, rusted, matte or irregular surfaces ($0.80 < \varepsilon < 0.95$).

The emissivity of a material such as plastic sheet should be determined at its temperature, whereas its energy absorption efficiency (absorptivity, a) should be at the emitter temperature. Strictly speaking, $a \neq \varepsilon$, but practically a and ε can be assumed equal.

All surfaces radiate energy. The maximum amount of energy absorbed by a plastic sheet is determined from a net radiant energy balance between the grey-body emitter (heater) and the grey-body sheet:

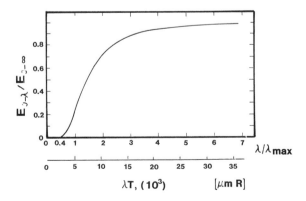

Figure 3.6 Fraction of Total Emissive Power $E_{0-\lambda}/E_{0-\infty}$ at or below Wavelength λ. (9). $\lambda_{max} T = 5215.6$ μm · R. (Figure used by permission of copyright owner.)

Figure 3.7 Schematic of Various Types of
Radiative Bodies. A: Black Body, ε = 1. B:
Grey Body, ε < 1. C: Real Body, ε = f(λ).

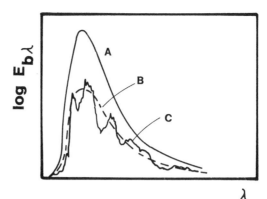

TABLE 3.6 EMISSIVITIES AND ABSORPTIVITIES FOR VARIOUS MATERIALS
USED IN THERMOFORMING (from (21), with permission of copyright owner)

Material	Temperature and Peak Wavelength, (μm).				
	38 C [100 F] 9.3	260 C [500 F] 5.4	538 C [1000 F] 3.6	1371 C [2500 F] 1.8	Abs*
Aluminium					
Polished	0.04	0.05	0.08	0.19	0.26
Oxidized	0.11	0.12	0.18	–	–
Anodized	0.94	0.42	0.60	0.34	–
Chromium					
Polished	0.08	0.17	0.26	0.40	–
Iron, Steel					
Polished	0.06	0.08	0.13	0.25	0.45
Cast, oxidized	0.63	0.66	0.76	–	–
Galvanized					
New	0.23	–	–	0.42	0.66
Dirty	0.28	–	–	0.90	0.89
Steel Plate	0.94	0.97	0.98	–	–
Oxide	0.96	–	0.85	–	0.74
Steel Tube, Oxidized	–	0.80	–	–	–
Stainless Steel					
Polished	0.15	0.18	0.22	–	–
Weathered	0.85	0.85	0.85	–	–
Tungsten Filament	0.03	–	–	0.18	–
Paper, white	0.95	–	0.82	0.25	0.27
Plaster	0.91	–	–	–	–
Enameled Steel, White	–	–	–	0.65	–
Paints					
Black Lacquer	0.96	0.98	–	–	0.97–0.99
Oil (all Colors)	0.94	0.90	–	–	–
White (ZnO)	0.95	–	0.91	–	0.12–0.26
Water	0.96	–	–	–	–
Wood	0.93	–	–	–	–
Glass	0.90	–	–	–	–

* Absorptivity values for solar radiation from (20).

$$Q/A = \sigma F_g (T_h^4 - T_s^4)$$

T_h is the heater temperature and T_s the sheet temperature, in K [R]. σ is the Stefan-Boltzmann constant used earlier. F_g is a factor that corrects black-body energy for the grey body nature of the emitter (ε_h) and plastic sheet (ε_s). For planar heaters and flat sheet, F_g, the *grey body correction factor*, is:

$$F_g = 1/(1/\varepsilon_h + 1/\varepsilon_s - 1)$$

For an 800 C [1472 F] source with $\varepsilon_h = 0.95$ and a 20 C [68 F] semi-matte ABS sheet with $\varepsilon_s = 0.85$, $F_g = 0.814$ and $Q/A = 60.9$ kW/m^2 [= 19,320 Btu/ft$^2 \cdot$h]. At a sheet forming temperature of 150 C [302 F], the net energy interchange decreases to $Q/A = 59.8$ kW/m^2 [= 18,960 Btu/ft$^2 \cdot$h] or about 2% less than at RT. ABS absorbs preferentially in the 3.2 to 3.7 and 6.4 to 7.4 μm wavelength ranges. About 18% or 10.8 to 11 kW/m^2 [3410 to 3480 Btu/ft$^2 \cdot$h] of the grey body energy is available in these wavelength ranges. Other examples of grey body correction factors are given below.

In addition to a correction factor for the nonblack nature of the source and sink, a correction factor is sometimes needed for compensating for relative sheet and heater geometries. If both can be considered infinite planar surfaces, the *view factor*, F, is unity. Similarly, the view factor F is unity if the sheet can be considered as completely enclosed by the heater. The nonplanar nature of rod heaters and the radiation losses at the sheet edge yield values of F that are not unity. These cases are described below. The general net radiant energy balance between heater and sheet can then be written as:

$$Q/A = \sigma F F_g (T_h^4 - T_s^4)$$

Constant Heat Flux – An Interesting Application

Earlier, constant heat flux was mentioned as a way of determining the effect of energy transfer *to* a plastic sheet. It can also be used as a way of analyzing radiant heater output efficiency.

Consider a square aluminum plate, L units on a side by t units thick. The aluminum plate weight is known [$m = \rho L^2 t = (2.7$ g/cm$^3)L^2$t] and its heat capacity is cp = 0.224 cal/g C [Btu/lb F]. The plate is mounted on a thermally insulated rod such as a broom handle. A thermocouple is imbedded in the center of the plate and its output is monitored on a strip chart recorder. The plate is sprayed with matte black oven paint to increase emissivity. The plate, initially at room temperature, is inserted into the radiant oven and its rate of temperature increase measured for several seconds over a 20 C (or so) temperature range near room temperature.

A heat balance on the plate is:

$$m \; cp \; dT/d\theta = A \; (Q/A) = A \; F\sigma T_\infty^4$$

The latter equation is assumed since $T_\infty \gg T$. F is a combined view factor and source emissivity. σ is the Stefan-Boltzmann constant, as before, and A is the plate area, $A = 2 L^2$ (ignoring the plate edges). Now $T = T_0$ when $\theta = 0$. So:

$$T = T_0 + \left[\frac{F\sigma T_\infty^4}{(mcp/A)} \right] \theta = T_0 + \left[\frac{F\sigma T_\infty^4}{(\rho t \; cp/2)} \right] \theta$$

For very short times, the temperature increases linearly with time, with the slope containing information about the efficiency of the radiant heating source.

Consider a 15.2×15.2 cm [6 in $\times$ 6 in] aluminum plate, 0.32 cm [0.125 in] thick, being heated on both sides from 37.8 to 51.7 C [100 to 125 F] in 9.43 s by exposure to ceramic heaters having a temperature of 315.6 C [600 F]. The plate mass is m = 199 g [0.439 lb]. The increase in energy is 64.5 cal/s and the flux is 0.139 cal/cm$^2 \cdot$s = 0.582 W/cm^3 = 1844 Btu/ft$^2 \cdot$h = 3.75 W/in^2. Ideally, the heat flux at this source temperature should be $(Q/A) = \sigma T_\infty^4 =$ 0.164 cal/cm$^2 \cdot$s = 0.685 W/cm^2 = 2172 Btu/ft$^2 \cdot$h = 4.42 W/in^2. So the radiant heating efficiency is 85%.

Heaters are rated in "watt density", viz, W/cm^2 or W/in^2 of heater surface. The heaters used in this example were rated at $I^2R = 8$ W/in^2 at 315.6 C [600 F]. Thus the heater efficiency is 46.9%. This constant heat flux example illustrates a practical way of measuring and monitoring radiant heater performance.

Real Heaters – Efficiencies

As noted earlier, only a fraction of the energy supplied by utility companies is converted into radiant energy to heat the sheet (Figure 3.8 (10)). Efficiencies of actual radiant heater materials for various thermoformable sheet materials are given in Table 3.8. These values represent net efficiencies. The energy conversion from power source to radiant thermal energy at the heater surface is relatively efficient. Ceramic heaters are more efficient at higher temperatures (Figure 3.9). About 50% of the electrical power input is converted to radiant energy at 316 C [600 F] and essentially 100% at 760 C [1400 F]. Tubular and spiral wire heaters have similar efficiencies (Table 3.7). Gas combustion efficiency at 900 C [1650 F] for one type of surface IR burner is reported to be 82 to 84% (11), with an average heat flux of 236.5 kW/m^2 [75,000 Btu/ft$^2 \cdot$h]. The ideal black body energy emitted at this temperature is 107.1 kW/m^2

Figure 3.8 Schematic of Heat Transfer Energy Distribution to Thermoforming Sheets (After (10)). A: Energy Supplied to Heating Source. B: Energy Loss in Conversion to Radiant Heat. C: Energy Convected Away from Heaters. D: Radiation Loss to Surroundings. E: Reradiation from Surroundings. F: Reradiation from Heaters. G: Radiation from Sheet to Heaters. H: Convection Heat Loss to Surroundings. I: Energy Absorbed by Sheet. (Modified figure used by permission of Society of Plastics Engineers, Inc.)

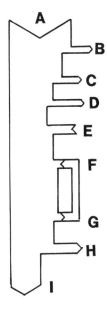

TABLE 3.7 EFFICIENCIES OF COMMERCIAL RADIANT HEATING SOURCES (Adapted from Singleton (25))

Radiant Source	Maximum Energy Input		Maximum Temperature		Black Body Energy		Max. Eff., %	Response Heating	Time Cooling	Comments
	(kW)*	[Btu]*	C	F	(kw)*	[Btu]*				
Bulb: R-40 Reflector	16.1	5120	2200	4000	2140	678,000	<1	3s	10s	Spot output – Color sensitive.
G-30 Bulb	6.4	2030	2200	4000	2140	678,000	<1	3s	10s	Needs reflector – color sensitive.
Ceramic Spot	1.4	1535	870	1600	97.3	30,900	1.4	5–10 m	5–10m	Spot output.
Quartz Lamp	310	98295	2200	4000	2140	678,000	14.5	3s	10s	Needs reflector – Color sensitive. Seals may need cooling – must be kept clean.
Tube: Metal Sheathed	46.5	14745	870	1600	97.3	30,900	48	5m	5m	Needs reflector – surface exposed – airflow causes large heat losses. Resists shock, vibration.
Quartz Tube	77.5	24575	980	1800	141	44,700	55	1m	20s	Needs reflector.
Strip: Quartz Faced	58.1	18430	760	1400	64.7	20,500	90	2– 4m	2– 4m	Very even heating. Low temp. leads to airflow surface losses.
Panel: Coated Glass	14.4	4555	315	600	6.8	2,200	**	5m	5m	Even heating. Can be zoned.
Fiberglass	12.9	4095	595	1100	32.0	10,200	40	5m	5m	See comments on metal sheathed tube.
Metal Sheathed	31	9830	595	1100	32.0	10,200	97	5m	5m	
Ceramic Faced	31	9830	760	1400	64.7	20,500	48	5– 10m	5– 10m	Available with soft or hard face.
Quartz or Hard Ceramic	62	19660	980	1800	141	44,700	44	5–20m	5– 20m	Thermal shock sensitive.
Exposed Foil	59.2	18770	815	1500	79.7	25,300	74	4s	10s	Shock hazard. Convective heat losses can be high.
Exposed Coil	85.2	27030	815	1500	79.7	25,300	**	3m	3m	Shock hazard. Convective heat losses can be high.
Gas IR-Impingement: Ceramic Plate	1890	600000	1260	2300	314	99,460	(5–35)+	2– 3m	2– 3m	Efficiency decreases with increased output.
Gas IR-Surface Burn: Ceramic Plate	252	80000	930	1700	117.7	37,300	(20–55)+	2– 3m	2– 3m	Same as above.
Screen	126	40000	870	1600	97.3	30,900	(20–55)+	1m	1m	Same as above. Screen maintenance can be problem.
Ceramic Fiber	148	47000	900	1650	107.1	34,000	(35–65)+ **	4– 8s	4– 8s	Emitter can be damaged by force or fluids.
Catalytic	15.8	5000	370	700	9.8	3,100		30m	5m	Low temp. Emitter can be damaged by force or fluids.

*   Units are kW/m² or Btu/ft² h.

** Greater than 100%.

+   Listed efficiency, but greater than 100% of black body efficiency.

Figure 3.9 Quartz Heat Output as Function of Temperature (24). q: W/in^2. T: Heater Temperature, [× 100 F]. (Figure used by permission of copyright owner.)

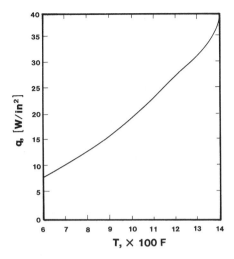

[33,970 Btu/ft^2·h]. Other types of surface burners have efficiencies somewhat lower than this. Note in Table 3.7 that the effective surface heat fluxes are substantially greater than the values predicted by black body radiation. Convective energy transport is apparently a major factor here. Since all radiant heaters operate in a fluid (air) environment, convection losses from heater surfaces reduce heater efficiency, by as much as 30 to 50%. An estimate of this loss is given below. Heaters radiate energy to *all visible surfaces*, including plastic sheet, reflectors, other heaters, rails, sheet clamping devices, and heater guards, sidewalls and shields. As much as 20 to 30% of the energy emitted by radiant heaters is lost to the environment in this way. Further, a fraction of net radiant energy absorbed by the plastic sheet is convected to the environment. Thus, only about 20 to 70% of utility-supplied power is converted into plastic sheet enthalpic increase. The actual efficiency depends upon matching source temperature with plastic radiation absorption range, minimizing all thermal sinks other than the plastic sheet and controlling the convective energy losses from solid surfaces (including the plastic sheet).

TABLE 3.8 RADIANT HEATER EFFICIENCIES FOR SEVERAL POLYMERS
(Adapted from Höger (19))

Material	Heater Type			
	Ceramic	Metal Rod	Quartz	
	510 C [950 F] 4.0 µm	550 C [1022 F] 3.8	680 C [1256 F] 3.0	760 C [1400 F] 2.8
LDPE	13%	15%	17%	20%
HDPE	13	15	17	20
PS	13	15	17	20
PVC	5	5	22	25
PMMA	0	2	50	65
PA-6	30	28	24	28
Cellulose Acetate	18	28	48	56
For the typical thermoforming wavelength range, 1.4 to 3.6 µm	28	33	70	77

Radiation Heat Transfer Coefficient

Convective energy losses can be determined from an energy balance around the solid surface (heater or plastic sheet). The effect of radiation heat transfer must also be included, however. This can be done by examining the surface boundary condition for the transient one-dimensional heat conduction equation, given earlier:

$$\frac{Q}{A} = -k\frac{\partial T}{\partial x}(\theta, L) = f(T, T_\infty, F, \varepsilon's)$$

For radiation absorption on a solid surface ($x = L$), the proper form for $f(T, T_\infty, F, \varepsilon's)$ is:

$$f(T, T_\infty, F, \varepsilon's) = \sigma FF_g (T_\infty^4 - T^4)$$

σ is the Stefan-Boltzmann constant, $= 5.674 \times 10^{-11}$ kW/m$^2 \cdot$ K^4 [$= 0.1714 \times 10^{-8}$ Btu/ft$^2 \cdot$ h $\cdot$ R^4], T_∞ is the source temperature and T is the solid surface temperature, in K [R]. F is the view factor between the solid surface and the source and F_g is the grey-body correction factor. The radiation heat transfer boundary condition is nonlinear [unlike the convection heat transfer boundary condition, $f = h(T_\infty - T)$]. When $T = a \cdot T_\infty$ (and a is approximately constant), the condition can be linearized as:

$$f(T, T_\infty, F, \varepsilon's) \simeq h_r (T_\infty - T)$$

where:

$$h_r = FF_g T_\infty^3 (a+1)(a^2+1) = FF_g R$$

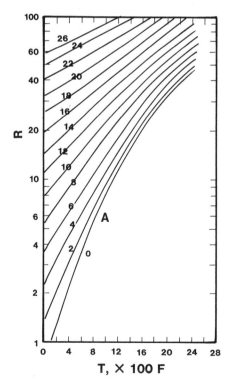

Figure 3.10 Radiation Factor, R (3; pg. 231). R: Radiation Factor. T: Radiant Surface Temperature, [× 100 F]. A: Absorbing Surface Temperature, [× 100 F]. (Figure used by permission of copyright owner.)

Values of R are obtained from Figure 3.10. If $T_\infty \gg T$ throughout the heating cycle, R is approximately constant and an average value can be used. The radiation heat transfer coefficient for an infinite planar 800 C [1472 F] black body source radiating to an infinite planar 20 C [68 F] black body sink (F, $F_g = 1$) is 0.096 kW/m$^2 \cdot$C [16.9 Btu/ft$^2 \cdot$h$\cdot$F]. If the sink temperature is 150 C [302 F], the coefficient value is 0.113 kW/m$^2 \cdot$C [19.9 Btu/ft$^2 \cdot$h$\cdot$F]. An average value of 0.104 kW/m$^2 \cdot$C [18.3 Btu/ft$^2 \cdot$h$\cdot$F] is accurate to within 11%. Actual values can be substantially less than these ideal values. Typical values are 1 to 10 times those for moving air convection heat transfer coefficients (Table 3.2).

Convection Heat Transfer Coefficient

Air trapped between heater banks and plastic sheet surfaces is very slow moving or quiescent, and so attains a nearly-isothermal temperature between the sheet surface temperature and the radiant source temperature. The convection heat transfer coefficient is found from:

$$h = K\,(\Delta T/G)^{\frac{1}{4}}$$

G is the length of a plate heater or the diameter of a rod heater, ΔT is the temperature difference between the hot surface and the air. The proportionality constant (K) depends upon the heater geometry (G) and whether the heater plate faces up or down (Table 3.9). For 93 C [200 F] trapped air, sheet at 150 C [302 F], and 800 C [1472 F] flat plate radiant sources on both sides of the sheet, the four heat transfer coefficients are:

h (sheet top) $= 4.71 \times 10^{-3}$ (kW/m$^2 \cdot$C) {0.83 [Btu/ft$^2 \cdot$h$\cdot$F]}
h (sheet bottom) $= 2.35 \times 10^{-3}$ {0.414}
h (heater, facing down) $= 4.43 \times 10^{-3}$ {0.78}
h (heater, facing up) $= 8.86 \times 10^{-3}$ {1.56}

The range of 2.4 to 10×10^{-3} (kW/m$^2 \cdot$C) [0.4 to 1.6 Btu/ft$^2 \cdot$h$\cdot$F] is consistant with values in Table 3.2 for quiescent air, and is a factor of 10 or so below the typical range for radiation heat transfer coefficients. If the air temperature is greater than the plastic sheet temperature, energy is convected *to* the sheet. If the sheet is hotter than the air, energy is convected *from* the sheet. A combined convection and radiation heat transfer coefficient can be written as:

$$h_{eff} = h + h_r$$

TABLE 3.9 CONVECTION HEAT TRANSFER COEFFICIENTS FOR NATURAL CONVECTION FROM FLAT PLATES AND RODS
$h = K(\Delta T/G)^{1/4}$

Geometry/Attitude	K (metric) (h, kW/m^2 C)	K (English) [h, Btu/ft^2 h F]
Heated Plate (G = L)		
Facing Upward	1.49×10^{-3}	0.263
Facing Downward	0.746×10^{-3}	0.131
Rod (G = D)	1.533×10^{-3}	0.27
	(2.839×10^{-3})	(0.50)*
	ΔT in C	ΔT in F
	G = D, L in m	G = D, L in ft

* J. H. Perry (23).

The initial effective heat transfer coefficients at the sheet surfaces for the ideal radiant source/sink case above are:

h(sheet top)	$= 0.096 + 0.005 = 0.101 \ (kW/m^2 C)$
	$= 16.9 + 0.96 = 17.9 \ [Btu/ft^2 \ h \ F]$
h(sheet bottom)	$= 0.096 + 0.003 = 0.099$
	$= 19.9 + 0.48 = 20.4$

The final values are:

h(sheet top)	$= 0.113 - 0.005 = 0.098 \ (kW/m^2 \ C)$
	$= 19.9 - 0.83 = 19.1 \ [Btu/ft^2 \ h \ F]$
h(sheet bottom)	$= 0.113 - 0.003 = 0.110$
	$= 19.9 - 0.4 = 19.5$

In this ideal case, the radiation contribution to the overall heat transfer coefficient over-whelms the convection contribution. In practical thermoforming, the radiation contribution is diminished by heat losses, but still dominates the overall heat transfer.

An effective heat transfer coefficient can be obtained from an overall heat balance on a given plastic sheet. Effective values in Table 3.1 are obtained from thin-gage heating rate data (Figure 3.2) and typical forming conditions. Except for polyethylene, the values range from about 0.0255 to 0.0548 $kW/m^2 \cdot C$ [4.5 to 9.7 $Btu/ft^2 \cdot h \cdot F$]. If the convection contribution is essentially constant at about 0.005 $kW/m^2 \cdot C$ [1 $Btu/ft^2 \cdot h \cdot F$], the radiation contribution is about 4 to 9 times that of the convection contribution (which is net energy transfer *from* the sheet). Further, if the average black body net radiant interchange yields an effective radiation heat transfer coefficient of about 0.093 $kW/m^2 \cdot C$ [16.4 $Btu/ft^2 \cdot h \cdot F$], the radiant inter-change efficiency is about 35 to 65%. These effective heat transfer coefficient values are typical of experimental data obtained in other ways (12).

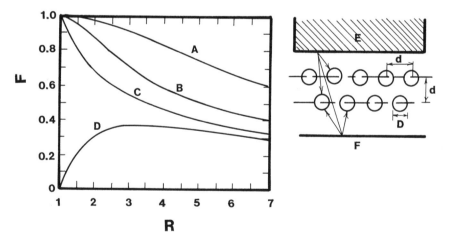

Figure 3.11 Radiation Between Rods and a Plane (20). R: Ratio, Center-to-Center Distance Between Tubes to Tube Diameter, d/D. F: Fraction of Heat Transferred When Compared with Infinite Planes. A: Total of Both Rows. B: Total When Only One Row is Present. C: Total to First Row. D: Total to Second Row. E: Non-Conducting Absorber. F: Plane. (Figure used by permission of McGraw-Hill Book Co., Inc.)

TABLE 3.10 ROD HEATER REFLECTOR EFFICIENCIES-EFFECTIVE HEAT TRANS-
FER COEFFICIENTS (from (12), by permission of Society of Plastics Engineers)

Material	Emissivity	Heater Temp, C	Reflector Temp, C	Convective Heat Trans. Coeff. kW/m^2 C
Gold				
New	0.92	690	220	0.0244
Aged	–	683	323	0.0176
Stainless Steel				
New	0.60	686	304	0.0125
Aged	–	668	352	0.0142
Aluminium				
New	0.30	719	274	0.0199
Aged	–	693	287	0.0199

Length of time to aged values unknown.

Rod Heaters

In some thermoformers, rod heaters (with or without reflectors) are used to heat sheet. The
energy emitted from rod heaters is related to that emitted by a heated plane. Figure 3.11 assumes that the surface behind the rod heaters is nonconducting. As an example, consider
25 mm dia tubular heaters spaced 125 mm apart. From Figure 3.11 the black body emitted
energy is only 70% of that of a plane at the same temperature. The grey-body correction factor F_g for grey surface radiation between a plane and a tube bank is given as:

$$F_g = \varepsilon_1 \varepsilon_2$$

For $\varepsilon_1 = 0.9$ source and $\varepsilon_2 = 0.85$ sink, the energy interchanged is 76.5% of ideal black body
interchange. The effective energy interchange is 70% × 76.5% = 53.6% of maximum black-
body parallel plane interchange. Radiant energy loss from the back of rod heaters is minimized by reflectors. New aluminum and gold-fired porcelain enamel give the greatest reflector efficiencies, but efficiencies deteriorate with age. Stainless steel appears to provide
the best long-term efficiency (Table 3.10). The effective heat transfer coefficient from the
top of the reflector is essentially independent of reflector material or temperature (Figure 3.12).

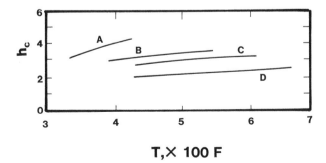

Figure 3.12 Convection Heat Transfer Coefficients for Rod Heater Reflectors (12). h_c: Experimentally Determined Heat Transfer Coefficient [Btu/ft$^2 \cdot$h$\cdot$F]. T: Reflector Temperature, [× 100 F]. A: New Gold Plated. B: Aluminum. C: Oxidized Gold. D: Stainless Steel. (Figure used by permission of Society of Plastics Engineers, Inc.)

Radiant Heater Efficiency

Radiant heater efficiency also decreases with time (Table 3.11). The values represent overall efficiencies (effective energy conversion) for several commercial heaters. Efficiency is thought to decrease as a first-order system response with time:

$$\xi = \xi_0 \exp[-a\theta]$$

a is the time constant of the heater, (1/month). The expected efficiencies of heaters at various times (assuming the heaters are still functioning) are shown in Table 3.11.

Since heater efficiency is directly related to the radiant heat transfer coefficient, any decrease in heater efficiency at constant heater temperature increases the time to achieve sheet forming temperature. Since heater efficiency loss is gradual, cycle times can lengthen imperceptibly over days. If heater temperature is increased to compensate for decrease in efficiency, the radiant wavelength range can shift to less efficient regions of the spectrum. Further, energy losses to the surroundings increase with increasing heater temperature. Since efficient sheet heating is a key to optimum economic performance, all heater manufacturers now recommend strict scheduled periodic replacement of all elements, regardless of their apparent performance.

TABLE 3.11 COMMERCIAL RADIANT HEATER OVERALL EFFICIENCIES
(Adapted from McConnell (8))

Heater Type	ξ_0, Efficiency		Average Life, hr.	Time Constant, a, 1/mo (***)	Efficiency at end of life	Expected Efficiency at (***)		
	New	After 6 mos (**)				12 mo	18 mo	24 mo
Coiled Wire, Nichrome	16–18	8–10	1500	0.0926–0.1155	11–13	4–4.5	2–2.3	1–1.1
Tubular Rods*	42	21	3000	0.1155	19	10.5	5.3	2.6
Ceramic Panels	62	55	12–15,000	0.020	31–36	49	43	38
Quartz Heaters	55	48	8–10,000	0.0227	33–36	42	37	32
Gas-Fired IR Panels	40–45	25	5– 6,000	0.0926–0.104	11–12	13	7	4

*   Sanding, polishing increases efficiency by 10–15%.
** After 6 mo. use, 4–8% efficiency can be gained by replacing all reflectors.
*** One month = 440 hr (assumed for time constant only).

Edge Losses

Ideally, radiant net energy interchange does not depend upon the distance between the plane of the emitting source and that of the sheet surface. Radiation losses to the frame holding the sheet and the sheetmetal at the edge of the heater frame are a small fraction of the net energy interchange so long as the sheet width dimension is much larger than the gap dimension. The radiant energy interchange between black bodies of equal finite dimension connected by reradiating walls is given in Figure 3.13. For 600 × 600 mm [24 × 24 in] sheet with radiant heaters spaced at 150 mm [6 in], the view ratio is 4 and the view factor (F) is 77%. If the heaters are spaced at 75 mm [3 in], the spacing ratio is 8 and the view factor is 86%. To obtain the proper net energy interchange value between gray surfaces, this view factor must be then multiplied by the *grey-body correction factor*, F_g:

$$F^* = FF_g = F\varepsilon_1\varepsilon_2$$

F* is a grey-body corrected view factor. For the $\varepsilon_1 = 0.9$ source and $\varepsilon_2 = 0.85$ sink considered above, $F_g = 76.5\%$. For finite sheets with a 4:1 spacing ratio, the actual net energy interchange is 58.9% of maximum and at an 8:1 ratio, is 65.8%. In these examples, edge losses amount to 14% and 23%, respectively. Although spacing has been used to control heat to sheet without changing heater temperature, it is now recognized as an inefficient use of energy. Heater spacing is now governed by sheet sag and minimization of sheet "striping" or local overheating beneath rod heaters.

Figure 3.13 View Factor (F) for Radiant Interchange Between Parallel *Finite* Surfaces (20). R: Ratio, Diameter (or Side) to Distance Between Surfaces. A: Total Radiation if Surfaces are Connected by Non-Conducting, Reradiating Surfaces. B: Squares. C: Circular Disks. (Figure used by permission of McGraw-Hill Book Co., Inc.)

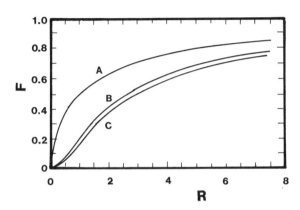

Pattern Heating

Radiant screens are frequently used in pattern heating to achieve uniform wall thickness in odd-shaped parts (13–15). Fine wire mesh is cut to shape and placed between the heater plane and the sheet surface (Figure 3.14). If f_s is the fraction of open area in the screen and T_{sc} is its (absolute) temperature, then the energy interchanged between the heater and the sheet beneath the screen is given as:

$$Q/A = \sigma f_s F^* \, (T_\infty^4 - T_s^4)$$

The energy interchanged between the heater and the screen is:

$$Q'/A = \sigma \, (1 - f_s) \, F^{*\prime} \, (T_\infty^4 - T_{sc}^4)$$

And that interchanged between the screen and the sheet is:

$$Q''/A = \sigma \, (1 - f_s) \, F^{*\prime\prime} \, (T_{sc}^4 - T_s^4)$$

Values for the various grey-body corrected view factors (F*, F*', F*'') are determined from individual emissivities and the relative wire dimensions. For example, if the spacing-to-diameter ratio is 3 and $f_s = 0.67$, the black body correction factor for discrete rods is $F = 0.70$. If the wire emissivity is 0.4, that of the heater is 0.9 and that of the plastic is 0.85, the values for F* are:

$$
\begin{aligned}
F^* &= 0.9 \times 0.85 &&= 0.765 \\
F^{*\prime} &= 0.7 \times 0.4 \times 0.85 &&= 0.238 \\
F^{*\prime\prime} &= 0.7 \times 0.4 \times 0.9 &&= 0.252
\end{aligned}
$$

(F* does not contain the rod correction factor, since the sheet is *seeing* the heater plane.) For an 800 C [1472 F] emitter, a 150 C [302 F] sheet and a screen at 350 C [662 F], the net energy interchange values are:

$$Q/A = 37.67\,kW/m^2 \,[= 11\,940\ Btu/ft^2\ h]$$
$$Q'/A = 0.53\,kW/m^2 \,[=\ 170\ Btu/ft^2\ h]$$
$$Q''/A = 5.55\,kW/m^2 \,[=\ 1760\ Btu/ft^2\ h]$$

Since the unshaded energy interchange is $Q_0/A = 56.22\ kW/m^2$ [= 17 800 Btu/ft² h], screening reduces the energy interchange in this case by about 32% [$(Q/A + Q'/A)/(Q_0/A)$]. The fraction of open area in the screen is the primary method of controlling pattern heating.

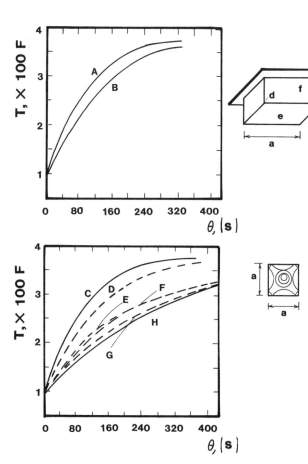

Figure 3.14 Effect of Patterning on Thermoforming Part Thickness and Temperature (14). PS, 2.1 mm [0.082 in] Vacuum Formed into Female Mold. T: Sheet Temperature, [× 100 F]. A: Top Surface. B: Bottom Surface. a: 178 mm [7 in]. b: 178 mm [7 in]. c: 76 mm [3 in]. Thickness Ratio (t/t_0) at d: = 0.049; at e: = 0.17 to 0.23; at f: = 0.38. For Four Thicknesses of Tissue Paper (Pattern Shown in Insert). C: Top Center Temperature Location. D: Top Side. E: Top Corner. F: Bottom Center. G: Bottom Side. H: Bottom Corner. Patterned Part Thickness Ratio $(t/t_0) = 0.29$ to 0.32 Throughout the Part. (Figure used by permission of Krieger Co. and Society of Plastics Engineers, Inc.)

Thin-Gage Sheet – Approximate Heating Rates

For thin-gage sheet, especially rollfed film for packaging and blister-pack applications, the time-dependent heating model can be significantly simplified. The net enthalpic change in the sheet is simply equated to the rate at which energy in the sheet is exchanged with its environment. In essence then, as a first approximation, the temperature across the plastic film is *assumed to be constant:*

$$d\,(VH) = V\rho c_p\,dT = hA\,(T_\infty - T)\,d\theta$$

V is the sheet volume, $= A \cdot t$, A is the sheet surface area and t is its thickness. The convective heat transfer coefficient is h. Now:

$$dT/(T_\infty - T) = (h/t\rho c_p)\,d\theta$$

If $T_0 = T(\theta = 0)$ and T_∞ is constant:

$$\ln\,[(T_\infty - T)/(T_\infty - T_0)] = -(h\theta/t\rho c_p)$$

or:

$$(T_\infty - T)/(T_\infty - T_0) = \exp(-h\theta/t\rho c_p)$$

This *lumped-parameter transient heat transfer* model is valid only where conduction through the sheet thickness is less significant than energy transmission from the environment to the sheet surface. A dimensionless group, the Biot Number (Bi), $Bi = h \cdot t/k$, is the ratio of internal to external heat transfer. The lumped-parameter model should be applied *only* when $Bi < 0.1$, or when internal resistance is relatively low. For air moving over plastic sheet, the sheet thickness should be less than 0.3 to 5 mm (10 to 200 mils) (Table 3.12 (4)).

TABLE 3.12 LUMPED-PARAMETER MAXIMUM SHEET THICKNESS

Moving Air Heat Transfer Coefficient (Table 3.2):

   1.4 ($\times 10^{-3}$ cal/cm^2 s C)
   1   [Btu/ft^2 h F]

Plastics Thermal Conductivity (Table 2.7):

   4.1 – 8.3 ($\times 10^{-4}$ cal/cm s C)
   0.1 – 0.2 [Btu/ft h F]

Maximum Thickness, $Bi = 0.1$:

   0.025–   0.5 (cm)
   10   –200 [mils]

Practical heating times for various thin-gage materials over a wide range in sheet thicknesses are given in Figure 3.2 (5). The linear relationship is apparent. The energy source temperature is not given, but a radiant heater at $T_\infty = 760$ C [1400 F] produces an energy spectrum with a peak wavelength of about 2.8 µm. The energy source output is 40 kW/m^2. The sheet temperature at forming time is not given. At a lower source temperature, $T_\infty = 510$ C [950 F], the forming time is not linear with sheet thickness. If the heat flux to a thin sheet is constant (Q/A = constant), then:

$$Q/A = \text{constant} = t\rho c_p\,(dT/d\theta)$$

Rearranging:

$$dT = [(Q/A)/t\rho c_p] \, d\theta$$

or:

$$T - T_0 = [(Q/A)/t\rho c_p] \, \theta$$

For a given set of processing conditions, the time to heat a very thin sheet with a high temperature source to a given forming temperature should be approximately proportional to the sheet thickness. This supports the data of Figure 3.2.

The heating efficiencies for several materials can be determined by using the normal forming temperatures from Table 3.1. The enthalpic change between room temperature and the normal forming temperatures are then determined (Figure 3.1). The individual heating rates are determined from the slopes of the curves of Figure 3.2 and the net energy increases calculated. As seen (Table 3.1), most thin-gage materials absorb 40 to 60% of the energy supplied by the heating source. The relatively low efficiency for LDPE is unexplained. PP efficiency is also reported to be low (6), indicating that the 760 C source temperature may be improper for efficient heating of olefins. This is amplified below.

This analysis is restricted to one very specific processing area (thin-gage materials) and very stringent conditions (lumped-parameter, with linear approximation of the logarithmic function). But it serves to illustrate that only a fraction (about half in this case) of the input energy is taken up by the sheet. The rest is lost to the environment.

Heavy-Gage Sheet – Internal Temperature

For thin-gage sheet and film, energy transmission to the sheet controls the heating cycle time. Radiant heating, seen to be far more efficient than convection heating, is preferred. For thick sheet however, energy absorbed on the sheet surface must be conducted to the interior. For very thick sheets, the heating cycle time is controlled by the sheet centerline temperature and so heating rate must be controlled to prevent surface overheating. This can be seen by reviewing the graphical solution to the transient one-dimensional heat conduction equation with the convection boundary condition (Figure 3.15). The ratio of effective energy convected to the surface to that conducted to the interior is the Biot Number, $Bi = h_{eff}L/k$, as before. If the sheet is heated uniformly from both sides, L is its half-thickness. The Fourier Number, $Fo = \alpha\theta/L^2$, is a dimensionless conduction time. α is the polymer thermal diffusivity (Table 2.7) and θ is time. Y is a dimensionless temperature, $= (T_\infty - T)/(T_\infty - T_0)$. T_∞ is the environmental temperature and T_0 is the initial sheet temperature, in consistant units. Y is unity initially and approaches zero in infinite time. The slab time-temperature profiles at various fractional thicknesses (x/L) are given in Figure 3.16.

An example illustrates the use of this Figure. For an 800 C [1472 F] source and an initial sheet temperature of 20 C [68 F], with L=0.32 cm [0.125 in], $k = 1.73 \times 10^{-4}$ kW/m·C [0.1 Btu/ft·h·F], $\alpha = 5.7 \times 10^{-4}$ cm^2/s [2.2 × 10^{-3} ft^2/h], and $h_{eff} = 0.0568$ kW/m^2·C [10 Btu/ft^2·h·F], Bi = 1.04, and Fo = 20.27θ (θ in h). The surface reaches the 150 C [302 F] forming temperature (x/L=0; Y= 0.833) when Fo = 0.038 or θ = 6.8 s. At that time, the centerline temperature is Y=0.96 or T_{cl} = 70 C [160 F]. When the centerline reaches the forming temperature, Fo=0.38 or θ = 67.6 s, and the surface temperature is Y=0.56 or T_s = 363 C [686 F]. Since the polymer would probably blister, degrade or discolor at this temperature, either a lower rate of effective convective energy is needed or the sheet must be removed from the heating environment before the centerline reaches the forming temperature (or both).

Figure 3.15 Unaccomplished
Temperature Change,
$Y = (T_\infty - T)/(T_\infty - T_0)$, for
Transient Heat Conduction
Through a Slab. Fo: Fourier
Number, $\alpha\theta/L^2$. x/L: Thick-
ness Ratio. $x/L = 0$: Center-
line. $x/L = 1$: Surface. L: Half-
Slab Thickness. Bi: Biot Num-
ber, hL/k. A: Bi = 0.25. B:
Bi = 0.5. C: Bi = 1. D: Bi =
2. E: Bi = 4. F: Bi = 10. G:
Bi = ∞.

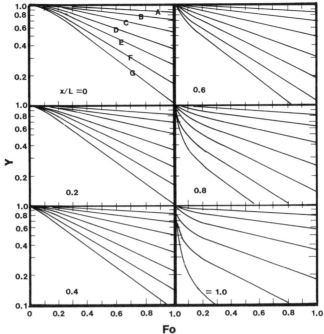

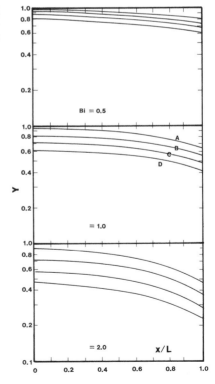

Figure 3.16 Unaccomplished Temperature Change, Y,
for Conduction Through a Slab. X/L: Half-Slab Thickness Ratio. Bi: Biot Number, hL/k. A: Fo = 0.2. B:
Fo = 0.4. C: Fo = 0.6. D: Fo = 0.8.

The most effective way of lowering the effective convective heat transfer coefficient is to lower the radiant heater temperature. If $T_\infty = 760$ C [1400 F], $h_{eff} = 0.0284$ kW/m$^2 \cdot$C [5 Btu/ft$^2 \cdot$h$\cdot$F]. Let $T_{cl} = 120$ C [248 F]. Then Y$= 0.865$, Bi$=0.52$ and Fo$=0.5$ or $\theta = 89$ s. The surface temperature at this time is Y$=0.7$ or 242 C [468 F]. The average sheet temperature at any time is obtained by averaging the individual values of Y at the various x/L increments. This is given in Table 3.13 for the example given above where $T_{avg} = 149$ C [300 F] at $\theta = 89$ s.

The effect of sheet thickness can be seen as well. If the sheet thickness is doubled, all things equal, the Biot Number, Bi$= hL/k$, doubles. If the centerline temperature is to attain a fixed value (say, 120 C in the last example), the surface temperature must increase, to Y$=0.5$ or $T_s = 390$ C [734 F], again probably above the normal processing temperature for the material. This occurs at Fo$=0.35$ or $\theta = 249$ s (since the material thickness is doubled). To minimize surface degradation, the energy flux to the surface must once again be reduced. Since conduction clearly governs the heating time for very heavy-gage sheets, less expensive albeit less efficient heating means, such as hot convection air ovens are used. There is experimental corroboration that heating cycle times for thick sheets are proportional to the square of sheet thickness for PVC/PMMA and PMMA (Table 3.14).

TABLE 3.13 CONVECTIVE AND CONDUCTION HEAT TRANSFER THROUGH HEAVY-GAGE PLASTIC SHEET (From Figure 3.16)

At $T_\infty = 800$ C Fo$=0.34$ ($\theta = 67.6$ s) Bi$=1.04$			$T_\infty = 760$ C Fo$=0.5$ ($\theta = 89$ s) Bi$=0.52$		
x/L	Y	T (C)	Y	T (C)	$T_{calc}*$(C)
0	0.833	150	0.865	120	120
0.2	0.82	160	0.84	138	131
0.4	0.78	192	0.82	153	147
0.6	0.74	223	0.80	168	169
0.8	0.65	293	0.75	205	200
1.0	0.56	363	0.70	242	242
		$T_{avg} =$ 225		$=169$	$=166$

* $T_{calc}(x) = 151.65 \exp(-0.51x) + 90.35$ where $0 < x < 3.2$ cm.

TABLE 3.14 THERMOFORMING HEATING CYCLE TIMES FOR HEAVY-GAGE PVC/PMMA AND PMMA SHEET
(Adapted form H.R. Osmers (24), with his permission) (Sheet heated on both sides) [Note: Heating time controlled by conduction through plastic is proportional to square of sheet thickness]

Sheet Thickness cm	(x/x_o)	$(x/x_o)^2$	PVC/PMMA		PMMA	
			time, s	$(0/0_o)$	time, s	$(0/0_o)$
0.102	1.0	1.0	15	1.0	13	1.0
0.152	1.49	2.22	35	2.33	29	2.23
0.203	1.99	3.96	61	4.07	51	3.92
0.236	2.31	5.35	82	5.47	–	–
0.254	2.49	6.20	–	–	80	6.15
0.318	3.12	9.72	150	10.0	126	9.69
0.475	4.66	21.7	324	21.6	276	21.2
0.635	6.23	38.8	594	39.6	495	38.1
0.953	9.34	87.3	–	–	1122	86.3

Thus if Bi < 0.1, the sheet heating process is controlled primarily by the rate at which energy is delivered to the sheet surface. If Bi > 1, the heating process becomes controlled by the rate at which heat is conducted to the interior of the sheet. Although the range in values for plastic thermal conductivity is relatively narrow, a factor of two or so, the effective heat transfer coefficient can range in value a factor of 20 or more. Thus the range in sheet thicknesses where neither conduction nor convection dominate heating rate is quite broad. Further, this range spans most of the common sheet thermoforming thicknesses, requiring case-by-case analyses.

Equilibration

When the sheet has reached its forming temperature and has been removed from the heating environment, its temperature gradually approaches an average value. This effect is known as *equilibration*. The time to equilibration is sometimes referred to as *soaking time*. Equilibration time values are strongly dependent upon temperature profile through the sheet and the sheet thickness and can be obtained (approximately) either from Figure 3.17 or from:

$$Fo_{eq} = (\alpha\theta/L^2) =$$

$$(\pi^{-2}) \ln \{4000 \, bL \, [1 - e^{(-bL)}]/[(bL)^2 + \pi^2]\}$$

This equation and the curves in Figure 3.17 are determined by assuming that the sheet has a temperature profile $T(x) = a \, \exp(bx) + c$ at the instant the heat source is removed. Strictly, this profile does not accurately mirror typical heat conduction temperature profiles, but

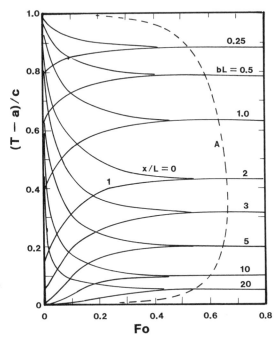

Figure 3.17 Adiabatic Equilibration Temperature (22). Initial Temperature Profile: $T(x) = a \cdot \exp(-b/x) + c \cdot A$: Equilibration Line. bL: Thermal Time Constant. L: Half-Slab Thickness. Fo: Fourier Number, $\alpha\theta/L^2$. (Figure used by permission of McGraw-Hill Book Co., Inc.)

practically it yields useful approximate information. For the second example of Table 3.13, curve-fitting yields $a = 151.65c$, $b = 0.51$ cm^{-1}, and $c = 90.35C$, and an integrated-average temperature of 166C. For the $L = 3.2$ cm sheet, the equilibration time is $Fo_{eq} = 0.65$. This sheet attains a uniform forming temperature of 166 C in $\theta = 115$ s. Forming at times substantially less than this equilibration time can lead to differential and uneven drawing, internal stress generation, and optical distortion. The dimensionless equilibrium time (Fo_{eq}) is rather constant over a wide range in values for bL ($0.5 < bL < 10$). As a first approximation, Fo_{eq} can be assumed to be about 0.6. This means that equilibration time is approximately proportional to the square of the sheet thickness.

Transparent Materials

Many thermoformable polymers that are optically transparent (PMMA, PET, PS, PC, PVC) may not be transparent to incident radiant energy. The visible light wavelength range is 0.38 to 0.7 μm. Less than 1% of the total black body radiation is emitted in the visible region for radiant heater temperatures less than 800 C [1472 F]. For some materials (PS, PMMA, PET), the transparent region extends into the infrared region. For these materials, in the transparent region, energy is absorbed volumetrically (Figure 3.18). The exact determination of the effect of volumetric energy absorption on temperature profiles in semi-transparent sheet has been made using opposing heat flux energy balances to obtain expressions for wavelength-dependent reflectance (r), transmittance (t), and absorptance (a) (16, 17). Surface or interfacial reflectance can be obtained from:

$$r = (n-1)^2/(n+1)^2$$

n is the index of refraction of the polymer. Reflectance for most transparent polymers is quite small. For PET, for example, $n = 1.65$ and $r = 0.06$. Transmittance is given as:

$$t = t_0 (1-r)^2 \exp(-\mu x)$$

t_0 is the wavelength-specific transmittance at the polymer surface and μ is Beer's Law absorption coefficient, also wavelength-dependent. Examples of wavelength-dependent absorption coefficients are given for several materials in Chapter 2. Absorption curves cannot be mathematically modeled, and so the curves are approximated with a series of step functions, as seen for PMMA in Table 3.15. An infinite value for the absorption coefficient indicates that all energy is absorbed on the sheet surface. Over the 0.4 to 2.2 μm range, the average absorption coefficient is 0.8 cm^{-1}. For a $L = 1.25$ cm thick sheet, the transmittance over this range is $t/t_0 = (0.94)^2 \cdot \exp(-1) = 28.7\%$. Since the reflectance is about 6%, about 65% of

TABLE 3.15 ABSORPTION COEFFICIENT VALUES STEP-FUNCTION APPROXIMATION PMMA (Lucite) (Adapted from (14))

Wavelength, μm	Absorption Coefficient, μ, cm^{-1}
0 –0.4	∞
0.4 –0.9	0.02
0.9 –1.65	0.45
1.65–2.2	2.0
2.2 – ∞	∞

the incident radiant energy in this wavelength is absorbed. If the black body radiant source temperature is 800 C [1472 F], it can be shown that about 15% of its energy is emitted at wavelengths of 2.2 μm or less. Thus volumetric energy absorption for this very thick sheet is about 10% of the total. Typically, volumetric absorption accounts for no more than about 10 to 15% of the total net radiant energy interchange.

Absorption coefficient values for unpigmented materials are independent of sheet thickness (17). Average values for pigmented PET show a decrease with increasing thickness (Figure 3.19 (18)). Organic dyes increase the absorption coefficient values primarily in the visible wavelength range. Pigments are primarily inorganic and act to increase scattering within the polymer (Figure 3.18), thus increasing absorption coefficient values across the entire wavelength spectrum in proportion to concentration. Very fine particles, such as talc and TiO_2, cause less scattering, as seen by comparing absorption coefficients of unpigmented with carbon- and TiO_2-pigmented PET (Figure 3.20).

The general effect of volumetric energy absorption is to flatten the temperature profile within the sheet. For thin-gage sheet, low energy absorption implies low heating efficiency. Pigments increase energy absorption and improve heating rates of thin-gage sheet. At a given energy input rate, they serve to increase sheet surface temperature in otherwise transparent materials. Most optically transparent materials, however, are opaque to incident infrared energy and so the volumetric absorption effects are secondary.

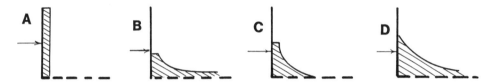

Figure 3.18 Schematic of Radiant Energy Absorption *Within* a Semitransparent Sheet. A: Surface Absorbing, Opaque. B: Volumetrically Absorbing, Semitransparent. C: Scattering, Translucent. D: Diathermanous, Semitransparent.

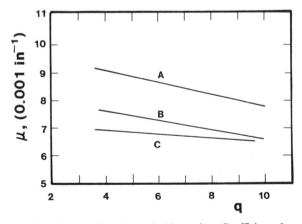

Figure 3.19 Absorption Coefficient for PET (18). μ: Experimental Absorption Coefficient, [× 0.001 in^{-1}]. q: Electrical Heat Flux, [× 1000 Btu/ft$^2 \cdot$h]. Quartz Heater. Sheet Thickness. A: 0.05 mm [0.00195 in]. B: 0.1 mm [0.0039 in]. C: 0.13 mm [0.0051 in]. (Figure used by permission of Society of Plastics Engineers, Inc.)

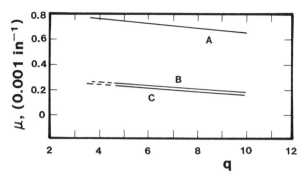

Figure 3.20 Absorption Coefficient for Pigmented PET (18). μ: Experimental Absorption Coefficient, [× 0.001 in^{-1}]. q: Electrical Heat Flux, [× 1000 Btu/ft^2·h]. Quartz Heater. A: Carbon Pigmented Sheet Thickness, 0.1 mm [0.0039 in]. B: Unpigmented, 0.1 mm [0.004 in]. C:TiO$_2$ Pigmented, 0.11 mm [0.0044 in]. (Figure used by permisssion of Society of Plastics Engineers, Inc.)

Guidelines for Determining Heating Cycle Times

When a new material is to be thermoformed, estimates of energy consumption, heater temperature and heating cycle time are needed. The best source for this information are experimental data on homologous materials. Some of this might be available from the supplier of this resin or its competitors. Carefully documented prior observations are also invaluable aids in estimating the needed data. If these sources cannot provide the information, certain guidelines can be extracted from the information given above. Heating rate guidelines depend upon whether the sheet can be considered as *thin-gage* or *heavy-gage*. These definitions can be partially quantified in terms of the value for the *Biot Number*, the *ratio of energy input to the surface to that conducted to the sheet interior*. Bi = hL/k. If Bi < 0.1, the sheet can be considered as thin-gage. If Bi > 1.0, the sheet can probably be considered as heavy-gage. In the discussion that follows, these definitions are used.

Thin-Gage Guidelines. Relatively speaking, the sheet is thin. Therefore the surface temperature is not significantly greater than the either the centerline or average sheet temperature. Sheet surface blistering, degradation or burning are not primary concerns. *Energy input* to the sheet surface *controls* cycle time. Therefore, *radiant heating* provides the *most efficient* means of heating. In order to minimize cycles, the maximum net energy exchange should occur in the wavelength range where the polymer has the greatest absorptivity. Usually this implies *high heater temperatures* and relatively short cycles. The effective heat transfer coefficient is on the order of 0.057 to 0.114 kW/m^2·C [10 to 20 Btu/ft^2·h·F] and is dominated by the radiation contribution, which can be as much as 10 times the natural convection contribution. Therefore convection effects can be ignored. For *very thin films*, such as those used in blister and bubble packaging, the *cycle time is directly proportional to the film thickness*. A lumped-parameter model that ignores temperature gradients through the sheet can be used to estimate average sheet temperature at any time. Cycle time can then be determined when the sheet reaches the forming temperature. From net energy balances, it appears that *about 50% of power* supplied to radiant heaters is *actually used to heat the sheet* to its forming temperature. If h_{eff} = 0.0567 kW/m^2·C [10 Btu/ft^2·h·F] and k = 1.73 × 10^{-4} kW/m·C [0.1 Btu/ft·h·F], Bi = 0.1 for L = 0.03 cm [0.012 in], or a total sheet thickness of 0.06 cm [0.024 in].

Heavy-Gage Sheet Guidelines. The rate of heating of thick sheet is governed by the *maxi-

mum allowable surface temperature. Energy transmitted to the surface from the surroundings must be conducted to the sheet interior. If the rate of conduction is low compared with the input energy rate, the sheet surface temperature may reach an undesirable level. Thus, highly efficient heating methods such as radiant heating may, in fact, be undesirable. Forced *hot air convection* ovens are used to heat very heavy-gage sheet. Relatively low surface temperatures imply relatively *low input energy* levels, manifested as relatively low values of the effective convection heat transfer coefficient. Typically, values on the order of 0.0114 to 0.0284 $kW/m^2 \cdot C$ [2 to 5 $Btu/ft^2 \cdot h \cdot F$] are seen. *Cycle times* are controlled by conduction into the sheet and therefore are *proportional to the square of the sheet thickness.* Overall *energy efficiency* is considered to be relatively low *(20 to 30% or so)* with heat losses to surroundings and low conversion efficiencies for heating air considered the primary reasons. For $h_{eff} = 0.0284$ $kW/m^2 \cdot C$ [5 $Btu/ft^2 \cdot h \cdot F$] and $k = 1.73 \times 10^{-4}$ $kW/m \cdot C$ [0.1 $Btu/ft \cdot h \cdot F$], when $Bi = 1$, $L = 0.610$ cm [0.240 in] or the overall sheet thickness is 1.22 cm [0.480 in]. Further, *equilibration times* are also proportional to the square of sheet thickness.

References

1. J. L. Throne, *Plastics Process Engineering*, Marcel Dekker, 1979, pp. 714–735.
2. J. L. Throne, *Plastics Process Engineering*, Marcel Dekker, 1979, "Conduction Heat Transfer", Section 6.2, pg. 316.
3. F. Kreith, *Principles of Heat Transfer*, 2nd Ed., International Textbook Co., 1965, pg. 142.
4. F. Kreith, *Principles of Heat Transfer*, 2nd Ed., International Textbook Co., 1965, pp. 128–135.
5. A. Höger, *Warmformen von Kunststoffen*, Hanser, 1971, Table 3, pp. 36–37.
6. H. Gross and G. Menges, "Influence of Thermoforming Parameters on the Properties of Thermoformed PP", SPE Tech. Papers, *28*, 1982, pg. 840.
7. J. Frados, Ed., *Plastics Engineering Handbook*, 4th. Ed., Van Nostrand Reinhold, 1976, pp. 278, 281.
8. W. McConnell, "Industrial Thermoforming Symposium and Workshop", SPE Thermoforming Division, Arlington TX, 12–14 March 1985, distributed handout.
9. F. Kreith, *Principles of Heat Transfer*, 2nd Ed., International Textbook Co., 1965, pg. 215.
10. F. Brinken and H. Potente, "Some Considerations of Thermodynamics in Thermoforming", SPE Tech. Papers, *24*, 1978, pg. 65.
11. "The Bratko Burner", Slyman Manufacturing Corp., Parma OH, undated brochure.
12. R. R. Kraybill, "Emission Efficiency of Reflector Materials for an Infrared Tubular Heater", SPE Tech. Papers, *29*, 1983, pg. 466.
13. N. Platzer, "Rigid Thermoplastic Sheeting", Mod. Plastics, *31*: 11, 1954, pp. 3, 144.
14. N. Platzer, "Sheet Forming", in E. C. Bernhardt, Ed., *Processing of Thermoplastic Materials*, Reinhold, 1959, pg. 485.
15. J. L. Throne, *Plastics Process Engineering*, Marcel Dekker, 1979, pg. 657.
16. R. C. Progelhof, J. Quintiere, J. L. Throne, "Temperature Distribution in Semitransparent Plastic Sheets Exposed to Symmetric, Unsymmetric, and Pulsed Radiant Heating and Surface Cooling", J. Appl. Polym. Sci., *17*, 1973, pg. 1227.
17. R. C. Progelhof, J. Franey, T. W. Haas, "Absorption Coefficient of Unpigmented Polym(methyl Methacrylate), Polystyrene, Polycarbonate, and Poly(4-methylpentene-1) Sheets", J. Appl. Polym. Sci., *15*, 1971, pg. 1803.
18. W. J. Hennessey and R. R. Kraybill, "Infrared Heating Characteristics of Pigmented Polyethylene Terephthalate Webs", SPE Tech. Papers, *28*, 1982, pg. 826.
19. A. Höger, *Warmformen von Kunststoffen*, Hanser, 1971, Table 2, pg. 31.
20. A. I. Brown and S. M. Marco, *Introduction to Heat Transfer*, McGraw-Hill, 1951, pg. 68.
21. F. Kreith, *Principles of Heat Transfer*, 2nd Ed., International Textbook Co., 1965, Table 5-1, pp. 215–216.
22. P. J. Schneider, "Conduction", in W. M. Rohsenow and J. P. Hartnett, Eds., *Handbook of Heat Transfer*, McGraw-Hill, 1973, pg. 3–42. See also, P. J. Schneider, "Thermal Equilibration", J. Spacecraft and Rockets, *4*, 1967, pg. 402.

23. J.H. Perry, Ed., *Chemical Engineers' Handbook*, 4th Ed., McGraw-Hill, 1963, pp.10-11 to 10-13.
24. H.R. Osmers, "Industrial Thermoforming Symposium and Workshop", SPE Thermoforming Division, Arlington TX, 12–14 March 1985, distributed handout.
25. R.W. Singleton, "Electric Infrared: Textile Applications in the 1980's", Proceedings, AATCC National Technical Conf., 1980, pg.201.
26. A.G. Rowe, "Thermoforming of Polyethylene Sheeting", paper presented at ACS Meeting, Sept.1957. Referenced in Platzer (14).

4 STRETCHING THE SHEET

Introduction

Once the plastic sheet is at the proper forming temperature, it can be stretched. There are many ways of stretching and prestretching the sheet, as seen in Chapter 1. Vacuum, air pressure, mechanical aids such as plugs, rubber diaphrams, and combinations of these can be used to shape the rubbery sheet. The extent to which a given material at a given temperature can be stretched limits the ways in which it can be thermoformed. Part design, especially local part wall thickness, depends upon the extent of materials deformation. Deep drawing, drawing into sharp corners, and replication of mold surface details (patterns, lettering) require materials that can be rapidly and uniformly stretched. Chapter 7 examines part design in great detail.

This chapter focusses on the interaction between the inherent nature of the rubbery plastic and the forces needed to stretch it into shape. This interaction, as noted in Chapter 2, is related directly to the stress-strain behavior of the plastic at the forming temperature. Typically, at low temperatures, the plastic sheet is quite stiff, does not stretch easily, and does not faithfully replicate the mold details. It therefore requires high forming forces. But the sheet cools quickly and so cycle times are short. At high temperatures, the sheet is quite limp, is easy to stretch and replicates well at very modest forming pressures (such as vacuum). But sagging may be a serious problem, cooling may increase the overall cycle time, and part wall uniformity may be compromised. Processing guidelines are given in the first part of Chapter 7, especially Table 7.9.

Intuitively knowing when a sheet is hot enough for processing is an acquired skill. One way to gain a technical understanding of this skill is to examine the fundamental nature of plastic material deformation. As noted below, thermoplastic sheet at the forming temperature can be considered *either* as a rubbery elastic solid *or* as a highly viscous fluid *or* as something in between. An extensive body of knowledge has been created on this topic because of the commercial interest and because this mode of deformation leads to a very basic understanding of material behavior during stretching.

The objective of examining this topic in such technical detail is a better understanding of the process fundamentals. The parts designer does not necessarily need to understand these nuances to design quality parts, but the material should be reviewed for general concepts.

What is Stretching?

Stretching is material deformation. The extent of deformation depends upon sheet temperature, level of applied force, level of molecular order and orientation, and general material stress-strain behavior. Above Tg, most amorphous polymers have sufficient chain mobility to deform and even dislocate (flow) under load. If a material flows, it can retain permanent deformation once the load is removed. For crystalline polymers above Tg, those chain segments that are not involved in the crystallite formations (either in the spherulites or captured in dendritic structures) can deform. The extent of deformation then depends upon the level of crystallinity.

Thermoforming involves a complex mixture of material deformation processes (Table 4.1 (1)). In most cases, when the sheet is prestretched by air pressure prior to forming (snap-back, pillowing, billow forming), it is biaxially stretched (Figure 4.1) and is undergoing *unconstrained deformation*. Free-blown shapes (skylights, blisters and bubbles for packaging) are also biaxially stretched. When the sheet is mechanically prestretched (plug-assist, web breakers) or when it contacts a mold surface almost immediately upon initiation of stretching, the stretching may be uniaxial (Figure 4.2). The sheet is undergoing *constrained deformation*. Unconstrained deformation gives the clearest analysis of material behavior under load. It also provides a practical means for determining the thermoformability of a material and so is examined here in detail.

TABLE 4.1 TYPE OF VISCOSITY EXPECTED FOR SEVERAL TYPES OF PLASTIC PROCESSING (Adapted from Denson (1), by permission of Society of Plastics Engineers)

Process	Type of Extensional Viscosity		
	Uniaxial	Uniform Biaxial	Pure Shear
Injection Molding (Radial Flow)			X
Blow Molding (Cylindrical Parison) (Spherical Parison)		X	X
Fiber Spinning	X		
Converging Entry Flows-Rectangular Die Circular Die	X		X
Thermoforming*	X	X	X

* Depends upon particular configuration and whether plug assist is used.

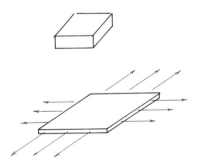

Figure 4.1 Schematic of Biaxial Stretching.

Figure 4.2 Schematic of Uniaxial Stretching.

Polymer Hot Strength

As noted in Chapter 2, for amorphous and crystalline polymers alike, tensile strength and modulus decrease and elongation increases with increasing temperature. Simply put, polymer sheets become rubbery when heated to the forming temperature. Typically, the tensile test is a standard procedure for measuring the strength of solid polymers. From a uniaxial tensile test on a dogbone-shaped sample, the initial elongation under load yields Young's Modulus, E. As the applied load increases, neck-down and elongation begin. The polymer response becomes one of plastic yielding. The yield point is noted as the point where an abrupt change in strain occurs. Ductile and rubbery polymers continue to bear load while yielding. The sample fails at its ultimate tensile strength and ultimate elongation. Brittle polymers normally exhibit very little yielding before failing.

The sample *strain rate*, in sec^{-1}, is the slope of the elongation-time curve. Thermoforming is a high-deformation-rate process with momentary strain rates of 0.1 to 10 sec^{-1} (or higher). In a typical laboratory tensile test, the crosshead speed of 25.4 cm/min yielded a sustained strain rate of about 0.3 to 0.6 sec^{-1} (13, 35). In other words, high laboratory speeds yield data at the low end of the practical process.

Carefully controlled hot tensile tests can yield important data about the general formability of resins. For example, the tendency for abrupt sheet sag is thought to be related to a rapid drop in tensile modulus with temperature (35). As noted in Figure 4.3, amorphous polymers (represented by ABS) have less sag tendency than crystalline ones (HDPE, PP) even when the latter are filled. As expected, the thermoforming windows for crystalline polymers increase with increased filler loading. Fillers act to lower the hot tensile strength and modulus at a given temperature. This makes forming at a lower temperature easier. Polymers that exhibit load retention after yielding are thought to produce parts with more uniform wall thicknesses, particularly in deep draw applications (35). Crystalline polymers are candidates if formed at temperatures within 10 C [20 F] of their melt temperatures.

Hot tensile tests are difficult experiments to carry out with any degree of reliability or confidence in the data. At elevated temperatures, uniaxial stretching is not confined to the neck-down region of the sample and grip slip is common. Sample conditioning at the desired

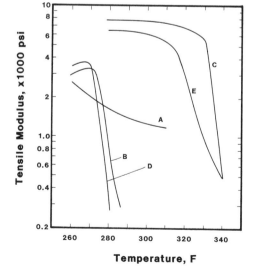

Figure 4.3 Temperature-Dependent Tangent Tensile Moduli for Amorphous (A: ABS) and Crystalline (B: HDPE, C: PP) Polymers. D: 40%(wt) Mineral Filled HDPE. E: 40%(wt) Mineral Filled PP. (35). (This figure used by permission of Society of Plastics Engineers, Inc.)

temperature is arduous since the sample is usually quite limp and the grips and even the load cells conduct heat from the environmental chamber. Conditioning times of 12 minutes have been recommended (13). Appreciable annealing and strain relaxation can occur during thermal conditioning and initial elongation values under load (initial values of Young's Modulus, for example) can be suspect. In short, high temperature tensile tests are difficult to master and may yield suspect data.

Hot creep is another uniaxial test that has been used extensively in attempts to evaluate material candidates for thermoforming. In tensile creep, a fixed load (or fixed stress) is applied to a sample and the strain level and strain rate monitored. Usually creep is a long-term test, involving relatively low loads and temperatures. Hot creep is a modification of this test. Here a fixtured sample is placed in a high-temperature oven and allowed to condition with no applied load. A very high load is then applied instantaneously and a high speed camera is used to measure time-dependent elongation to break (14). Instantaneous strain rates of $5 \sec^{-1}$ are commonly measured this way.

The hot creep test yields temperature-dependent ultimate elongation values as well. In one reported experiment, the ultimate elongation or strain for RPVC increased linearly from about 1.2 at 100 C to 5 (or so) at 122 C, then dropped to about 3 (or so) at 140 to 180 C (14). This would indicate that local draw ratios should not exceed 3 to 4 in parts to be made from RPVC. The effect of strain hardening owing to increasing strain rate at a given temperature can only be found implicitly in the hot creep test. Hot uniaxial creep test data can be compromised by the same testing vagaries that could occur in hot tensile testing. Nevertheless there is a strong indication that ultimate uniaxial strain can be related to areal draw ratios in simple geometries (14).

The hot creep test is more sensitive to changes in polymer character at a given strain level and temperature. The hot tensile test provides a clearer picture for stress-strain behavior at high strain levels. However, hot creep and hot tensile tests do not predict processing conditions necessary for obtaining accurate mold replication. Prediction of sheet performance in practical draw-down situations cannot be obtained from these tests. Neither test truly replicates the nature of the biaxial sheet stretching so common in even the simplest thermoforming process. As a result, recent studies have focussed on the development of biaxial stretching laboratory tests that more closely mirror reality. An important aspect of these efforts is to find and define a more useful material design parameter, $\varphi(T)$, that can be used to better evaluate the performance of a given material in a given stretching situation. The parameter identified in this chapter should be useful to the process engineer, for it helps establish a minimum value for forming temperature for a given material, mold geometry, and applied forming force. It is based on fundamental concepts in biaxial orientation of rubbery sheet.

Stress-Strain-Rate-of-Strain

At forming temperature, polymers are *incompressible, time-dependent elastic* materials. When a low-level load is applied for a long time, polymers have fluid-like properties. They flow or creep. At impulse loading levels, polymers exhibit solid-like springback or brittle fracture. Thermoforming is usually considered a short-time, high deformation-rate process.

Tensile stress-strain behavior is written as:

$$\sigma = f(\varepsilon, \dot{\varepsilon})$$

σ is the applied stress (MPa) [lbf/in^2], ε is the true material strain or deformation per unit length, and $\dot{\varepsilon}$ is the true rate-of-strain or deformation rate (s^{-1}). This interrelationship is temperature-sensitive. For purely elastic solids in uniaxial extension, stress is proportional to strain. The proportionality is Young's Modulus of Elasticity:

$$\sigma = E\,\varepsilon$$

In biaxial stretching:

$$\sigma_i = E\,\varepsilon_i/(1-\upsilon)$$

υ is Poisson's ratio and i is direction ($=1, 2$). For purely Newtonian fluids, stress is proportional only to rate of strain. For uniaxial stretching:

$$\sigma = \eta_e(\dot{\varepsilon})\,\dot{\varepsilon}$$

$\eta_e(\dot{\varepsilon})$ is the fluid elongational viscosity. For a deformation-rate-independent fluid, the uniaxial elongational or Trouton viscosity is $\frac{1}{3}$ the Newtonian shear viscosity:

$$\eta_{Newt} = 3\,\eta_{Trout} \qquad \text{(uniaxial)}$$

For uniform biaxial stretching, the Trouton viscosity is $\frac{1}{6}$ the Newtonian shear viscosity:

$$\eta_{Newt} = 6\,\eta_{Trout} \qquad \text{(biaxial)}$$

However most polymer melts have shear-dependent (nonNewtonian) shear viscosities (2).

The time-dependent elastic nature of polymers at the thermoforming temperature can be understood in terms of solid or fluid behavior. The time dependency can be included in a typical stress-strain analysis of a solid. Or conventional rheological stress-rate-of-strain models can be altered to include solid-like behavior at high strain rates (3). Both approaches have merit. Both are simplified conditions of the general cases of viscoelastic mechanical analyses (2, 4, 5). The common methods for determining polymer strain-rate-of-strain response to applied stretching stresses include extensional rheometry (3, 6), biaxial or bubble inflation of a tube or sheet (7–10), biaxial stretching of a blow film (11), free blowing of a preform (12), uniaxial stretching of fibers (6) and creep experiments (13–15).

Creep experiments are the easiest to conduct to obtain information on material response to constant low-level load at isothermal conditions (13–17). Rate-dependent terms are considered negligible. At room temperature, many polymers follow a (near-)ideal strain-hardening ductile material creep rupture response to constant load:

$$\sigma = \sigma_0 \exp(m\varepsilon)$$

σ is stress, σ_0 is initial stress, and m is a strain-hardening factor. If the material is ideally ductile, $m = 1$. Bahadur shows $0.92 < m < 1.6$ for many polymers at strain-rate levels of less than $0.0333\ s^{-1}$ (Table 4.2 (17)). At high loading levels and/or elevated temperatures, creep rates are so high that measuring and conditioning errors make accurate interpretation difficult (13, 14). Time-dependent behavior can be added to the creep model as (18–20):

$$\sigma = \sigma_0\,f(\varepsilon)\,g(\theta)$$

For amorphous polymers such as PMMA and HIPS, at normal forming temperatures, the data favor an ideal elastic (non-strain-hardening) model (Table 4.3):

TABLE 4.2 STRAIN HARDENING CONSTANTS FOR SEVERAL POLYMERS
(from Bahadur (17), by permission of Society of Plastics Engineers)
$\sigma = \sigma_0 \exp(m\varepsilon)$

Material	Strain Rate, s^{-1}	From Plot		From least square	
		σ_0 (MPa) [psi]	m	σ_0 (MPa) [psi]	m
POM (Delrin)	0.00027	67.9 [9850]	1.12	65.8 [9539]	1.312
POM (Delrin)	0.0027	68.95 [10000]	1.19	68.3 [9910]	1.257
PA-66 (Nylon)	0.0027	49.6 [7200]	0.919	51.5 [7468]	0.894
Mod. PPO (Lexan)	0.0027	48.3 [7000]	1.061	48.8 [7079]	1.06
PVC	0.0027	38.6 [5600]	0.974	38.0 [5518]	1.029
PE	0.0333	7.93 [1150]	1.182	8.26 [1198]	1.144
PP	0.0133	12.93 [1875]	1.103	13.0 [1889]	1.102
PP	0.0333	13.5 [1960]	1.182	13.4 [1943]	1.169
PTFE (Teflon)	*	10.34 [1500]	1.58	10.3 [1495]	1.603
PFEP (Teflon)	*	12.41 [1800]	1.203	12.51 [1815]	1.203

* Not reported.

TABLE 4.3 STRESS-STRAIN BEHAVIOR OF TWO PLASTICS IN BIAXIAL EXTEN-
SION (From Lai and Holt (19), by permission of Society of Plastics Engineers)
$\sigma = \sigma_0 \varepsilon^m \theta^n$

Material	n	m
PMMA	-0.05	1.0
HIPS	-0.33	1.1

$$\sigma = \sigma_0 \varepsilon^m \theta^n$$

HIPS appears to have little time-dependent behavior, with $n \simeq 1$. On the other hand, ABS/
PVC and PVC exhibit substantial strain-hardening at processing temperatures (Figure 4.4
(14)).

If a material deforms uniformly during uniaxial stretching, a tensile strength can be obtained from:

$$T^* = \sigma_0 \exp[(m-1)\varepsilon_f]$$

ε_f is the true strain at fracture. If $m \simeq 1$ (as is the case with most polymers in Table 4.2),
$T^* \simeq \sigma_0$. Polymer tensile strength decreases with temperature, as shown in Figure 4.5 (13,
18). At normal (vacuum) forming temperatures, tensile strengths for these polymers are
about 0.07 to 0.7 MPa [10 to 100 psi].

Since the polymer sheet forming temperature is substantially above Tg, amorphous materials (at least) can be considered as fluids. Behavior under load can be correctly considered in
terms of elongational viscosity. Isothermal elongational viscosity usually increases with
time (Figure 4.6). At very low strain rates, $\eta_e \propto \theta^n$, where $n < 1$. (Table 4.4 (19)). Isochronous
biaxial elongational viscosities for olefins at forming temperature and very low strain rates
(0.000015 to 0.006 s^{-1}) are inversely proportional to strain-rate (16).

As the strain-rate increases, the apparent viscosity deviates from the asymptote at earlier
and earlier times. As seen for LDPE (Figure 4.7 (4)), at 2 s, for $\dot{\varepsilon} = 1.0\ s^{-1}$, the material has a
viscosity 10 times greater than at $\dot{\varepsilon} = 0$. At 10 s, the elongational viscosity is about 1000 times

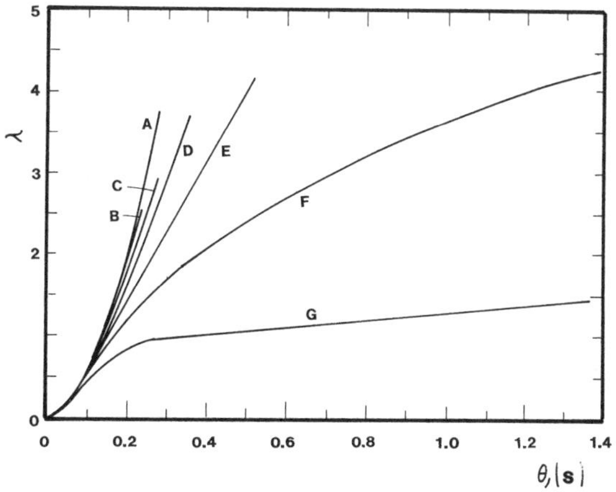

Figure 4.4 Effect of Temperature on Strain Rate for RPVC (14), by permission of Gordon & Breach, copyright owner. λ: Strain. θ: Time, s. A: 181 C [357 F]. B: 161 C [321 F]. C: 150 C [302 F]. D: 141 C [286 F]. E: 129 C [264 F]. F: 116 C [240 F]. G: 107 C [224 F].

Figure 4.5 Tensile Yield Strengths of Several Polymers (Adapted from Vincent (18), permission granted by Imperial Chemical Industries, Petrochemicals and Plastics Division, copyright owner). A: POM (Acetal). B: PA-66 (nylon). C: RPVC. D: PC. E: PP. F: 4-Methyl-Pentane-1. G: LDPE. H: PTFE.

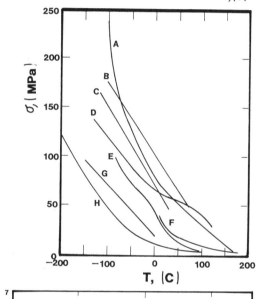

Figure 4.6 Strain-Rate Dependent Extensional Viscosity for HDPE at 180 C (3), by permission of John Wiley & Sons. η: Extensional Viscosity, Pa·s. θ: Time, s. A: $\dot{\varepsilon} = 1.15$ s^{-1}. B: 0.726. C: 0.461. D: 0.288. E: 0.115. F: 0.0726. G: 0.0115. H: 0.

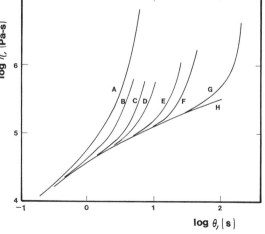

TABLE 4.4 BIAXIAL EXTENSIONAL VISCOSITIES FOR OLEFINS AT VERY LOW STRAIN RATES
(Adapted from Hoover and Tock (16), by permission of Society of Plastics Engineers)

Material	Strain Rate $\dot{\varepsilon}$, ($\times 10^{-6}$, s^{-1})	Viscosity (GPa s)
PP (3 mil) Unoriented*	2310	4.99
	196	71.6
	19.1	762
PP (1.5 mil) Unoriented	2260	6.51
	219	50.9
	15.1	719
PP (3 mil)	5110	28.1
	262	496
	28.8	4150
Ethylene-Propylene Copolymer (3 mil)	181	890
	24.3	6310

* Least squares fit, $\eta = 0.015/\dot{\varepsilon}$.

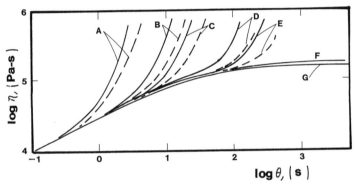

Figure 4.7 Comparison of Experimental and Theoretical Strain-Rate Dependent Extensional Viscosity for LDPE. See (4) for Additional Details. η: Extensional Viscosity, Pa s. θ: Time, s. Solid Lines: Theory. Dashed Lines: Experiment. Experimental Lines for F, G Fall on Theoretical Lines. A: $\dot{\varepsilon} = 1.0$ s^{-1}. B: 0.2. C: 0.1. D: 0.02. E: 0.01. F: 0.002. G: 0.001. This figure used by permission of John Wiley & Sons, copyright owners.

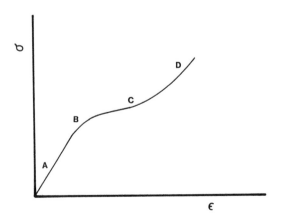

Figure 4.8 Elastic Liquid Behavior of LDPE (Data From Figure 4.7 (4). This figure used by permission of John Wiley & Sons, copyright owners.) σ: Tensile Stress. ε: True Strain, as $\dot{\varepsilon}\theta$. A: Linear Region. B: Yield. C: Strain Hardening. D: Fracture.

greater than at $\dot{\epsilon}=0$. In short, the material is rapidly becoming solid-like in its response to applied load. At $\dot{\epsilon}=0.1\ s^{-1}$, it takes about 100 s to achieve this relative level of stiffness and at $\dot{\epsilon}=0.1s^{-1}$, about 1000 s. In terms of true stress and true strain, $\epsilon=\dot{\epsilon}\theta$, the data show an initial linear region, a yield, then strain-hardening and fracture (3) (Figure 4.8). In other words, both amorphous and crystalline polymers behave as *elastic liquids* at typical thermoforming temperatures (21).

Basic Understanding

When a thermoformed shape is placed in an environment having a temperature (substantially) greater than Tg and typically approaching that of its forming temperature, it quickly returns to a flat sheet. Schmidt and Carley (22) record 90% recovery in less than 0.002 s. They argue therefore that thermoforming is a solid phase deformation process. Others (5, 23) argue that the material response is proper for a highly strained elastic liquid. Sheet stretching behavior is best viewed in terms of relative orders of magnitude for process times and material memory. To understand this, consider a simple "Maxwell fluid", (Fig 4.9 (24)) consisting of an ideal elastic spring and a purely viscous dashpot in series. If this fluid is strained to a fixed value, the resulting stress will decay. This can be represented as:

$$\sigma = \sigma_0 \exp(-\theta/\theta_1)$$

σ_0 is the initial stress and $\theta_1=\mu/G$, μ is the (Newtonian) viscosity of the dashpot and G is the elastic modulus of the spring. θ_1 is the relaxation or *retardation time* for this fluid.

This is a linear viscoelastic model. More complex models use complicated spring and dashpot models to obtain spectra of retardation times. Creep data can be used to obtain values for the "first" retardation time in terms of the creep compliance, J (15):

$$J = J_0 \left(1 - \exp(-\theta/\theta_1)\right)$$

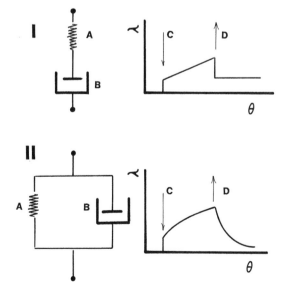

Figure 4.9 Simple Time-Dependent Elastic Models. I: Maxwell Model. II: Voigt Model. A: Spring. B: Viscous Element. λ: Strain. θ: Time. C: Stress Applied. D: Stress Removed.

White shows that for the simple Maxwell fluid at low strain rates ($\dot{\varepsilon}_0 \sim 0$), the tensor stress-strain-rate-of-strain elastic liquid equation reduces to a simple relationship between stress and compliance:

$$\sigma_j = 6\,G_1\,\theta_1\,\dot{\varepsilon}_0\,[1 - \exp(-\theta/\theta_1)] \qquad (j = 1, 2)$$

For long times, $\theta \to \infty$:

$$\sigma_j = 6\,G_1\,\theta_1\,\dot{\varepsilon}_0 \equiv \mu\,\dot{\varepsilon}_0 \qquad (j = 1, 2)$$

The model yields the Trouton-Newton form for a purely *viscous fluid*.

At high strain rates ($\dot{\varepsilon}_0 \to \infty$), the tensor form yields:

$$\sigma_j = G_1[(1 + \Delta/2)\exp(2\,\dot{\varepsilon}_0\,\theta) - (\Delta/2)\exp(4\,\dot{\varepsilon}_0\,\theta)] \qquad (j = 1, 2)$$

Δ is proportional to the ratio of second to first normal stress difference of the polymer and is negative (5). Thus the model predicts that under constant deformation rate, stress increases exponentially with time. In other words, at high strain rates, the rate of stress increase is greater than the rate of internal material stress relaxation. The material behaves as if it were an *elastic solid.* (5, 6; pg. 65).

It is highly unlikely that constant biaxial deformation rate can be sustained (or is desirable) in commercial thermoforming. Schmidt experimentally measures deformation rates that, for the most part, decrease with time (25). For *constant velocity stretching*, the deformation rate decreases with time (5). This stabilizes the initially rapidly growing stress.

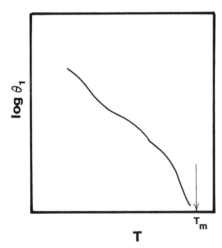

Figure 4.10 Temperature-Dependent   Retardation Time - Schematic. θ: Retardation Time. T: Temperature. Tm: Melt Temperature.

First retardation times can be obtained from creep experiments. Usually these values decrease monotonically with increasing temperature (Figure 4.10). A discontinuity in the retardation time curve for PP occurs at 110 C [230 F] (15). This is attributed to a deformation mechanism change on the molecular level. The importance of creep data in parts design has produced a substantial library of information. If temperature-dependent relaxation times for a given polymer are not available, approximate values can be obtained at any temperature T (18):

$$\theta_1(T) = \eta_0(T)/G(T)$$

η_0 is the zero-shear *shear viscosity* and G is the tensile modulus (or initial slope of the stress-strain curve). If the processing time is substantially less than θ_1 (about 10% θ_1), the material behaves as an elastic membrane. Snap-back thermoforming depends upon elastic membrane response. If the processing time is substantially greater than θ_1 (about 10 times θ_1), the material should behave as a fluid. Pressure forming, backward extrusion and high surface replication depend upon plastic (anelastic) material response.

Solid Mechanics Behavior

In conventional thermoforming of 1.25 mm (0.060 in) PP sheet, stretching rates of up to 26.8 s^{-1} have been reported (26). Schmidt (25) records instantaneous values of 2.4 s^{-1} for 2.54 mm (0.100 in) HIPS sheet. At these rates, most polymers should respond as *elastic solids*. Principal stresses in elastic solids are defined in terms of a *strain energy function*, W:

$$\sigma_i = \partial W/\partial\lambda_i$$

λ_i is the extension ratio in direction i ($=1, 2$). ∂W is the incremental amount of work done when the material is stretched an incremental amount $\partial\lambda$ under stress, σ. In general, the strain energy function is written in terms of three principal invariants of the Cauchy strain tensor (5, 15), as $W = W(I, II, III)$:

$$I = \lambda_1^2 + \lambda_2^2 + \lambda_3^2$$

$$II = 1/\lambda_1^2 + 1/\lambda_2^2 + 1/\lambda_3^2$$

$$III = \lambda_1^2 \lambda_2^2 \lambda_3^2$$

A stress-strain energy expression can be written in terms of these invariants as:

$$\sigma_i = (\partial W/\partial I)(\partial I/\partial\lambda_i) + (\partial W/\partial II)(\partial II/\partial\lambda_i) + (\partial W/\partial III)(\partial III/\partial\lambda_i)$$

For an incompressible solid, $\lambda_1\lambda_2\lambda_3 = 1$. So $III = 1$, and the last term drops. For *uniaxial stretching*, $\lambda_1 = \lambda$, $\lambda_2 = \lambda_3 = 1/\lambda^{1/2}$:

$$\sigma\lambda = (\lambda^2 - 1/\lambda)[2(\partial W/\partial II) + (2/\lambda)(\partial W/\partial I)]$$

($\sigma\lambda$ is the tensile stress, σ is the force per unit area of unstrained cross-section.) For *biaxial stretching*, $\lambda_1 = \lambda_2 = \lambda$, $\lambda_3 = 1/\lambda^2$. The stress-strain relationship becomes:

$$\sigma\lambda = (\lambda^2 - 1/\lambda^4)[2(\partial W/\partial II) + 2\lambda^2(\partial W/\partial I)]$$

The bracketed terms represent a specific solid polymer material response to applied load. The exact form for W(I, II) depends to a great degree on curve-fitting elongational data. For large deformations in rubbery solid membranes, Treloar recommends a simple power-law form for W:

$$W(I, II) = \sum_{i, j} C_{ij}(I-3)^i(II-3)^j$$

TABLE 4.5 STRAIN ENERGY DENSITY FORMS FOR POLYMERS AND ELASTO-MERS

Name	Form	Material	Source of Data
NeoHookean	$W = C_{10}(I\text{-}3)$	Treloar (27) PMMA (Williams (28))	Uniaxial stretching
Mooney	$W = C_{10}(I\text{-}3) + C_{01}(II\text{-}3)$	Vulcanized natural rubber (Treloar (27)) HIPS (Schmidt (25))	Uniaxial stretching Bubble inflation
Funt	$W = C_{01}(II\text{-}3)$	PP (15)	Creep data
Schmidt	$W = C_{10}(I\text{-}3) + C_{02}(II\text{-}3)^2$	HIPS (25)	Bubble inflation (gross)

(27). A neoHookean solid yields one of the simplest forms for W:

$$W = C_{10}(I - 3)$$

Mooney applied another simple form to rubber stress-strain curves:

$$W = C_{10}(I - 3) + C_{01}(II - 3)$$

Other forms that have been used to curve-fit rubbery elastic sheet deformation are given in Table 4.5. As an example, consider that a polymer is best described by the Mooney equation; $W = C_1(I - 3) + C_2(II - 3)$. Now, $\partial W/\partial I = C_1$ and $\partial W/\partial II = C_2$. The stress-strain relationships for a Mooney-type rubbery solid sheet in uniaxial and biaxial extension are:

$$\sigma\lambda = (\lambda^2 - 1/\lambda)[2\,C_1 + C_2/\lambda]$$

$$\sigma\lambda = (\lambda^2 - 1/\lambda^4)[2\,\lambda^2\,C_1 + 2\,C_2]$$

C_1 and C_2 are therefore curve-fitting constants. Further, since stress-strain relationships are temperature-sensitive, $C_1 = C_1(T)$ and $C_2 = C_2(T)$. In the limit, as the strain goes to zero, the constants can be defined in terms of an elastic modulus (25):

$$E/6 = \partial W/\partial I + \partial W/\partial II$$

For the Mooney form for W:

$$E/6 = C_{01} + C_{10}$$

For the Schmidt model, $E/6 = C'_{01}$ (where the prime denotes a different value for the first constant (25)). For HIPS and PS, predicted modulus values range from 427 to 1192 MPa [62 to 173 psi], whereas actual values range from 310 to 3900 MPa [45 to 566 psi], with errors ranging from -100% to $+50\%$. If the polymer modulus temperature dependency is known, a good first approximation of the temperature dependencies of the strain function coefficients can be had. For many materials, $\partial W/\partial I \gg \partial W/\partial II$ (28). For the Mooney model, $C_{01} \gg C_{10}$, and the curves are approximated best with the neoHookean model. (Figure 4.11). Treloar (27; pg. 162) shows C_{10} about 0.05 to 0.15 times C_{01}. The neoHookean model works best at low levels of deformation, at or just above the linear viscoelasticity region (27; pg. 169, 25). The Schmidt model works best at very high levels of deformation. Schmidt rec-

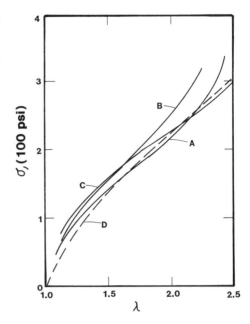

Figure 4.11 Stress-Strain Behavior for PMMA at 160 C (28). σ: Stress, [100 psi]. λ: Strain. A: ε̇ = 2 min⁻¹. B: 2.5. C: 5.0. D: Theory, φ = [130 psi]. This figure used by permission of Ellis Horwood Ltd., copyright owner.

ognized however that although his sheet was being deformed rapidly to large deformation, it was not isothermal and was not being deformed at a constant rate. Funt, on the other hand, correlated PP isochronous creep data best with $C_{01} = 0$ (15).

It appears that no single rubbery solid model can describe the behavior of a material undergoing isothermal high-speed, gross deformation. Some guidelines can be obtained, however, by selecting the simplest model (the neoHookean) for illustration. Table 4.6 lists values for most available experimental strain-energy function coefficients.

TABLE 4.6 TYPICAL STRAIN-ENERGY FUNCTION COEFFICIENTS FOR RUBBERY SOLIDS $C_1 = C_{10} = \partial W/\partial I$ $C_2 = C_{01} = \partial W/\partial II$ $C_3 = C_{02} = 2(\partial W/\partial II)$ (II-3)

Material	Temperature, C	C_1 (MPa)	C_2 (MPa)	C_3 (MPa) × 10⁶	Source	Comments
HIPS	123,3*	0.0758	–	0.001179	Schmidt/	No representa-
HIPS	124.7	0.08598	–	0.001331	Carley (30)	tive values for
HIPS	124.4	0.14445	–	0.002234		Mooney C2 given.
Vulcanized Natural Rubber	25.0	0.1618	0.0147**	–	Treloar (27)	Data on rubber, taken by Rivlin/ Saunders
PP	A = 165-T	0.0	0.080.A	–	Funt (15)	Creep data is source.
Cellulose Acetate Butyrate	***	0.1236	–	3400.	Schmidt/ Carley (30)	No temperature given. C_3 value seems high.

* At pole, about 29 C higher than at edge.
** Average value. Range is 0.010 to 0.022. Value decreases with increasing value of II.
***Not reported.

A Material Parameter, $\varphi(T)$

A typical thermoforming process applies (near-)instantaneous (near-)constant differential pressure to the rubbery plastic sheet to deform it. If the pressure is insufficient or the sheet is not soft enough, the part will not replicate the mold details or will not be fully formed. Earlier sections focussed on basic material behavior under load. Williams (28, 29) proposed a logical solid mechanical approach to the development of a parameter, $\varphi(T)$, that can be used to determine proper processing conditions for a given material. $\varphi(T)$ is a material parameter related to the derivative of the strain energy function with respect to the first principal invariant of the Cauchy strain tensor. As seen in Appendix 4.I, the relationship between φ and inflation pressure P, for a uniform disk of radius a and initial thickness h_0 forming a dome δ units above the horizontal is (29):

$$Pa/2 \, h_0 = \varphi \, (2 \, \delta/a)/[1 + (\delta/a)^2]$$

Since φ is related to the temperature-sensitive strain-energy function, it is written as $\varphi = \varphi(T)$. $\varphi(T)$ has the units of force per unit area (MPa) [lbf/in^2]. $\varphi(T)$ can be determined by heating a sheet of radius a and initial thickness h_0 to a fixed, uniform temperature, then measuring the extent of bulging (δ/a) as a function of applied pressure. Other methods are described below.

This analysis is approximate and inaccurate at the clamped sheet edge (29). If the deforming sheet is assumed to have a constant thickness everywhere $(\lambda_h = [1 + (\delta/a)^2]^{-2}$ and $\lambda_1^2 = 1 + (\delta/a)^2)$, then at a maximum value $\lambda_1 = 1.61$, $(\delta/a) = 1.26$ and the applied pressure is:

$$P_{max} = \sqrt{3} \, \varphi(T) \, (2 \, h_0/a)$$

Unfortunately, this is also an approximate relation between applied pressure and material property. Experiments indicate that biaxially stretched sheet does not have constant thickness (20, 30).

The Williams analysis can be extended to constrained biaxial deformation as sheet drawdown into a cone or funnel of wall angle α. The material not in contact with the wall is biaxially stretching. $\lambda_1 = \lambda_\theta$ and $r_0 = a$:

$$r/a = (r_0/a)^{\cos \alpha}$$

The thickness is:

$$\lambda_1 = (h/h_0) = 1/\lambda_\theta^2 = (r/r_0)^2 = (r/a)^{2(\sec \alpha - 1)}$$

and pressure is:

$$P = (2 \, \varphi(T) \, h_0/r) \, G(\alpha)$$

where:

$$G(\alpha) = \sin \alpha \, [1 - \sin^6 \alpha/\delta \, (1 - \cos \alpha)^3]$$

If s is the distance down the cone side from the cone opening to the point where the sheet leaves the cone wall (Fig. 4.12):

$$r/a = [1 - s/(2 \tan \alpha)]$$

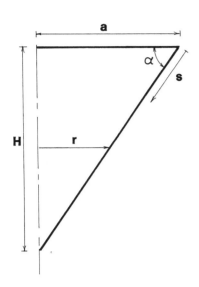

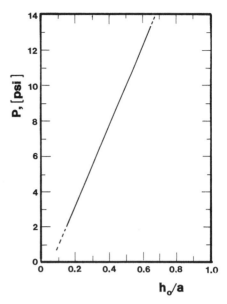

Figure 4.12 Geometric Factors For a Conical Female Mold. a: Initial Radius. α: Cone Angle. s: Distance Down Cone Side. r: Radius at Any Point. H: Horizontal Cone Depth.

Figure 4.13 Elastic Deformation as a Function of Inflation Pressure for Polyisobutylene (10). Data Points Omitted. h_0/a: Ratio, Inflation Height to Disk Radius. P: Applied Pressure, Above Atmospheric, [psi]. This figure used by permission of Society of Rheology.

$$h/h_0 = [1 - s/(a\tan\alpha)]^{2\,(\sec\alpha - 1)}$$

$$P = 2\,\varphi(T)\,(h_0/a)\,G(\alpha)/[1 - s/(a\tan\alpha)]$$

For most commercial funnels, $\alpha = 60°$, $G(\alpha) = 0.5$, $r/a = 1 - (0.577\,s/a)$, $h/h_0 = (r/a)^2$ and $P = \varphi(T)\,(h_0/a)[1 - 0.577.s/a]^{-1}$. Further, for a cylindrical or straight side mold (a can, for example), $\alpha = \pi/2$ and:

$$h/h_0 = \exp(-2s/a)$$

$$P = 2\varphi(T)(h_0/a)[1 - 0.125\,\exp(-6s/a)]$$

Note that the deformation pressure is directly proportional to both the material parameter $\varphi(T)$ and the relative sheet thickness (h_0/a). If P is fixed by the process (viz, vacuum forming, where $P < 0.1$ MPa [< 15 psi]), then the ability to deform a sheet of specific thickness, h_0/a, into a specific shape or depth of draw (s/a), depends entirely upon the material parameter, $\varphi(T)$:

$$\varphi(T) = [(1 - s/(a\tan\alpha))\,P/2G(\alpha)]/(h_0/a)$$

Usually $\varphi(T)$ decreases with increasing temperature. Thus to form thicker sheets in the same mold and with the same pressure as thinner sheets, it is necessary to increase the sheet temperature. And this is true for any geometry and any predetermined applied pressure (Fig. 4.13).

For the straight-walled cavity, once s/a exceeds about 0.5, the depth of draw is no longer a factor (Table 4.7), and the effect of geometry can be neglected. Thus:

$$P = 2\varphi(T)(h_0/a) \quad (s/a > 0.5)$$

For simple vacuum forming, $P < 0.1$ MPa [15 psi], and for a 50 mm [2 in] diameter cavity and a 1 mm [0.040 in] thick sheet, $\varphi(T)$ must be less than 1.3 MPa [187.5 psi]. As an example, consider creep data for unplasticized PVC (Table 4.8 (14)). These data are taken at 1.4 seconds under constant stress of 2.9 MPa [426 psi]. $\varphi(T)$ has been calculated in accordance with the last equation. The temperature should exceed about 100 C for 1 mm thick sheet to be vacuum formable into a 50 mm diameter cylinder at $s/a > 0.5$.

Note that $\varphi(T)$ also establishes a minimum value for forming temperature, given the material, the geometry and the applied pressure. Consider again the straight-walled cavity. When $s/a = 0$:

$$P = 2\varphi(T)(h_0/a) \cdot 0.875$$

For the simple vacuum forming case above, $h_0/a = 0.04$, $P = 0.1$ MPa [15 psi], and $\varphi(T) < 1.5$ MPa [214.3 psi]. If the sheet temperature is below 100 C (Table 4.8), it will not begin to draw. One definition for the thermoforming window then is the temperature range from the value below which the sheet is too stiff to deform under applied pressure to that above which the sheet can be deformed to $s/a > 0.5$. In the example above, the forming window is only a few degrees, at best. Note that increasing the temperature above this minimum forming window allows the sheet to be formed at much lower pressure. The practical upper limit on formability is the point where the sheet is plastically drawn to rupture.

TABLE 4.7 REDUCED THICKNESS AND FORCE FOR VARIOUS VALUES OF DRAW RATIO, s/a (Williams (29))

Draw Ratio, s/a	h/h_0	$P/2\Phi(T)\,(h_0/a)$
0	1.0	0.875
0.1	0.819	0.931
0.2	0.670	0.962
0.3	0.549	0.979
0.4	0.449	0.989
0.5	0.368	0.994
0.6	0.301	0.997
0.7	0.247	0.998
0.8	0.202	0.999
0.9	0.165	0.999
1.0	0.135	1.000

TABLE 4.8 CREEP DATA (HARRIS AND BRUINS (14)) AND MATERIAL PARAMETER $\Phi(T)$ FOR PVC $\sigma = 2.9$ MPa [426 psi]

Temp, C	ε (measured)	λ	$\Phi(T)$ MPa [psi]
98	1.2	2.2	1.5 [213.7]
100	1.45	2.45	1.3 [186.7]
110	3.6	4.6	0.65 [93.6]
118	3.6	4.6	0.65 [93.6]

Practical Aspects of Stretching

As noted, there are many ways of generating stretching data on plastics. $\varphi(T)$ is a material parameter extracted from one analysis using a simple isothermal stress-strain model. Several precautions are important. Creep data over a relatively wide range in temperatures are easy to obtain, but normally yield uniaxial stretching data at *fixed stress*. The effect of strain-rate-dependency is masked. Further Treloar (27; pg. 170) cautions against using uniaxial data to predict biaxial performance. He notes that for rubber, experiments that

> "... cover only one type of strain may, and usually do, appear to conform to [a given strain-energy function] equation. [However,] they provide very little real evidence regarding the form of the strain energy function *in general strain*, and any use of them is an unwarranted extrapolation".

For uniaxial extension for $\lambda = 7$ (say), $I_{max} = 49.3$, $II_{max} = 14$ and $(I/II) = 3.52$ (for a Mooney-type solid). In biaxial extension at the same value ($\lambda = 7$), $I_{max} = 98$, $II_{max} = 2401$ and $(I/II) = 0.041$. There is a relationship between uniaxial extension and biaxial extension for the special case of a "simple" fluid, however (31).

In order for biaxial extension data to be relevant (6; pg. 90, 210), inflation experiments must be at isothermal, uniform, constant rate conditions. Practical stretching rates are rarely achieved under these conditions. When practical rates are used (25, 16, 19), inflation rates are not constant and the sheet may not be isothermal. Middleman (32) cautions that the natural process time may be so short that the material may never behave as a fluid in dynamic steady state elongation. It appears, then, that elastic liquid models can serve only as signposts for thermoforming. No current analytical model can be used a priori to predict the thermoformability of a given polymer. Practical methods of comparing the performance of one material with another must remain relatively empirical for the time being.

Biaxial constrained stretching into a funnel is a relatively simple way of obtaining qualitative information about $\varphi(T)$. An isothermal sheet is stretched using either vacuum or positive air pressure. Sheet temperature and differential pressure must be accurately measured. Positive air pressure is easier to control (8). The funnel temperature should be substantially below the material Tg so that the sheet freezes instantaneously upon contact with the funnel surface. The surface should be relatively smooth to allow a good seal between the sheet and the surface. In practice, once the sheet contacts the surface it does not slide (33). At a given temperature and applied differential pressure, deformation should occur to a depth (s/a). s is the point along the funnel surface where the sheet last touches it (Figure 4.12). If s cannot be determined, $s + \delta$ can be measured. δ is a function of the radius, R, of the cap (Appendix 4.I). Further, (h/h_0) can be measured at every point along the part surface, and compared with (s/a) at any set of conditions. For a $60°$ cone, $(h/h_0) = [1 - 0.5773 \, (s/a)]^2$ (Figure 4.14). All material in the cone should be accounted for with a simple material balance:

$$\text{Volume} = \int_0^s 2\pi rh \, dr + h(s) \, 2\pi R \, \delta$$

If the measured values of h/h_0 do not exactly agree with calculated values, the measured values should be used. $\varphi(T)$ can be obtained once P, T, (h/h_0) and (h_0/a) are known (Figure 4.14). Note that extension ratios for draw down into a cone are initially rather small, with λ_θ, λ_l values of only 2.4 when the sheet has been drawn a distance $(s/a) = 1$. Values rapidly increase as the material is drawn into the tip of the cone. Schmidt's maximum values of $\lambda \simeq 11$ are achieved when $(s/a) > 1.5$.

A straight-walled cylinder can also be used but draw-down is extreme. High pressure and rapid rate-of-pressurization can lead to premature diaphram rupture.

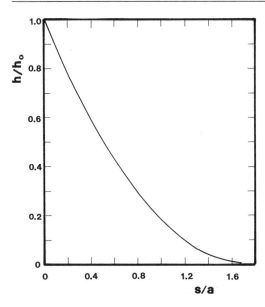

Figure 4.14 Sheet Thickness Ratio for Draw-Down into 60° Cone. h/h_0: Thickness Ratio. s/a: Ratio, Distance Down Cone Side to Cone Mouth Radius.

Results from experiments such as these should be used only to roughly define the processing parameters (pressure, temperature) for any given material, and a given ratio of sheet thickness to part dimension. These experiments suffer many of the same limitations on interpretation as the fiber spinning and film blowing processes (6, 32; pg. 48).

Bursting Conditions

Rapid biaxial stretching is common thermoforming practice for thin-gage sheet. Instantaneous strain rates of 2 to $30\,\mathrm{s}^{-1}$ have been reported at the pole during bubble blowing. It was noted above that for elastic liquids at constant stress (constant applied pressure), material deformation rate increases without bound. This can result in membrane rupture. An interesting relationship between applied pressure and bursting time has been proposed in terms of an elastic liquid response to applied stress $(\sigma)(9)$:

$$\sigma = \eta_e \dot{\varepsilon}$$

η_e is the biaxial extensional viscosity and $\dot{\varepsilon}$ is the principal biaxial rate-of-strain. Now:

$$\sigma \simeq (P/2)[(R/2\,h)_o + (R/2\,h)_b]$$

$$\dot{\varepsilon} \simeq (\varepsilon_b - \varepsilon_o)/\theta_b$$

R is the radius of the cap, h is the membrane thickness, P is constant applied pressure, θ_b is the time to burst, and "o" and "b" represent initial and bursting conditions. This can be rewritten as:

$$P\,\theta_b = \eta_e \left\{ 2\Delta\varepsilon / [(R/2\,h)_o + (R/2\,h)_b] \right\}$$

Now $(1/\theta_b)$ is a strain-rate-like term (s^{-1}) and $(P\theta_b)$ is a viscosity-like term (MPa s) [lbf · s/in²]. If the term in the bracket $\{\}$ is essentially constant, $(P\theta_b)$ is proportional to η_e, the biaxial extensional viscosity. A comparison of bursting time data and viscosity data for room-temperature bubble inflation of polyisobutylene rubber is seen in Figure 4.15. If the biaxial extensional viscosity is essentially inversely proportional to strain rate, (16), the bursting time is independent of applied pressure. More important, even if direct comparison is fortuitous, the effect of sheet temperature on bursting time can be found by applying an Arrhenius-type temperature correction factor:

$$(P\,\theta_b)(T) = A \exp[-E_{vis}/RT]$$

A is a preexponential term, E_{vis} is a viscous energy of activation for biaxial extension and R is the gas constant.

Bursting should be of concern only in the early stages of bubble deformation, however. At later stages, the process approaches one of constant velocity, and the falling sheet temperature helps to stabilize the bubble against rupture. Sheet splitting is a similar problem seen in constrained deep drawing into rather sharp corners. Perforation of sheet nipples during draw-down into oversized vacuum holes can also be analyzed in terms of this bursting phenomenon.

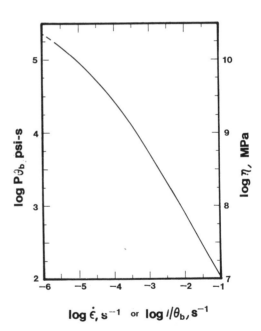

Figure 4.15 Comparison of Bursting Time with Viscosity for Polyisobutylene Rubber (9). $P\theta_b$: Applied Pressure Times Bursting Time, [psi s]. η: Viscosity, Pa s. $\dot{\varepsilon}$: Strain Rate, s^{-1}. θ_b: Bursting Time, s. This figure used by permission of Society of Rheology.

Sheet Sag

When a polymer sheet is clamped in a frame and heated, it begins to sag. If the extruded sheet has some residual stress, the sag will be reduced as the sheet temperature increases. If the sheet has substantial residual stress, sag will be minimal and the sheet may be pulled from its frame. The extent of sag for a "worst case scenario", a sheet with no residual stress, is determined from (34):

$$y = -\alpha \, q \, b^4/Eh^3$$

y is the extent of sag, m [in], q is the weight of the sheet, kg/m^2 [lb/in^2], b is sheet width, m [in], E is Young's Modulus, kg/m^2 [lb/in^2], h is sheet thickness, m [in], and α is a function of sheet length to width (Table 4.9). $q = \rho \cdot h$ ($g/cm^3 \cdot cm$). $b = b(T)$, since all polymers have finite thermal expansion coefficients. This effect is small when compared with $E = E(T)$, with a rapid drop in value seen for all polymers above Tg. Both effects cause an increase in sag with increasing temperature. For continuous sheet, $\alpha = 0.1421$. For the same material in a square sheet, $\alpha = 0.0444$ or the sag is less than one-third. The effect of *sag bands* on continuous-sheet thermoformers is to reduce the effect of the span, b. If one sag band is used, $b' = b/2$ and the sag is reduced by 2^4 or 16 times. For two sag bands, $b'' = b/3$ and the sag is reduced by 3^4 or 81 times. As an example, for a sheet with zero residual stress and zero thermal expansion coefficient, b = 61 cm [24 in], h = 0.3 cm [0.12 in], $\rho = 1.05$ g/cm^3, E = 69 MPa [10,000 lb/in^2], y = 31.5 cm [12.4 in]. With one sag band, y = 2 cm [0.78 in]. If the sheet thermally expands 10% in width (and length) during heating, b = 67 cm [26.4 in]. Without sag bands, y = 46.1 cm [18.2 in], a 46% increase. The increase is the same for a sheet with sag bands.

TABLE 4.9 SCALE FACTOR FOR SHEET SAG EQUATION (from Roark and Young (34))

Sheet length/width	α
1.0	0.0444
1.2	0.0616
1.4	0.0770
1.6	0.0906
1.8	0.1017
2.0	0.1110
3.0	0.1335
4.0	0.1400
5.0	0.1417
∞	0.1421

References

1. C.D. Denson, "Implications of Extensional Flow in Polymer Fabrication Processes", Polym. Eng. Sci., *13*, 1973, pg. 125.
2. Z. Tadmor and C.G. Gogos, *Principles of Polymer Processing*, John Wiley & Sons, 1979, "Elongational Flows", Section 6.8, pg. 184.
3. C.W. Macosko and J.M. Lorntson, "The Rheology of Two Blow Molding Polyethylenes", SPE Tech. Papers, *19*, 1973. pg. 461.
4. R.B. Bird, R.C. Armstrong, O. Hassager, *Dynamics of Polymeric Liquids*, Vol. 1, John Wiley & Sons, 1977, pg. 451.
5. J.L. White, "Theoretical Considerations of Biaxial Stretching of Viscoelastic Fluid Sheets with Application to Plastic Sheet Forming", Rheol. Acta, *14*, 1975, pg. 600.
6. C.J.S. Petrie, *Elongational Flows*, Pitman, 1979, pg. 93, Section 3.3, "Spinning and Related Flows".

7. J. Meissner, "A Rheometer for Investigation of Deformation-Mechanical Properties of Plastic Melts Under Defined Extensional Straining", Rheol. Acta, *8*, 1969, pg. 78.

8. C. D. Denson and R. J. Gallo, "Measurements on the Biaxial Extension Viscosity of Bulk Polymers: the Inflation of a Thin Polymer sheet", Polym. Eng. Sci., *11*, 1971, pg. 174.

9. D. D. Joye, G. W. Poehlein, and C. D. Denson, "A Bubble Inflation Technique for the Measurement of Viscoelastic Properties in Equal Biaxial Extensional Flow. II", Trans. Soc. Rheol., *17*, 1973, pg. 287.

10. D. D. Joye, G. W. Poehlein and C. D. Denson, "A Bubble Inflation Technique for the Measurement of Viscoelastic Properties in Equal Biaxial Extensional Flow", Trans. Soc. Rheol., *16*, 1972, pg. 421.

11. C. D Han and J. Y. Park, "Studies on Blown Film Extension. I. Experimental Determination of Elongational Viscosity", J. Appl. Polym. Sci., *19*, 1975, pg. 3257.

12. L. Erwin, H. Gonzolez, M. Pollock, "Analysis and Experiments in Blow Molding of Oriented PET Bottles", SPE Tech. Papers, *29*, 1983, pg. 807.

13. V. E. Malpass and C. H. White, "Laboratory Comparison of the Thermoforming Properties of Two ABS Materials", in P. F. Bruins, Ed., *Basic Principles of Thermoforming*, Gordon and Breach, 1973, pg. 103.

14. R. L. Harris and P. F. Bruins, "A New Technique for Predicting Optimum Thermoforming Conditions", in P. F. Bruins, Ed., *Basic Principles of Thermoforming*, Gordon and Breach, 1973, pg. 81.

15. J. M. Funt, "An Analysis of the Rheology of Polypropylene Below Its Melting Point", Polym. Eng. Sci., *15*, 1975, pg. 817.

16. K. C. Hoover and R. W. Tock, "Experimental Studies on the Biaxial Extensional Viscosity of Polypropylene", Polym. Eng. Sci., *16*, 1976, pg. 82.

17. S. Bahadur, "Strain Hardening Equation and the Prediction of Tensile Strength of Rolled Polymers", Polym. Eng. Sci., *13*, 1973, pg. 266.

18. P. I. Vincent, "Short-Term Strength and Impact Behaviour", in R. M. Ogorkiewicz, Ed., *Thermoplastics: Properties and Design*, John Wiley & Sons, 1974, pg. 72.

19. M. O. Lai and D. L. Holt, "The Extensional Flow of Poly(Methyl Methacrylate) and High-Impact Polystyrene at Thermoforming Temperatures", J. Appl. Polym. Sci., *19*, 1975, pg. 1209.

20. M. O. Lai and D. L. Holt, "Thickness Variation in the Thermoforming of Poly(Methyl Methacrylate) and High-Impact Polystyrene Sheets", J. Appl. Polym. Sci., *19*, 1975, pg. 1805.

21. A. S. Lodge, *Elastic Liquids*, Academic Press, 1964, pg. 99.

22. L. R. Schmidt and J. F. Carley, "Biaxial Stretching of Heat-Softened Plastic Sheets: Experiments and Results", Polym. Eng. Sci., *15*, 1975, pg. 51.

23. T. Alfrey, Jr., "Plastics Processing and Fabrication Problems Involving Membranes and Rotational Symmetry", SPE Trans., *5*: 4, 1965, pg. 5.

24. J. A. Brydson, *Flow Properties of Polymer Melts*, Van Nostrand Reinhold, 1970, pp. 18–19.

25. L. R. Schmidt, *Biaxial Stretching of Heat-Softened Plastic Sheets*, PhD Thesis, Univ. Colorado, 1972.

26. H. Gross and G. Menges, "Influence of Thermoforming Parameters on the Properties of Thermoformed PP", SPE Tech. Papers, *28*, 1982, pg. 840.

27. L. R. G. Treloar, *The Physics of Rubber Elasticity*, Oxford Univ. Press, 1958.

28. J. G. Williams, "A Method of Calculation for Thermoforming Plastics Sheets", J. Strain Anal., *5*, 1970, pg. 49.

29. J. G. Williams, *Stress Analysis of Polymers*, John Wiley & Sons, 1973, pp. 211–220.

30. L. R. Schmidt and J. F. Carley, "Biaxial Stretching of Heat-Softened Plastic Sheets Using an Inflation Technique", Int. J. Engng. Sci., *13*, 1975, pg. 563.

31. J. M. Dealy, "On the Relationship Between Extensional Viscosities for Uniaxial and Biaxial Extension", Trans. Soc. Rheol., *17*, 1973, pg. 255.

32. S. Middleman, *Fundamentals of Polymer Processing*, McGraw-Hill, 1977, pg. 48.

33. R. Allard, J.-M. Charrier, A. Ghosh, M. Marangou, M. E. Ryan, S. Shrivastava and R. Wu., "An Engineering Study of the Thermoforming Process: Experimental and Theoretical Considerations", paper presented at First Annual Meeting, Polym. Proc. Soc., Akron OH, 28–29 March 1984.

34. R. J. Roark and W. C. Young, *Formulas for Stress and Strain*, Fifth Ed., McGraw-Hill, 1975, Table 26, pg. 386.

35. V. E. Malpass and J. T. Kempthorn, "Comparison of Polyolefin Thermoforming by Hot Tensile Testing", SPE Tech. Papers, *32*, (1986), pg. 63.

Appendix 4.I

BIAXIAL STRETCHING OF AN ELASTIC MEMBRANE

(Adapted from Williams (29), by permission of Ellis Horwood Ltd, copyright owner)

Consider the biaxial extension of a rubbery solid membrane of initial thickness h_0 and radius a inflated with a differential pressure P. The extensional stress-strain equations are written as:

$$p_l = (\varphi + \psi \lambda_\theta^2)(\lambda_l^2 - 1/\lambda_l^2 \lambda_\theta^2)$$

$$p_\theta = (\varphi + \psi \lambda_l^2)(\lambda_\theta^2 - 1/\lambda_\theta^2 \lambda_l^2)$$

φ and ψ are material parameters that are related to constants C_{01} and C_{10} in a Mooney-type rubbery solid strain-energy function. l and θ are the in-sheet (meridonal) and angular (hoop direction) coordinates (Figure 4.16). N is the force acting on the membrane, $=$ ph, p is the local stress and h is the local thickness. r is the radius from the center axis. $\lambda_h = h/h_0$, $\lambda_\theta = r/r_0$, and $\lambda_l = 1/\lambda_h \lambda_\theta$. β is the angle of the membrane from horizontal. Thus, $r/R = \sin\beta$ where R is the radius of the spherical cap (Fig 4.17). If δ is the height above the horizontal, $R = (a^2 + \delta^2)/2\delta$. At the top of the dome:

$$\lambda_h = h/h_0 = [1 + (\delta/a)^2]^{-2}$$

For $\psi \ll \varphi$, and λ_l, $\lambda_h \gg 1$, e.g., for large deformations of a neoHookean solid:

$$p_l = \varphi \lambda_l^2$$

$$p_\theta = \varphi \lambda_\theta^2$$

The forces acting on the membrane are:

$$N_l = p_l h = p_l h_0/\lambda_l \lambda_\theta = \lambda h_0 (\lambda_l/\lambda_\theta)$$

$$N_\theta = p_\theta h = p_\theta h_0/\lambda_l \lambda_\theta = \varphi h_0 (\lambda_\theta/\lambda_l)$$

$N_l N_\theta = (\varphi h_0)^2 = N_0^2$, a constant. Further, stress equilibrium yields $N_l = N_0$ and so $N_\theta = N_l$. A hoop stress condition is:

$$p_l h_0/N_l^2 = PR/2$$

So:

$$p_l = \lambda_l^2 (PR/2 h_0) = \varphi \lambda_l^2$$

And since $R = R(a, \delta)$ above:

$$Pa/2 h_0 = \varphi (2 \delta/a)/[1 + (\delta/a)^2]$$

Figure 4.16 Membrane Stretching Geometry (Adapted from Williams (29) and used with permission of Ellis Horwood Ltd., copyright owner). P: Applied Force. N_l: In-Sheet (Meridonal) Stress. N_θ: Angular (Hoop) Stress. β: Membrane Angle from Horizontal. θ: Membrane Equatorial Angle. h: Sheet Thickness. δl: Differential Meridonal Length. r: Meridonal Radius. R: Radius of Spherical Cap.

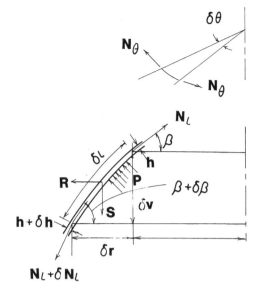

Figure 4.17 Geometry of a Stretched Cap (Adapted from Williams (29) and used by permission of Ellis Horwood Ltd., copyright owner). a: Initial Radius. R: Cap Radius. δ: Cap Height Above Horizontal. β: Membrane Angle from Horizontal. r: Local Radius.

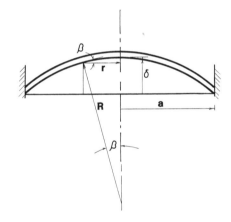

5 COOLING AND TRIMMING THE PART

Introduction

Once the part has been heated and formed to shape, it must be rigidified and trimmed from the web. When thermoforming a reactive material such as polyurethane or a crystallizing one such as nucleated CPET, the part is rigidified by holding it against a heated mold to continue the crosslinking reaction or crystallization. In most cases, rigidifying implies cooling while in contact with a cold mold. For automatic thin-gage formers, the molds are usually actively cooled with water flowing through channels. Free surfaces of medium- and heavy-gage sheet are frequently cooled with forced air, water mist or water spray. Cooling of the formed part against a (near-)isothermal mold should rarely control the overall thermoforming cycle. However, when cooling crystalline and crystallizing polymers such as PP, HDPE, and PET, the cooling cycle can be relatively long and can govern overall cycle time.

When the sheet has cooled sufficiently to retain its shape and (to a large extent) its dimension, it is stripped from the mold and transferred to a trimming station, where unwanted web material is removed. Requisite holes, slots and cut-outs are drilled or milled into the part at this time. Thin-gage roll-fed sheet can be trimmed on the mold surface immediately after forming or on an in-line mechanical trimming press. Heavier-gage sheet is usually removed from the mold and saw- or router-cut at a remote station. Trimming can be thought of as a mechanical shearing process, controlled crack propagation by brittle (or ductile) fracture. Care must be taken when trimming brittle polymers (PS, PMMA) to minimize microcracks. The very fine sander and saw dust can be a serious problem with brittle heavy-gage plastics. Other polymers such as PP are quite tough and require special cutting tool materials. Dull steel-rule dies can cause fibers or hairs at the cutting edge of thin-gage fiber-forming plastics such as PP and PET. Slowly crystallizing polymers (PP, PET) can pose registry problems when an in-line trimming press is used. The speed of trim cutting and the nature of the cutting surface control the rate of crack propagation through the plastic. The material presented in this chapter is gleaned from studies on machining of plastics. The trimming and cutting problems that are unique to thermoforming have not been addressed.

The chapter deals with fundamental aspects of cooling and cutting. The parts designer would do well to survey the material as it pertains to wall thickness control and parting line location.

Cooling Heat Balance

Typically the formed part is cooled to an average temperature at least $20\,C$ [40 F] below material Tg before being removed from the mold. Stretching is a (near-)isothermal process. Thus the heat to be removed is given as:

$$Q = V\rho c_p \left[T_f - (Tg - 20)\right] = V\rho c_p \Delta T$$

T_f is the equilibrated forming temperature discussed in Chapter 3. Heat is removed from one surface by conduction to the mold and from the other by convection to the surroundings. Further, the heat absorbed by the mold is usually removed by coolant flowing through channels in the mold. The heat load at any point on the mold surface depends upon the sheet thickness, t, at that point. Sheet thickness, as noted in Chapters 4 and 7, is not uniform across the mold surface. Thus the heat load at any point is obtained from:

$$q' = \rho c_p t \Delta T$$

The *average heat flux at that point* depends upon the number of parts formed per unit time (P):

$$q' = \rho c_p t P \Delta T \qquad\qquad \text{(W/cm}^2\text{) [Btu/ft}^2\text{ h]}$$

The total heat load on a mold of surface area A is given as:

$$Q = \rho c_p\, t_{avg}\, AP\Delta T \qquad\qquad \text{(W) [Btu/h]}$$

At steady state conditions, this heat must be transferred to the surroundings and to the coolant flowing through the mold. The mold and ambient temperatures will increase until this condition is satisfied.

Cooling the Formed Shape

Consider a typical cooling step. The sheet of variable thickness but known temperature is pressed against a (slightly) irregular surface of a mold. The properties of the mold material are known and uniform throughout its volume (see Chapter 6). Coolant of known properties flows through uniformly spaced channels in the mold. The free surface of the part is also cooled. At any instant, the temperature profile through the various layers of material is as shown in schematic in Figure 5.1. The rate at which energy is removed from the plastic to ambient air and coolant depends on the sum of resistances to heat transfer through each of these layers. This can be written as:

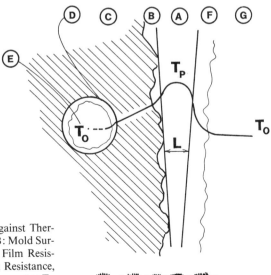

Figure 5.1 Schematic of Part Cooling Against Thermoform Mold Surface. A: Plastic Sheet. B: Mold Surface Irregularity, Air Gap. C: Mold. D: Film Resistance, Coolant. E: Coolant at T_0. F: Film Resistance, Free Surface Cooling. G: Ambient Environment at T_0.

$$R_{total} = R_{coolant} + R_{mold} + R_{interface} + R_{plastic} + R_{air}$$

For example, if the free surface is exposed to a water spray, the heat transfer resistance at that interface would be very small ($R_{air} \rightarrow 0$). If the free surface is insulated instead, the resistance would be nearly infinite. Some effects are small and can be either ignored or adequately accounted for with simple approximations. Others can become very significant and can act to dominate the entire cooling cycle.

In order to understand the relative importance of these resistances, consider building a "resistance" model, beginning with a simple (and quite significant) conduction model. Consider a plastic sheet of thickness L and uniform temperature T_i. One surface is pressed against a mold (conduction heat transfer) at a constant temperature T_0. At the same time, the other surface, the free surface, is exposed to a fluid (convection heat transfer) also at temperature T_0. The time to cool the sheet to an average temperature T_a is desired.

The transient one-dimensional heat transfer equation described in Chapter 3 is used here:

$$\rho c_p \, (\partial T / \partial \theta) = k \, (\partial^2 T / \partial x^2)$$

$$-k \, (\partial T / \partial x) \, (x = L) = h \, (T - T_0)$$

$$T(0, x) = T_i$$

$$T(\theta, 0) = T_0$$

h is the convection heat transfer coefficient between the free plastic surface and the ambient fluid (see Table 5.1). Two limiting conditions bound the solution.

TABLE 5.1 CALCULATED COOLING TIMES FOR PS SHEET
(Combined Conduction-Convection Heat Transfer)
Initial sheet Temperature, $T_i = 190.6$ C [375 F]
Mold Ambient Temperature, $T_0 = 23.9$ C [75]
Final Average Temperature, $T_a = 79.4$ C [175 F]
Thermal Conductivity, $= 3 \times 10^{-4}$ cal/gm s C
$\qquad\qquad\qquad [= 0.073$ Btu/ft h F]
Thermal Diffusivity, $\quad = 5.7 \times 10^{-4}$ cm^2/s
$\qquad\qquad\qquad [= 2.2 \times 10^{-3}$ ft^2/h]

$Y = 0.333$
$Fo = 0.0863 \, [1 + 3 \exp(-0.667 \, Bi^{0.667})]$
$Fo = \alpha\theta/L^2 \qquad Bi = hL/k$

Type of Free Surface Cooling	Convection Heat Transfer Coefficient, h		Thin-Gage Sheet L = 0.111 cm [= 0.0438 in]			Heavy-Gage Sheet L = 1.11 cm [0.438 in]		
	W/m^2 C	[Btu/ ft^2 h F]	Biot No.	Fourier No.	Cycle Time, s	Biot No.	Fourier No.	Cycle Time, s
Insulated	0	0	0	0.345	7.46	0	0.345	746
Ambient Air	5.7	1	0.05	0.323	6.98	0.5	0.256	554
Forced Air	57	10	0.5	0.256	5.54	5.0	0.123	266
Water Spray	570	100	5.0	0.123	2.66	50	0.086	187
Direct Contact	∞	∞	∞	0.086	1.87	∞	0.086	187

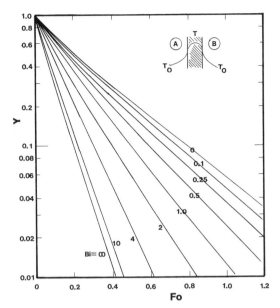

Figure 5.2 Average Sheet Temperature, Combined Conduction-Convection Heat Transfer. Y: Unaccomplished Temperature Change, $(T-T_0)/(T_i-T_0)$. Fo: Fourier Number, $\alpha\theta/L^2$. Bi: Biot Number, hL/k. A: Mold, Conduction. B: Free Surface, Convection.

When the heat transfer coefficient is very small relative to the rate of energy conducted to the mold (h→0), as with natural convection of heat from the free surface to the air, the free surface can be approximated by an insulated surface. Since $Y=(T_a-T_0)/(T_i-T_0)$ is known, the dimensionless time, $Fo=\alpha\theta/L^2$, can be obtained from Figure 5.2 for Bi=hL/k=0. L is the actual thickness of the plastic shape. On the other hand, when the free surface heat transfer coefficient is very large, as is the case when water is sprayed directly against the free surface, the plastic surface temperature drops rapidly to T_0. Again Figure 5.2 can be used to determine the dimensionless time, Fo (given Y and Bi = ∞). But now L=L/2. The actual cooling time, θ, is ¼ that of the first condition. Actual cooling times should be between these extremes.

In Figure 5.2, the conduction equation is numerically solved for the specific case where the mold surface and ambient fluid temperatures are equal. The Biot Number, Bi=hL/k, is the ratio of conduction to convection heat transfer. L is the actual sheet thickness. Consider a heavy-gage PS sheet, L=1.11 cm [0.438 in] initially at $T_i=$ 190.6 C [375 F], to be cooled to an average temperature of $T_a=$ 79.4 C [175 F], by pressing it against a mold at $T_0=$ 23.9 C [75 F] and cooling the free surface with a fluid at $T_0=$ 23.9 C [75 F]. The polymer properties are given in Table 5.1. From Table 3.8, for ambient or natural convection air cooling, h= 5.68 W/m²C [= 1 Btu/ft²hF] and Bi=0.5. For Y=0.333, Fo=0.256 and the cooling time is 554 s. If the air is fan-forced across the free surface, h= 57 W/m²C [= 10 Btu/ft²hF], the cooling time drops to 266 s, or an improvement of 50% in the cooling time. If water is mist-sprayed, h= 570 W/m²C [= 100 Btu/ft²hF] and the cooling time is 187 s, or an improvement of 67% over ambient air conditions. These results are summarized in Table 5.1.

For thin-gage PS sheet, L=0.111 cm [0.0438 in], under the same free surface cooling conditions, water mist-spray reduces cooling time by about 50% (Table 5.1).

The effect of altering free surface cooling conditions is seen in Figure 5.3 (1). The nature of the material and details about the processing conditions are unknown. For L=0.15 cm [0.060 in] sheet, water spray reduces the cooling time by about 60%. For the thicker sheet, L=0.45 cm [0.180 in], it reduces the cooling time by about ⅔. The cooling time increases

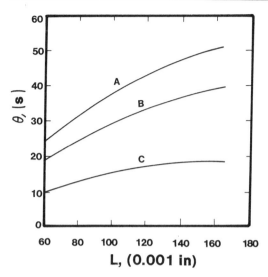

Figure 5.3 Typical Observed Cooling Times for Various Surface Cooling Techniques (1). θ: Cooling Time, s. L: Sheet Thickness, [0.001 in]. A: Ambient Air. B: Forced Air. C: Water Spray. Figure used by permission of copyright owner.

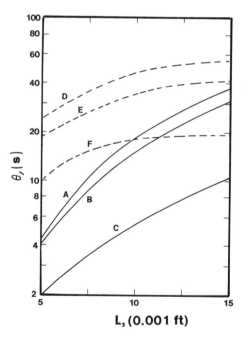

Figure 5.4 Effect of Sheet Thickness on Cooling Time – Conduction-Controlled (Thick) Sheet (Including Data from (1)). θ: Cooling Time, s. L: Sheet Thickness, [0.001 ft]. A: Calculated, h = 0.5 [Btu/ft²hF]. B: Calculated, h = 5. C: Calculated, h = 50. D: Observed, Ambient Air. E: Observed, Forced Air. F: Observed, Water Spray.

with increasing sheet thickness. As expected, the effect is most obvious with ambient air cooling. If conduction heat transfer through the plastic sheet controls the cooling time, the effect of sheet thickness can be easily determined. At any given average sheet temperature, the dimensionless time, Fo, is a simple function of the Biot Number:

$$Fo = f(Bi) \qquad (Y \text{ is fixed})$$

For the earlier example, Y = 0.333, a simple empirical relationship can be used to illustrate:

$$Fo = Fo_0 [1 + 3 \exp(- a \, Bi^a)]$$

Fo_0 is the value of Fo when $Bi \rightarrow \infty$, one limiting case where both sides of the sheet contact solid surfaces. When $Bi = 0$ (insulated free surface), $Fo = 4 \, Fo_0$. Since $Fo = \alpha\theta/L^2$, the cooling time θ is proportional to the square of the sheet thickness for both limiting cases. When conduction from the plastic sheet controls heat transfer, doubling the sheet thickness increases the cooling time by a factor of four (Figure 5.4). Actual cooling times show a near-linear relationship with thickness, with observed values substantially higher than values obtained from Figure 5.3. This is an indication in this case that the experimental sheet is not being cooled in a conduction-controlled environment. Again the exact conditions used to obtain the experimental data are unknown.

Interfacial Resistance

Cooling times calculated using the transient conduction equation represent ideal, conduction-controlled times. Additional resistances to heat flow increase the effective values, as noted in Figure 5.1. For the conduction model, perfect contact between the isothermal mold and the cooling sheet was assumed. Imperfect contact causes resistance to heat flow. Mold surface waviness and microscopic roughness (asperities) cause reduced physical contact (Figure 5.5). Increasing pressure against the sheet increases physical contact and reduces the resistance to heat transfer. In general, energy is transmitted across the interstices by a combination of conduction at contacting asperities, conduction through the interstitial fluid, and radiation. The resistance is thus a function of the properties of the contacting materials (relative hardness, thermal conductivity, surface roughness, flatness), the conductivity and pressure of the interstitial fluid, and the pressure applied against the free surface of the sheet. The interface coefficient, h_c, is a measure of thermal resistance across the gap. It is similar in concept to the convection heat transfer coefficient in that resistance to heat flow decreases with increasing value of h_c. For perfect contact, $h_c \rightarrow \infty$.

In thermoforming, the interstitial fluid is air, perhaps at substantially reduced pressure. If the interface is a uniform air gap of $\delta = 0.025$ cm [0.010 in] and air thermal conductivity is,

Figure 5.5 Interfacial Resistance Schematic. A: Stiff, Heavy-Gage Sheet, Rough, Cold Mold. B: Flexible, Thin-Gage Sheet, Smooth, Hot Mold.

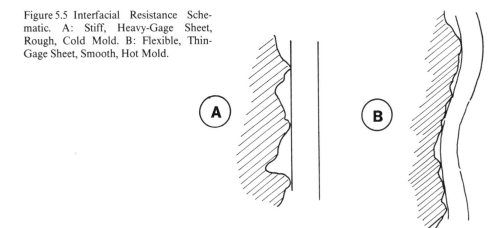

$k_{air} = 0.029$ W/m C [0.0167 Btu/ft h F], the value for h_c is about 114 W/m²C [20 Btu/ft²h F]. Contact heat transfer coefficient values between flowing polymer melt and mold surfaces of about h = 568 W/m²C [100 Btu/ft²h F] have been reported in injection molding (2). Similar values are expected here.

For two rigid surfaces in contact, $h_c = h_{co} p^{1/6}$, where p is the applied pressure and h_{co} depends upon the relative waviness and roughness of the two surfaces (Table 5.2) (3). If one surface is deformable, the contact resistance is only weakly dependent upon pressure. The values for h_c with hard vacuum in the gap are orders of magnitude lower than those for interstitial atmospheric air.

There are no data available for interfacial resistance during thermoforming of softened plastic sheet against various types of mold surfaces. For hot sheet pressed against a smooth mold surface at a relatively high differential pressure, the contact coefficient, $h_c \rightarrow 568$ W/m²C [100 Btu/ft²h F] and can probably be neglected for the first cooling time estimate. For rapidly cooling sheet pressed against a highly textured mold surface with modest differential pressures or vacuum, contact coefficient values of about 114 to 284 W/m²C [20 to 50 Btu/ft²h F] can be used for first cooling time estimates.

TABLE 5.2 CONTACT RESISTANCE AND CONDUCTANCE
(Adapted from Schneider (3))
$h_c = h_{co} p^n$
$[h_c] = $ W/m² C [Btu/ft² h F]
[p] = MPa [psi]

Material Contact	Inner Layer	h_{co}		n
		W/m² C	[Btu/ft² h F]	
Elastic Deformation Theory	-	35.8	6.3	2/3
Hard-to-Hard	Vacuum	113.6	20	2/3
Hard-to-Hard	Air	5680	1000	1/6
Hard-to-Soft	Vacuum	170	30	2/3

Heat Transfer to Coolant

The molds on automatic, rollfed thin-gage thermoformers are frequently water-cooled. There is a thermal resistance between the cool bulk flowing fluid and the warmer tube wall (see Figure 5.1). Slowly flowing fluids are *laminar* with a Reynolds Number, Re = dVρ/μ < 2000 and heat transfer is relatively poor. d is the tube diameter, V is the coolant velocity, ρ is its density and μ its viscosity. The Reynolds Number is the ratio of inertial to viscous forces for the fluid. Rapidly flowing fluids are *fully turbulent* when Re > 10,000 and transfer heat very efficiently. As an example, 21 C [70 F] water flowing through a d = 1.27 cm [0.500 in] diameter conduit at a velocity of about V = 0.16 m/s [0.52 ft/s or 0.32 GPM] has Re = 2000 and is in laminar flow. At five times the flow rate, V = 0.79 m/s [= 2.6 ft/s], Re = 10,000 and the fluid is fully turbulent. Heat transfer coefficient values for these two fluid states for 21 C [70 F] water can be obtained from (4):

$$h = 3.52 \ (k/d) \ Re^{1/3} \ (d/L)^{1/3} \qquad \text{(laminar)}$$

$$h = 0.068 \, (k/d) \, Re^{0.8} \, (d/L)^{0.055} \quad \text{(turbulent)}$$

For $L/d = 100$, typical dimensions of a serpentine coil imbedded in an epoxy mold, (hd/k) = 9.55 for laminar flow $(Re = 2000)$ and $(hd/k) = 83.7$ for fully developed turbulent flow $(Re = 10,000)$. Increasing the flow rate by a factor of five (laminar to turbulent) increases the heat transfer coefficient by about 9 times. For $d = 1.27$ cm [0.500 in] diameter conduit, $h_{(laminar)} = 454 \, W/m^2C$ [80 Btu/ft^{2}h F], and $h_{(turbulent)} = 4000 \, W/m^2C$ [700 Btu/ft^{2}h F]. Approximate values for transition flow $(2000 < Re < 10,000)$ can be obtained by geometric averaging. For example, in this case at $Re = 5000$, $h_{(transition)} = 1200 \, W/m^2C$ [210 Btu/ft^{2}h F].

Since heat is conducted perpendicular to the mold plane, the fluid resistance must be corrected for the conduit diameter and the number of conduits in a given mold area (see Figure 5.1). If N are the number of conduits of diameter d, then the area ratio is $\pi dNL/L^2$, and the effective resistance is $(L/\pi dNh)$, or $(1/\pi dNh)$ per unit area. This resistance becomes small for turbulent water flowing in many closely-spaced large-diameter conduits.

Heat Transfer Through the Mold

For thin metal molds, heat is conducted very rapidly from the plastic to the coolant. For relatively thick molds of plaster, wood, epoxy or FRP (or any nonmetallic material), heat transfer is slowed by low mold material thermal conductivity. For planar cooling as in Figure 5.1, the resistance to heat transfer per unit area $(L = 1)$ across a mold D units thick is:

$$R_m = D/k_m$$

k_m is the mold material thermal conductivity. Thermal conductivity values for many mold materials are given in Table 2.7. For round conduits, a shape factor, S, is used to correct for non-planar heat conduction:

$$S = 2 \, \pi/\ln \left[(2 \, P/\pi d) \sin h \, (2\pi D/P) \right] \qquad (P/d > 2, D/d > 0.5)$$

For $P/d = 2$, $S = P/d$, equivalent to the planar cooling case. Thus the resistance can be written in terms of an effective mold thickness, D^*:

$$R_m = P/Sk_m = (D/k_m)(P/DS) = D^*/k_m$$

Consider some simple examples. For $P = 5.1$ cm [2 in], $D = 5.1$ cm [2 in], $d = 1.27$ cm [0.5 in], $P/d = 4$, $D/d = 4$, $S = 0.963$. Thus the resistance is given as $R_m = 1.04 D/k_m$. If $P = 10.2$ cm [4 in], $P/d = 8$, $S = 1.542$, and $R_m = 1.3 D/k_m$. And finally, if $P = 5.1$ cm [2 in], $d' = 2.54$ cm [1 in], $P/d = 4$, $D'/d = 2$, $S = 1.858$, and since $D' = D/2$, $R_m = 0.538 D/k_m$. As expected, increasing the spacing between coolant lines increases the resistance. Moving the coolant lines closer to the mold surface decreases the resistance.

For the case of a thin aluminum mold, where $P/d = 8$, $D/d = 4$, $D = 0.51$ cm [0.2 in] and $k_m = 227 \, W/mC$ [131 Btu/ft h F], the effective conductance $(1/R_m)$ is 34,330 W/m^2C [6000 Btu/ft^{2}h F] and is negligible. For a thick plaster mold, $D = 5.1$ cm [2 in] and $k_m = 1.4 \, W/mC$ [0.8 Btu/ft h F], the effective conductance $(1/R_m)$ is 21 W/m^2C [3.7 Btu/ft^{2}h F]. This low value cannot be ignored.

Sum of Resistances

To recap, the rate of heat loss by the plastic is dependent upon the relative values of the thermal resistances (Table 5.3). The most efficient cooling occurs when the free surface of a thick part is cooled with water spray and the formed surface is pressed firmly against a thin, smooth metal mold cooled with turbulent water flowing through large-diameter, closely-spaced conduits. At the other extreme, cooling efficiency will be very low if the free surface of a very thin part is cooled in ambient air and the formed surface contacts a thick, textured nonmetallic mold under vacuum, with the mold either cooled naturally or with laminar water flowing through small, widely spaced conduits. For this condition, the combined thermal resistances on the contact or mold side of the formed part may be as great as the natural convection heat transfer resistance through the free surface film layer. In the limit, the part can be envisioned as being *convectively cooled on both sides.*

TABLE 5.3 COOLING A PART ON THE MOLD RELATIVE VALUES OF THERMAL RESISTANCE

Physical Resistance	Form for Resistance	Typical (Reciprocal) Value	
		(W/m^2 C)	[Btu/ft^2 h F]
Free Surface Cooling			
Ambient Air	$1/h_{air}$	2.84 to 5.68	0.5 to 1
Forced Air	$1/h_{air}$	28.4 to 56.8	5 to 10
Water Spray	$1/h_{air}$	284 to 568	50 to 100
Interface Gap*	$1/h_c$	114 to 284	20 to 50
Mold	(D^*/k_m) aluminium 34,330		6000
	plaster 21		3.7
Coolant			
Laminar Water $(L/\pi dNh_{cool})$	(h_{cool})	454	80
Turbulent Water		4000	700

* See Table 5.2.
D* is effective mold thickness and includes shape factor.

As an extreme limiting case, the time required to cool a very thin plastic film of thickness L in ambient air can be obtained from the *lumped-parameter model:*

$$Y = \exp(-BiFo) = \exp(-\alpha h\theta/kL)$$

Note that $\theta \propto (L/h)$ or cooling time is linear with thickness. In contrast, for conduction-controlled heat transfer, $\theta \propto L^2$ (Figure 5.4). The lumped-parameter cooling time curves for various film thicknesses are compared with the experimental data in Figure 5.6. Since nothing is known about the experimental processing conditions or sheet material parameters, the curves are fit at $L = 0.15$ cm [0.060 in] by selecting artificial values for h, the convection coefficient. The shape of these convection-controlled curves agree better with the data than do the conduction-controlled curves.

One additional practical factor must be considered. Thermoformed parts shrink as they cool. When the forming stresses are released, part shrinkage accelerates (see below). For forming onto a male mold, material contact improves. When forming into a female mold, however, the sheet can pull away from the mold surface. This increases cooling resistance.

If shrinkage is excessive, heat transfer from the sheet to the mold can stop. In effect, then, convection at the free surface is the primary source of sheet cooling.

When sheet or formed shape cooling is dominated by conduction through the plastic, cooling is a material-intrinsic phenomenon and so very little can be done to optimize the cooling time. On the other hand, if convection (or quasi-convection) controls the cooling time, a substantial amount of process redesign can be envisioned. Convection-controlled cooling is characterized by relatively large resistances between the heat source (the sheet) and the heat sinks (the coolant and the free surface fluid). These resistances are caused by process design. Process improvements focus on minimizing the largest of these resistances. The effects of various mold and material parameters on the cooling cycle are summarized in Table 5.4.

Figure 5.6 Effect of Sheet Thickness on Cooling Time – Convection-Controlled Thin Sheet (Including Data from (1)). θ: Cooling Time, s. L: Sheet Thickness, [0.001 ft]. A: Calculated, $h = 10$ [Btu/ft^2 h F]. B: Calculated, $h = 12$. C: Calculated, $h = 24$. D: Observed, Ambient Air. E: Observed, Forced Air. F: Observed, Water Spray.

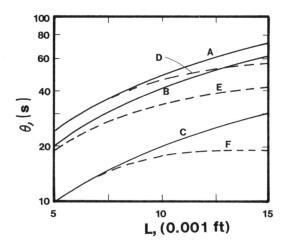

TABLE 5.4 MOLD, MATERIAL PARAMETERS EFFECT ON COOLING TIME

Increase in Parameter	Effect on Cooling Time	Approximate Relative Effect
Mold Thermal Conductivity	Decrease	$\theta \propto 1/k_m$
Mold Thickness	Increase	$\theta \propto D^n$ $(1 < n < 2)$
Mold Surface Roughness	Increase	Slight**
Applied Pressure	Decrease	Slight**
Coolant Flow Rate	Decrease	Moderate*
Free Surface Fluid Motion	Decrease	Significant for Heavy-Gage Sheets*
Cooling Channel Spacing	Increase	Slight to Moderate*
Sheet Thickness	Increase	$\theta \propto t^n$ $(1 < n < 2)$
Sheet Thermal Conductivity	Decrease	$\theta \propto (1/k_p)^n$ $(0 < n < 1)$
Sheet Heat Capacity	Increase	$\theta \propto c_p$
Sheet Density	Increase	$\theta \propto \rho$
Sheet Thermal Diffusivity	Decrease	$\theta \propto 1/\alpha$

* See text for specific guidelines.
**Could be significant for cool, heavy-gage sheets, vacuum-formed against highly textured molds. See text for guidelines.

Net Heat Balance on Mold

To this point, the analysis of conduction resistance has not taken into account the cyclical nature of heat transfer during thermoforming. Heavy-walled, nonmetallic molds alternately store and liberate heat during each forming cycle. An estimate of the rate at which heat penetrates the mold material is obtained by approximately integrating the heat conduction equation. If *constant energy flux* (W/m^2) $[Btu/ft^2 h]$ is supplied to the surface of a semi-infinite slab of known thermal diffusivity, α, the depth of penetration of heat is given (approximately) as:

$$\delta = \sqrt{(6 \; \alpha\theta)} \text{ (Constant Heat Flux)}$$

The penetration dimensionless time, $Fo = \alpha\theta/L^2$ has the value, $= \frac{1}{6}$. (6). If the surface is instead raised to a *constant temperature*, the penetration distance is given (again approximately) as:

$$\delta^* = \sqrt{(24 \; \alpha\theta)} \quad \text{(Constant Surface Temperature)}$$

or $Fo^* = \frac{1}{24}$. In thermoforming, the actual condition is probably between these two cases. If D is the effective thickness of the mold, then the time for the heat to be felt at the coolant interface is:

$$(D^2/24 \; \alpha) < \theta^* < (D^2/6 \; \alpha)$$

For a thin aluminum mold, $D = 0.51$ cm [0.2 in] and $\alpha = 0.49$ cm^2/s [1.9 ft^2/h], 22 ms $< \theta^* <$ 88 ms. The energy transfer is almost immediate. For a thick plaster mold, on the other hand, $D = 5.1$ cm [2 in] and $\alpha = 30 \times 10^{-4}$ cm^2/s [11.6 $\times 10^{-3}$ ft^2/h], 36 s $< \theta^* <$ 143 s. For many thermoforming operations using nonmetallic molds, the coolant probably would not see all the energy removed from the sheet until after the sheet has been removed from the mold. Thus, the mold, in effect, stores the sheet thermal energy during the part cooling cycle, then transfers it to the coolant after the cycle. During that time, heat is also convected away from the mold surface, as shown schematically in Figure 5.7.

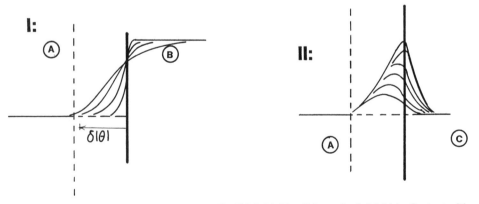

Figure 5.7 Transient Conduction into Thermally Thick Mold – Schematic. I: Mold in Contact with Plastic. δ: Penetration Distance. θ: Cooling Time. II: Mold Cooling in Air. A: Mold. B: Plastic. C: Ambient Air.

At the time the cooled sheet is removed from the mold, the average mold temperature has increased by about 25% of the difference between the time-average sheet temperature and the original mold temperature. For example, if the initial sheet temperature is $T_i = 190.6$ C [375 F] and the final value is $T_{avg} = 79.4$ C [175 F], the time-average sheet temperature is just $T_{ta} = 135$ C [275 F]. If the initial mold temperature $T_0 = 23.9$ C [75 F], the average mold temperature at the end of the sheet cooling cycle is about $T_0 + 0.25(T_{ta} - T_0)$ or 51.7 C [125 F].

The one-dimensional heat conduction model discussed earlier can be used to approximate (rather crudely) the time needed to cool the mold to within, say, 2% of its initial temperature, or $T_0' = 24.4$ C [75.9 F]. When $Y = 0.02$, $Fo = \alpha\theta/D^2 = 1.4$ and for the plaster mold, $\theta = 5000$ s.

Practically then, the average mold temperature continues to increase in value after each cycle until the energy added during the cooling portion of that cycle just equals that extracted during the entire cycle time. From above, the amount of heat added per unit area of the mold is:

$$q'' = \rho c_p t\, (T_i - T_a^*)$$

and this is to be removed in θ time. So:

$$q = t\rho c_p\, (T_i - T_a^*)/\theta$$

T_a^* is the time-average sheet temperature, such as $(T_i + T_{avg})/2$. The heat convected away by the cooling air is:

$$q_{conv} = h_{air}\, (T_a^* - T_0)$$

and that absorbed by the mold during this time is the difference:

$$q_{mold} = q - q_{conv}$$

The amount of heat transferred to the coolant over the *entire* cycle, $N\theta$, $(N \geqslant 1)$ is:

$$q_{cool} = h_{cool}\, (T_{mold} - T_0)$$

Thus the heat balance yields:

$$h_{cool}\, (T_{mold} - T_0) = [t\rho c_p\, (T_i - T_a^*)/\theta - h_{air}\, (T_a^* - T_0)]/N$$

T_{mold} is the only unknown temperature. Consider a plaster mold cooling a $t = 0.15$ cm [0.060 in] PS part in 20 s, with an additional 20 s delay ($N = 2$) for part removal and insertion and draw-down of the next part. Let $T_a^* = 135$ C [275 F], $T_0 = 23.9$ C [75 F]. Material properties are $\rho = 1.05$ g/cm^3 [65.5 lb/ft^3], $c_p = 0.45$ cal/g s [Btu/lb F]. $h_{air} = 28.4$ W/m^{2}C [5 Btu/ft^{2}h F], $h_{cool} = 284$ W/m^{2}C [50 Btu/ft^{2}h F], $q = 16.74$ kW/m^2 [1.474 Btu/ft^{2}s], $q_{conv} = 3.16$ kW/m^2 [0.278 Btu/ft^{2}s] and the net energy absorbed by the mold is 6.79 kW/m^2 [0.598 Btu/ft^{2}s]. From the expression above, the average equilibrium mold temperature is then $T_{mold} = 23.9$ C $+ 12.0$ C $= 35.9$ C [96.5 F].

As expected, average equilibrium mold temperature values increase with shortened time between forming steps and decrease with higher coolant flow rates, lower coolant temperatures, and more efficient convection cooling at the part free surface.

Trimming Basics

There are many acceptable ways of efficiently separating formed parts from surrounding plastic. Thin-gage, rollfed parts can be trimmed after forming but while still on the mold. Or they can be stripped from the molds and trimmed on a separate in-line mechanical (or hydromechanical) trim press. Heavy-gage parts are usually removed from the molds, placed in trimming fixtures and trimmed with routers, circular saws, bandsaws, abrasive wheels, hot knives or other cutting-off devices. In many cases, trimming fixtures are designed to accommodate other post-molding operations such as drilling, slotting, grooving, ultrasonic welding, gluing, ultrasonic insertion of fasteners and so on (13). Thin-gage part trimming is automatic. Very-heavy-gage parts are usually trimmed manually. Medium- and heavy-gage parts may be trimmed automatically once the parts are fixtured. Water-jet and laser-cutting devices are employed for automatic trimming of medium- and heavy-gage parts. In all cases, the cutting surface should be fed at a fixed rate in a plane perpendicular to the cutting direction. Prototype parts can be trimmed manually with bandsaws, routers, or for thin-gage parts, hand scissors or paper cutters. Steel rule dies are used to cut very soft plastics, such as olefins and low-density foams. Various cutting techniques are shown in schematic in Figure 5.8.

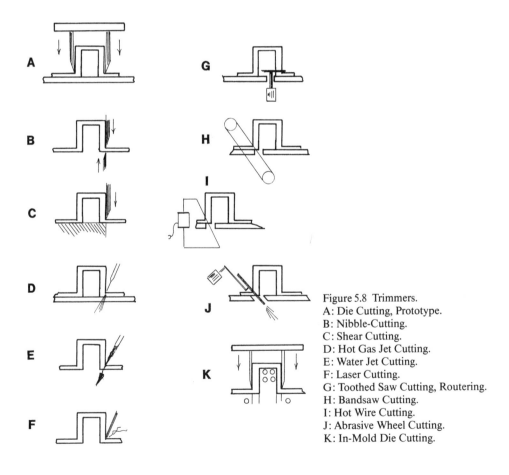

Figure 5.8 Trimmers.
A: Die Cutting, Prototype.
B: Nibble-Cutting.
C: Shear Cutting.
D: Hot Gas Jet Cutting.
E: Water Jet Cutting.
F: Laser Cutting.
G: Toothed Saw Cutting, Routering.
H: Bandsaw Cutting.
I: Hot Wire Cutting.
J: Abrasive Wheel Cutting.
K: In-Mold Die Cutting.

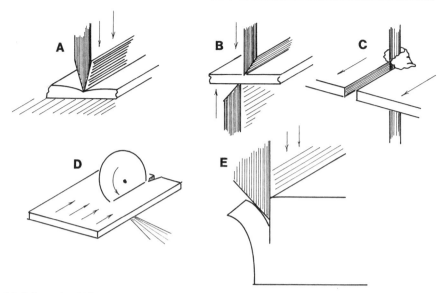

Figure 5.9 Schematic of Five General Mechanisms of Cutting. A: Compression. B: Shear. C: Thermal. D: Abrasion. E: Fracture, Chip Cutting. Adapted from Kobayashi (14) and used by permission of the author.

Five basic types of cuts are generally employed in trimming (Figure 5.9). They are in-plane uniaxial compression (die-cutting), Mode III antiplane pure shear (nibbling, shear cutting), abrasion (abrasive cutting, grinding, filing, buffing, water cutting), brittle tensile fracture (routering, drilling, sawing), and thermal (hot knife, hot wire, laser).

TABLE 5.5 FACTORS AFFECTING CUTTING CHARACTERISTICS OF PLASTICS
(Adapted from Kobayashi (14), with permission of the author)
X = Major Effect   x = Minor Effect

Factor	Effect				
	Chip Formation	Cut Surface Roughness	Tool Wear	Heat Generated	Gumming, Burning
Tool Design:					
Tool Geometry:*					
Rake Angle	X				
Relief Angle		X			
Point Radius			X	x	
Tool Material		X			
Machining Conditions:					
Depth of Cut	X		X	x	x
(Tooth Depth of Cut)					
Cutting Speed	X		X	x	x
Feeding Speed	X		X		
Ambient Work	x			X	X
Temperature					
Cooling System				X	X

* For single-edged cutting tools. Tool geometry effects more complicated for multiple-edged cutting tools.

TABLE 5.6 CLASSIFICATION OF PLASTIC MACHINING CHIPS (Adapted from Kobyashi (14), used by permission of author)

Classification	Nature of Chip	Thickness-to-Cut-Depth	Cutting Force Fluctuation	Surface Roughness	Nature of Deformation	Material Type	Cutting Speed	Typical Plastics	Comments on Cause
Continuous-Flow	Continuous	~1	Small	Small	Elastic	High Elongation (Rubberlike)	Slow	PE, PTFE, FEP, PP	High Elastic Deformation.
Continuous-Shear	Continuous	>1	Small	Irregular, Shear Marks	Plastic	Brittle	Medium-High	PS, ABS	Slippage Continuously by Shear Stress.
Discontinuous-Simple Shear	Discontinuous	>1, Irregular	Moderate	Irregular	Plastic	Brittle	Medium	PMMA	Plastic Fracture by Simple Shear Stress.
Discontinuous-Complex	Discontinuous	~1, Irregular	Large	Very Irregular, Wavy Hackle Marks	Elastic	Brittle	High (Sticky)	PMMA, PS	Plastic Fracture by Shear with Compressive and/or Tensile Stress.
Discontinuous-Crack	Discontinuous	>1, Irregular	Very Large		Brittle, Elastic Fracture	Brittle	High	PMMA, PS	Elastic Fracture, Brittle Fracture.
Discontinuous-Complex (Shear with Crack)	Discontinuous	Chips	Very Large	Gouges	Brittle Fracture	Brittle	High	high-mod, low-elongation	Plastic Fracture by Shear with Compressive and/or Tensile Stress.

Kobayashi (14) considers all mechanical cutting as controlled tensile fracture of the plastic. As a first step to understanding trimming parameters, examine the interaction of a single cutting-edge tool with the polymer (Figure 5.10). A single cutting-edge tool is used in machining, turning and shaping but not in trimming of thermoformed parts. But the cutting actions of tools having multiple edges such as saws, drills, and mills can be thought of as the sum of cutting actions of many single-edged tools. The physical factors affecting cutting actions on plastics are summarized in Table 5.5. Tool geometry factors are more complex for multiple-edged tools. The nature of the chip formed in cutting can be used to guide cutting tool selection, and as an indication of how cutting is proceeding (Table 5.6). For example, PS chips in multiple-edge (saw) cutting should be discrete and separate easily, with no evidence of softening, gumming, or threadlines.

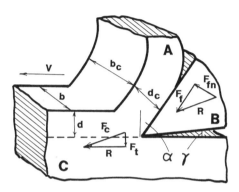

Figure 5.10 Orthogonal Single-Edge Cutting Geometry (From Kobayashi (14)). A: Chip. B: Cutting Tool. C: Work Material. R: Cutting Force. F_c: Cutting Force in Tool Direction. F_t: Thrusting Cutting Force. F_f: Frictional Force. F_{fn}: Normal Force. α: Rake Angle. γ: Relief Angle. V: Feed Rate. b: Cut Width. d: Cut Depth. b_c: Chip Width. d_c: Chip Thickness. By permission of the author.

Multiple-Edged Tool (Toothed Saw) Performance

Kobayashi presents extensive experimental results for plastics performance when cut with single-edged tools. A cutting force balance is shown in Figure 5.10. When the perpendicular cutting-force component F_t is zero, the cutting tool obtains the maximum cut surface accuracy. The cutting tool rake angle at this condition is known as the *critical rake angle*. All tools should have cutting angles equal to or greater than this value. The optimum cutting conditions for nearly all polymers should produce continuous chips of uniform thickness. If the cutting depth (tooth depth) is too large, discontinuous chips are produced and the cutting surface has many microcracks. If the cutting depth is too small, the plastic will heat from friction and will burn or gum the cutting tool.

Multiple-edged tool performance can be determined by comparing the tooth depth of cut and the cutting speeds with single-edged tool performance. For a circular saw (Figure 5.11), the tooth depth of cut, g, is:

$$g = (v/U)p \sin \varphi$$

U is the peripheral speed of the blade, m/min = πDN, D is its outside diameter, in m, = 2R, N is the blade speed, RPM, v is the cutoff speed or the work feed rate, in m/min, and p is the tooth spacing, in mm. The angle $\varphi = \cos^{-1}[(h - b/2)/R]$, where h is the cut-off height, the distance between the saw centerline and the bottom of the plastic sheet, in m, and b is the sheet thickness, in m.

Consider a D = 15.2 cm [6 in] diameter saw with p = 0.637 cm [0.25 in or 4 teeth/in], revolv-

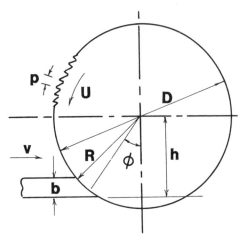

Figure 5.11 Toothed Saw Trimming (From Kobayashi (14)). P: Tooth Spacing. U: Peripheral Speed. D: Saw Diameter. R: Saw Radius. h: Cutting-Off Height. V: Feed Rate. b: Plastic Thickness. φ: Attack Angle. By permission of the author.

ing at 1000 RPM, cutting a sheet b = 0.254 cm [0.100 in] thick, with a cut-off height of h = 5.1 cm [2 in]. sin φ = 0.76. Consider a minimum tooth depth of g = 0.1 mm [0.00394 in], selected to minimize burning or gumming. The feed rate is v = 16.4 cm/s [6.5 in/s]. Feed rates much slower than this may cause the plastic to scorch, or gum and bind the blade. Note that the feed rate is proportional to blade speed and diameter and inversely proportional to tooth spacing. Wide tooth spacing (coarse tooth blades), small, low speed blades and high feed rates minimize thermal damage. But wide tooth spacing causes relatively rough cut edges with many relatively brittle materials (PS, ABS, SAN, PMMA, RPVC).

Hollow-ground blades with no tooth set and wide-kerf carbide blades yield smooth cut edges. Spring-set and swag-set teeth also produce quality cut edges (Figure 5.12).

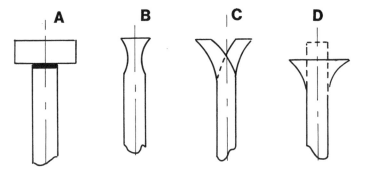

Figure 5.12 Schematic of Saw Tooth Design. A: Carbide. B: Hollow Ground. C: Spring-Set. D: Swaged.

Abrasive Wheel Cut-Off

Abrasive wheels with 30- to 200-grit surfaces produce relatively smooth cut surfaces at high cut-off rates with about one-half to one-third the heat generated by toothed saws (14). Typical abrasives include aluminum oxide (alumina), silicon carbide, tungsten carbide and diamond. Diamond abrasive wheels are most expensive and last longest. Abrasives are held together with thermosetting binders such as phenolics, ureas and epoxies.

Cutting forces are usually higher for abrasive wheels than for toothed wheels at the same feed rate (Figure 5.13). Abrasive wheel cut surface roughness is usually smaller (Table 5.7). Finer grit wheels produce smoother surfaces but at slower cut-off rates (Table 5.8).

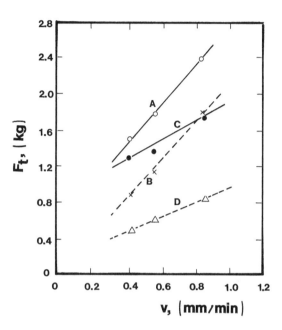

Figure 5.13 Cutting-Off Forces for Abrasive and Toothed Saws (After Kobayashi (14, pg. 156)). F_t: Tangential Cutting Force, kg (See Figure 5.10). V: Feed Rate, mm/min. Wheel Characteristics Given in Table 5.7. A: 36 Grit Silicon Carbide Abrasive. B: 36 Grit Aluminum Oxide Abrasive. C: Hollow-Ground Tooth Saw, No Set. D: Hollow-Ground Tooth Saw, Spring-Set. By permission of the author.

Machinability of a plastic, η, can be written as (14):

$$\eta = V_m / [V_w \, (HP) \, S_f]$$

V_m is the volume of material cut per unit time, mm^3/min, V_w is the amount of tool wear per unit time, mm^3/min, HP is power consumption, $kg \cdot m/min$, and S_f is the cut surface roughness, μm. For properly selected cutting wheels, the amount of tool wear is comparable (and essentially negligible) and so V_w can be ignored.

For cutting wheels:

$$\eta = vbB / F_t U S_f$$

B is the wheel thickness and F_t is the (tangential component of the) cutting force. The ratio of efficiencies of abrasive and toothed wheels operating at the same feed rates and peripheral speeds can be written as:

$$\eta_{ratio} = \eta_{(ab)} / \eta_{(tooth)} = B_a F_{tt} S_{ft} / B_t F_{ta} S_{fa}$$

Abrasive wheels are typically 2 to 5 times thicker than toothed wheels. Both produce about the same surface roughness on the cut edge at the same cut-off speeds (Table 5.7). The cut-off forces for abrasive wheels are about 2 to 5 times those for toothed wheels. So:

$$\eta_{ratio} = (2 \text{ to } 5)/(2 \text{ to } 5) \simeq 1$$

Although cut-off efficiencies are about equal, the cost of operating abrasive wheels is about 5 to 10% of that for toothed wheels. When loaded, abrasive wheels are simply redressed. Toothed wheels require resharpening and tooth resetting.

TABLE 5.7 CUTTING-OFF OPERATION - SURFACE ROUGHNESS
(After Kobayashi (14), with permission of author)
Peripheral Speed 2500 m/min

Materials	Surface Roughness, µm.			
	Abrasive Wheel		Circular Saw	
	A	B	C	D
SAN	32	23	8	200
ABS	28	16	10	200
PA-610 (nylon)	34	16	6	36
PC	8	6	5	25

A: 36 Grit Silicon Carbide, Resinoid - Medium Grade.
B: 36 Grit Aluminium Oxide, Resinoid - Medium Grade.
C: Saw, Hollow-Ground, Zero-Set Teeth, 300 mm Dia, 2 mm Thick. 2.3 teeth/cm [5.8 teeth/in], 0° Rake Angle, 60° Relief Angle.
D: Saw same as C, except 0.2 mm Set to Teeth.

TABLE 5.8 FINISHING OPERATIONS - SANDING BELT SURFACE ROUGHNESS
(Adapted from Kobayashi (14), with permission of author)
Silicon Carbide Sanding Belt: 2000 m/min, 0.5 kg/cm² Applied Force, 20 min.

Material	Surface Roughness, µm		Material Removed, g		Removal Rate, mg/s	
	60 Grit	240 Grit	60 Grit	240 Grit	60 Grit	240 Grit
PMMA	36	2	295	28	246	23.3
PVC (Rigid)	39	2	360	8	300	6.7
PC	41	2	235	9	196	7.5

Shear and Compression Cutting

Saw cutting depends upon brittle tensile fracture of the plastic under the force of the tooth. In solids, Young's modulus, E, is the proportionality between pure elastic tensile stress and strain:

$$\sigma = E\varepsilon$$

When a solid is sheared, the proportionality between pure shear stress and strain is the modulus of rigidity or shear modulus, G:

$$\sigma_s = G\varepsilon_s$$

The bulk modulus, B, is the ratio of hydrostatic pressure to solid volume change per unit volume. Solid compressibility is the reciprocal of the bulk modulus. These moduli are related through Poisson's ratio, the ratio of unit width change to unit length change (7):

$$E = 2\,G\,(1+\nu) = 3\,B\,(1-2\,\nu)$$

$\nu = 0.5$ for a material with constant volume under stress. For most plastics, $0.3 < \nu < 0.4$. PS and PMMA have values of 0.33. HDPE has a value of 0.35. LDPE has a value of 0.38. A value, $\nu = 0.35$, can be used if none is available for a given material. At this value, $E/G = 2.7$ and $E/B = 0.9$. Thus the expected resistance to shearing forces is only about 40% of that to stretching or tensile forces. Shear cutting should require lower specific energy than, say, saw cutting.

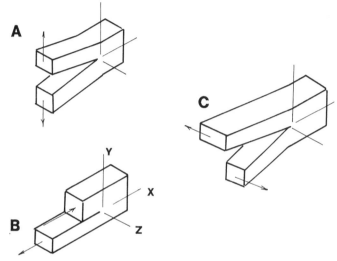

Figure 5.14 Characteristic Fracture Modes (After Caddell (5)). A: Mode I, Tensile Fracture. B: Mode II, In-Plane Shear or Sliding Fracture. C: Mode III, Anti-Plane Shear or Tearing Fracture. Adapted by permission from Prentice-Hall Publications, Inc.

Fracture mechanics is the study of crack propagation in plastics under stress. There are three general types of fracture (Figure 5.14). Mode I is a tensile mode where fracture surfaces are spread apart by the stress. Mode II is a shear mode, where stress forces the fracture surfaces to slide perpendicular to the advancing crack. Mode III is a tearing mode, where the fracture surfaces are forced apart by the stress in the direction parallel to the crack (8). Shear cutting can be considered as Mode III, antiplane shear. This fracture mode is also found in torsion of notched rods. Mode I fracture, cleavage or tensile-opening dominates classical fracture analysis since it is the most common form of material failure and since it is the easiest to study in the laboratory.

If the plastic is not held tightly, Mode III crack propagation control is difficult to maintain. The advancing crack tends to meander uncontrollably and tangent, secondary cracks can form. The amount of force required to propagate a crack (in any mode) and the rate at which a stable crack is propagated can only be estimated from the extensive studies of Mode I failures.

The amount of energy needed to initiate a crack in any polymer is substantially less than its theoretical cohesive strength. Cracks begin at flaws or defects in the material. They propagate when the decrease in elastic strain energy equals or exceeds the energy needed to create a new crack surface. When a tensile specimen with a small horizontal crack, 2 c in length, is stressed, it is in plane stress. The stress needed to propagate that crack is:

$$\sigma = \sqrt{(EG^*/\pi c)}$$

E is Young's modulus and $G^* = 2(\gamma + P)$. P is the plastic work done during yielding and γ is the surface energy of the polymer.

The stress required to *initiate* a crack is frequently far greater than that needed to *sustain* crack propagation (9). For PMMA, the ratio of stress levels is 1000. For vulcanized natural rubber, it is 325.

The plastic deformation stretching energy is much greater than the surface energy. For ductile plastics, such as PTFE, PP, PET and TPE, $P \gg \gamma$. Even for very brittle plastics, such as PS and PMMA, $P > 2\gamma$. For example, for PMMA, $2\gamma = 0.078$ kJ/m^2 [0.0683 ft-lb/in^2] and G^* to sustain the crack = 0.5 kJ/m^2 [0.48 ft-lb/in^2]. $2P = 0.422$ kJ/m^2 [0.37 ft-lb/in^2] and $P/\gamma = 5.4$. For a ductile material like vulcanized rubber, $P/\gamma = 555$ or a ratio 100 times that of the brittle one.

One measure of the fracture toughness of a polymer is the area under its tensile stress-strain curve. If the area is large, the material is tough. Materials that show great plastic flow after yielding (HDPE, PP, PET) have high fracture toughness. If the area is small, as with PS and PMMA, the material is brittle. The stress level that produces fracture is analogous to the crack tip stress *intensity* level that produces sustained fracture. A measure of this stress intensity level is *fracture toughness* or *stress intensity factor*, $K_c = f(\sigma, a)$, where a is the crack length. Characteristically, $K_c = C\sigma \sqrt{(\pi a)}$. C depends upon the geometry of the crack and the surface being fractured. One example of C is given in Figure 5.15 (8), for an edge crack of length a in a sheet of width W under uniaxial tension.

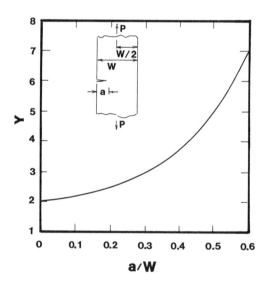

Figure 5.15 Stress Intensity Factor for Mode I Failure (8, pg.267). a: Crack Width. W: Sample Width. Y: Stress Intensity Factor, $= K_c dW/Pa^{1/2}$. d: Sample Thickness. P: Applied Tensile Load. Adapted by permission from John Wiley & Sons, Inc.

For unreinforced plastics, values for K_c range from about 0.5 to 10. Typical values for K_c for a few polymers are given in Table 5.9. The fracture stress is obtained from:

TABLE 5.9 STRESS INTENSITY FACTORS FOR SOME PLASTICS
(Adapted from Kinloch and Young (9))
Values in Parentheses Obtained from $K_c = /(G*E)$

Material	Youngs Modulus, E		G*		Stress Intensity Factor, K_c	
	GPa	[1000 psi]	kJ/m²	[ft-lb/in²]	MN/m³ᐟ²	[1000 lb/in³ᐟ²]
Vulcanized Rubber	0.001	0.145	13	11.4	(0.114)	(2.05)
Polyethylene	0.15	21.8	20*	17.5	(1.73)	(31.2)
PS	3.0	435	0.4	0.35	1.1	19.8
HIPS	2.1	305	15.8*	13.8	(5.76)	(104.)
PMMA	2.5	363	0.5	0.48	1.1	19.8
Epoxy	2.8	406	0.1	0.087	0.5	9.0
Rubber-Modified Epoxy	2.4	348	2	1.75	2.2	39.6
FRP	7	1015	7	6.12	7	126
Glass	70	10,150	0.007	0.0061	0.7	12.6
Wood	2.1	305	0.12	0.105	0.5	9.0
Aluminium	69	10,000	20	17.5	37	666

* J-Contour Integral. See (9; pg. 82).

$$\sigma = K_c/C \sqrt{(\pi a)}$$
$$= (\text{material parameter/geometric parameter})$$

In the tensile Mode I, an infinite stress is needed to initiate a crack of zero length. Once the crack is propagating, the stress diminishes rapidly.

The rate of crack propagation is also important. For fatigue failure, where the load is applied in a cyclic fashion, the following relationship is used:

$$da/dN = A_f \, \Delta K^m$$

N is the number of cycles, ΔK is the stress intensity factor range ($K_{max} - K_{min}$), and m and A_f are polymer material properties (9). Some values for A_f and m are given in Table 5.10. ΔK is proportional to K_c, the continuous loading stress intensity factor. For many polymers (9, 10), $0.5 < (\Delta K/K_c) < 0.67$.

Cyclic crack propagation rate can only be used as a guide to determining crack speed in Mode I tensile fracture. Cyclic fatigue crack growth occurs at substantially lower stress levels than those needed to sustain crack growth in continuous loading. In turn, this guideline can be used only as an estimate of the shear stress needed to control crack propagation in Mode III antiplane shear fracture. As noted, Mode III fracture is the apparent mode occurring during shear cutting of plastics (diagonal brake, nibbling, paper cutting). An appropriate relationship for the rate of crack propagation, $\dot{a} = da/d\theta$ might be:

$$\dot{a} \, (\text{mm/s}) = \beta \sigma^m \, \alpha^{m/2}$$

β includes geometric factors and material coefficients. If the crack length ahead of the shear is to remain stable (a = constant), the rate of shearing is proportional (approximately) to the applied force to the m power. For RPVC (Table 5.10), m = 2.2 and the shear rate should increase about four times when the applied load is doubled. On the other hand, for PMMA, m = 10 and the shear rate should increase about four times with only a 15% increase in applied load.

TABLE 5.10 CRACK PROPAGATION PARAMETERS

$da/dN = A_f \, \Delta K^m$

$[da/dN] = mm/cycle$ $[\Delta K] = MN/m^{3/2}$

$[A_f] = [MN/m^{3/2}]^{-m}$

Material	A_f ($\times 10^3$)	m	Range of ΔK
PS	2.65	3.73	0.5 to 1.2
PMMA	99	10.0	0.4 to 1.0
PES	1.5	9.5	0.6 to 1.2
HDPE	0.35	5.22	1.0 to 2.5
PC	0.118	4.81	1.0 to 3.0
PPO	0.0365	6.2	1.0 to 3.0
RPVC	0.164	2.2	0.5 to 1.0
PA-66 (nylon)	0.00728	3.63	1.5 to 8.0
PVF	0.0087	3.2	1.5 to 8.0

For crystalline polymers, the general relationship is:

$da/dN = A^*(\Delta K/E)^7$ $[\Delta K/E] = m^{1/2}$ $0.5 < A^* < 3$

Compression cutting occurs when a steel rule die is pressed perpendicularly into a plastic sheet resting on an unyielding surface. Steel-rule cutting is a common way of in-mold trimming of thin-gage rollfed sheet. Load-compression follows the true material stress-strain curve. A modification of compression cutting, employing uniaxial plane-strain compression, is used to determine stress-strain curves for polymers that neck or easily fracture (11). Compression cutting is particularly useful when a material yields in compression but fractures brittlely in tension or shear. RPVC and PMMA are typical materials that lend themselves well to compression cutting. Compression yield stresses are usually higher than tensile or shear yield stresses (Table 5.11). Thus more force per unit cutting area is required to die cut a plastic than to shear cut it.

TABLE 5.11 YIELD STRESSES AND CUTTING SHEAR STRESSES

Material	Tensile Yield Stress		Compressive Stress (Yield)		Flexure Stress (Yield)		Sharp Knife Cutting Stress	
	(MPa)	[1000 psi]	(MPa)	[1000 psi]	(MPa)	[1000 psi]	(MPa)	[1000 psi]
HDPE	28	4	20	3	–	–	–	–
LDPE	10	1.5	–	–	–	–	–	–
PP	34	5	41	6	45	6.5	–	–
PET	–	–	83	12	98	14	–	–
PC	62	9	86	12.5	94	13.5	–	–
RPVC	41	6	69	10	77	11	91–126	13–18
PS	–	–	83	12	77	11	110	15.8
HIPS	21	3	–	–	35	5	–	–
ABS	34	5	41	6	35	5	–	–
PPO	48	7	76	11	84	12	–	–
PA-66*	55	8	103	15	119	17	–	–
CA	–	–	–	–	42	6	–	–
CAB	–	–	–	–	35	5	–	–
CAP	–	–	21	3	28	4	–	–
PMMA	–	–	83	12	91	13	–	–
POM**	69	10	110	16	98	14	–	–

* Nylon, dry.   **Polyacetal Homopolymer.

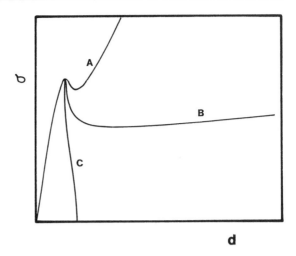

Figure 5.16 Load-Deformation Curves for RPVC (11). σ: Stress. d: Deformation. A: Uniaxial Compression. B: Uniaxial Tension. C: Tension on a Notched Specimen. Figure used by permission of John Wiley & Sons, Inc.

Comparison of typical stress-deformation curves (Figure 5.16 (11)) shows that the area under the compression curve continues to increase with increasing strain. As a result crack propagation in compression is more stable for materials that are brittle or neck badly. Compression cutting is a preferred method for cutting LDPE and should be considered for trimming PET, PA (nylon), POM (acetal), thin-gage OPS and PMMA and low-density foams. For prototype trimming, the trimming jig is frequently just a plywood table with a pneumatically (or manually) operated sharpened steel bandsaw blade mounted above it.

For very brittle materials, if a very sharp, wide die is used, a perpendicular crack is created ahead of the blade. It can propagate as a Mode I fracture (Figure 5.17) and can be uncontrollable, with an irregular reverse side cut surface and crazing. The stress required to cut through the material is then given in terms of the stress intensity factor above and is frequently much less than the compression yield strength. One way of (partially) controlling crack propagation in very brittle materials (PS, PMMA) is to place a very slightly resilient mat between the plastic sheet and the table. Very hard rubber can be used. A sheet of heavy-gage UHMWPE works well. If the plastic or rubber is too soft, the plastic may bind the cutting blade and chipping, splitting and uncontrolled fracture may be aggravated.

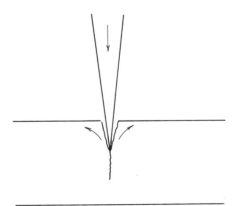

Figure 5.17 Schematic of Mode I Fracture During Die Cutting of a Brittle Plastic with a Very Sharp Edge.

Figure 5.18 Schematic of combined Shear and Compression Die Cutting. d: Gap to Allow Tough Polymer to be Pinched Between Cutter Surfaces.

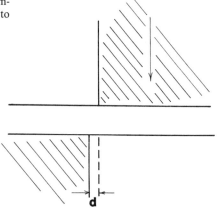

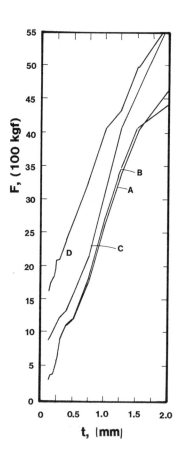

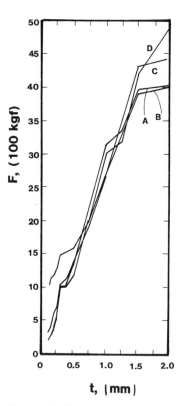

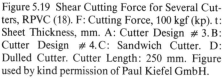

Figure 5.19 Shear Cutting Force for Several Cutters, RPVC (18). F: Cutting Force, 100 kgf (kp). t: Sheet Thickness, mm. A: Cutter Design # 3. B: Cutter Design # 4. C: Sandwich Cutter. D: Dulled Cutter. Cutter Length: 250 mm. Figure used by kind permission of Paul Kiefel GmbH.

Figure 5.20 Shear Cutting Force for Several Cutters, PS (18). F: Cutting Force, 100 kgf (kp). t: Sheet Thickness, mm. A: Cutter Design # 3. B: Cutter Design # 4. C: Sandwich Cutter. D: Dulled Cutter. Cutter Length: 250 mm. Figure used by kind permission of Paul Kiefel GmbH.

For a ductile polymer and a blunt die, the deformation stress can be obtained directly from the stress-strain curve. Since most materials strain-harden in compression, the force required to cut through a tough polymer increases with the depth of cut. For these materials, a combination shear and compression die cut can be used (Figure 5.18). With this type of cut, the lower force of a shear cut is combined with the stable crack propagation (increasing stress-strain) of a compression cut. Heavy-gage plasticized PVC, HDPE and PP are cut this way. Combination shear cutting forces for several cutter blade designs are linear with sheet thickness (Figures 5.19 and 5.20 (18)). Cutting forces for dull knives at 20 C [68 F] are measurably higher for polymers that yield (Table 5.12). Values for effective shear stress (cutting force per unit thickness and cutter length) are about the same as yield stress values (Table 5.11). Cutting forces at 60 C [140 F] are about 10% less.

TABLE 5.12 SHEAR CUTTING FORCES (Data from Figures 5.19 and 20 (18))
Blade length = 25 cm [10 in]   Sheet Thickness = 1 mm [0.039 in]

Material	Blade Design	Total Force		Cutting Stress	
		(kg-force)	[lb]	(MPa)	[1000 psi]
PVC	#3	2600	5720	104	15.1
	#4	2710	5960	108	15.8
	Sandwich	3100	6820	124	18.0
	Dull*	3900	8580	156	22.6
PS	#3	2680	5900	107	15.5
	#4	2680	5900	107	15.5
	Sandwich	2680	5900	107	15.5
	Dull**	2900	6380	116	16.8

* Exhibits a "zero thickness" resistance of 1360 kgf [2990 lb], or an equivalent shear stress of 54 MPa [7900 psi].
**Exhibits a "zero thickness" resistance of 460 kgf [1000 lb], or an equivalent shear stress of 18 MPa [2700 psi]. In addition, force-thickness curve does not appear linear.

Nibbling

Nibbling is a cyclic trimming process. An estimate of the nibbling force can be made from Mode I tensile fracture crack propagation. Consider a 1 mm [0.025 in] PMMA sheet, to be cut in one cycle. $da/dN \geq 1$ mm. $A_f = 0.1$ (MN/m$^{1/2}$)$^{-m}$ and m = 10. Thus $\Delta K = 1.26$ MN/m$^{1/2}$. If $\Delta K = 0.5 K_c$ and C = 20, $\sigma = 0.071$ MN/m^2 [10.3 psi]. This is the tensile stress needed to sustain the crack. The tensile yield stress for PMMA is about 45 MN/m^2 [8500 psi]. Since nibble-cutting should require about the same expenditure of force as compression-shear cutting, the apparent force needed to sustain a crack is only about 0.1% of the total force needed to cut the plastic. As noted above, the force required to initiate a crack is (as much as 1000 times) greater than that needed to sustain it. Nibbling is a process requiring crack initiation at each stroke. Further additional force is required to overcome friction between the nibbler blade and the plastic and to push the cut-off plastic piece from the kerf. As with compression cutters, a good first approximation for the value of the cutting-off shear stress is the yield strength value of the plastic (Table 5.11).

Thermal Trimming

Most plastics can be trimmed by localized melting, either with a hot wire or blade (contact melting) or with a hot gas jet or laser (noncontact melting). In addition to being energy inefficient, hot jet cutting torches are difficult to maintain. Typical problems include cut surface scorching, degradation, and discoloration, kerf width variability, hot gas temperature variability, polymer slag spatter, deposition and ignition, and threadlines. In laser cutting, the polymer is vaporized by the intense focussed energy beam. It is slower than hot gas cutting but more accurate and cleaner.

In contact melting, the heated wire temperature is typically only a few degrees above the polymer melt or flow temperature (12). Wires are electrically-heated, rheostat-controlled, PTFE-coated nichrome resistance wires. Heated blades are frequently resistance tapes placed over steel sawblades.

The plastic melting rate per unit width of heating surface, $\dot{m}$ (kg/m s) [lb/ft h] is given in terms of a convective heat transfer coefficient, h_p, for flowing plastic melt. Values of about $h_p = 200$ W/m^{2}C [35 Btu/ft^2 h F] are reported. The melting rate is:

$$\dot{m} = (\pi \Delta h_p / 2 \, c_p) \, (Nu/Pe)$$

c_p is the polymer heat capacity and D is the heated wire diameter ($\pi D = L^*$, the width of a heated blade). Nu, the Nusselt Number, is a ratio of conduction and convection heat transfer, $Nu = hL/k$, where h is a convection heat transfer coefficient, L is a characteristic fluid film thickness and k is the thermal conductivity of the polymer. Pe, the Peclet Number, = RePr, where Re is the Reynolds Number, and Pr is the Prandtl Number, $Pr = c_p \mu/k$, where c_p is the polymer specific heat, μ is its viscosity and k is its thermal conductivity. The ratio, Nu/Pe, occurs frequently in heat transfer to flowing fluids. Here the ratio is a function of two material parameters, A and B. A is a fluid film parameter and B is a solid parameter. For crystalline polymers, $0.5 < A < 3$ and $0.1 < B < 1$ (12). Over this range:

$$(Nu/Pe) \simeq (2/A)(B)^{0.26}$$

As an example, consider HPDE. Let $A = 3$ and $B = 0.1$ and $(Nu/Pe) = 0.37$. $c_p = 0.5$ cal/g C [0.5 Btu/lb F]. For $D = 0.76$ mm [0.030 in], $\dot{m} = 4.14 \times 10^{-5}$ kg/m s [0.1 lb/ft h]. If the part thickness, $L = 6.35$ mm [0.25 in], the mass rate of HDPE melted is $\dot{m}L = 2.53 \times 10^{-7}$ kg/s [0.002 lb/hr]. Since the projected cutting area is $\pi DL/2$ (only half the wire is cutting), the cutting speed probably cannot exceed 13 cm/s [5.1 in/s].

As noted, A is a melt shielding parameter, the ratio of melt sensible heat to latent heat of fusion. B is the equivalent ratio for the solid phase. For high latent heat crystalline polymers, a substantial fraction of heat is carried away by the melt. A and B are small and (Nu/Pe) is relatively large. Thus the cutting rate can be high. For materials with low latent heats, (Nu/Pe) is small and the cutting rate is low. The Griffin melting model (12) is not truly applicable to amorphous polymers, with no latent heats. Increasing the hot wire temperature increases the relative values of A and B. This effectively decreases the melting rate, since some cutting energy must be now be used to heat the polymer to a higher temperature. Of course, the cutting rate is inversely proportional to the sheet thickness.

Brittleness and Orientation

Many brittle plastics exhibit uncontrolled fracture, secondary crack propagation, reverse-side chipping, crazing and splitting when compression or shear cut. Brittle fracture occurs when the *brittle strength* of a polymer is less than the yield stress. The brittle strength of a polymer (below its Tg) is weakly dependent upon temperature over a wide range (100 C or so). On the other hand, polymer yield stress is essentially a linearly decreasing function of temperature (Table 5.13 (11)). As the polymer temperature increases, the probability of fracture at stresses below the yield stress decreases. The problems associated with brittle fracture trimming diminish as well. At elevated temperatures (approaching Tg), the material becomes ductile and high-speed cutting-off techniques that depend upon brittle fracture crack propagation, such as sawing, become inefficient.

Thermoformed shapes frequently have a high degree of orientation in the trim area. Part shape can enhance nonuniform orientation. Cutting can relieve local stresses. Although this can aid crack propagation to some degree, it can also cause nonuniform part dimensions, binding of the cutting tools, warping and distortion. Secondary fracture effects, crazing in

TABLE 5.13 TEMPERATURE EFFECT ON YIELD STRESS FOR VARIOUS POLYMERS
(Adapted from (11), with permission of John Wiley & Sons, Inc., copyright owner)

Polymer	Linear Region		Temperature Coefficient of Yield Stress,	
	(C)	[F]	(MPa/C)	[psi/F]
PMMA	50 to 100	122 to 212	0.97	78.2
PTFE	− 250 to − 140	− 420 to − 220	0.85	68.5
PE (Chlorinated)	− 60 to 20	− 76 to 68	0.82	66.1
RPVC	− 80 to 60	− 112 to 140	0.80	64.5
PP	− 40 to 20	− 40 to 68	0.74	59.6
PA-66 (nylon)	− 100 to 60	− 150 to 140	0.74	59.6
PET (Amorphous)	− 20 to 60	− 4 to 140	0.49	39.5
PC	− 40 to 120	− 40 to 250	0.32	25.8

particular, can result. Uncontrolled crack propagation can proceed in the orientation direction rather than in the desired cut path. This results in splitting and splintering.

Highly nonuniformly oriented parts of brittle materials can be trimmed by first partially annealing out residual stresses, then cutting away the trim while the material is still warm. Heavy-gage amorphous materials (such as RPVC and ABS) and easily oriented crystalline polymers (such as PA-66 and PP) may need to be trimmed in this manner also.

Trimming - A Summary

The selection of a trimming technique depends primarily on the stress-strain nature of the polymer at the trimming temperature. However many processing elements influence the choice. These include the gage of the sheet, the part size, the overall draw ratio, the complexity of the parting line between trim and part, the acceptable level of cut surface roughness, the required dimensional tolerance, the required speed of trimming, and the extent of fixturing. From a pragmatic view, equipment availability and operator skill probably substantially narrow and may actually dictate the choices. As noted, not all trimming devices are suitable for all types of plastics in all thicknesses. For example, automatic programmed laser cutting is clean and accurate but it is impractical for trimming thin-gage rollfed CAB. Die cutting is quicker, cheaper, can be installed as part of the in-mold forming process, and is the process of choice. Some techniques such as abrasive grit cutting are dusty and work best on high modulus, brittle polymers. Abrasive and toothed wheel cutting and routering generate dust. Heavy-gage parts of PMMA, ABS, and PS should be sprayed with an antistat prior to trimming to minimize an almost-impossible-to-remove cutting dust.

The ranking of trimming techniques in Table 5.14 is meant only as a guideline, in terms of matching the intrinsic natures of the cuts and the material stress-strain behavior. Economics and availability may dictate a less-than-optimum choice.

TABLE 5.14 SUITABILITY OF TRIMMING TECHNIQUES
9 = Preferred, Best   0 = Unsuitable   (Heavy Gage in Parentheses)

Material Nature	Typical Polymers	Die Cut	Shear Cut	Nibble Cut	Router	Circular Saw	Abrasive Wheel
Very Brittle	PS, PMMA, SAN	9 (0)	6 (2)	4 (4)	0 (4)	2 (6)	2 (9)
Brittle	ABS, RPVC, CA, CPET, CAB	9 (0)	7 (2)	5 (4)	2 (5)	3 (7)	4 (9)
Tough	PPO, CAP, PPS, PA-6, PA-66, PET, OPS	5 (2)	9 (6)	6 (8)	3 (8)	5 (9)	5 (7)
Ductile, Rubbery	LDPE, FPVC, HDPE, PP, PTFE, TPE	8 (2)	9 (8)	7 (8)	5 (3)	7 (6)	7 (5)

Material Nature	Typical Polymers	Band Saw	Hot Wire	Hot Gas Jet	Water Jet	Grit Blast	Laser Cut
Very Brittle	PS, PMMA, SAN	3 (4)	6 (7)	4 (6)	5 (2)	8 (8)	7 (8)
Brittle	ABS, RPVC, CA, CPET, CAB	3 (4)	4 (7)	5 (4)	6 (2)	8 (8)	7 (8)
Tough	PPO, CAP, PPS, PA-6, PA-66, PET, OPS	4 (7)	3 (8)	7 (6)	5 (2)	8 (2)	7 (8)
Ductile, Rubbery	LDPE, FPVC, HDPE, PP, PTFE, TPE	2 (3)	2 (8)	3 (6)	3 (5)	0 (0)	7 (9)

Shrinkage

Polymer density increases with decreasing temperature. Unoriented sheet usually decreases in length and width during cooling from forming temperature. If the sheet is substantially oriented during extrusion, severe handling problems can occur when it is heated to the forming temperature and the frozen-in stresses are relieved. Thermoforming is the deliberate attempt to highly orient the sheet, then freeze in orientation by forcing the hot sheet against a cold mold while quenching the free surface with cold air or water.

As the sheet cools, it shrinks. Applied stresses inhibit shrinkage. When the stresses holding the sheet against the mold are removed, shrinkage increases. The extent of shrinkage depends upon the material forming temperature, its glass transition temperature, and the mold temperature. It also depends upon the degree of crystallinity. Highly crystalline materials usually shrink more than amorphous ones. One reason is that they are usually formed at temperatures substantially higher than Tg.

Shrinkage values for many plastics are given in Table 5.15. Some injection molding values are given for comparison. Thermoforming values are in the middle to upper range of the latter.

TABLE 5.15 SHRINKAGE RANGE FOR THERMOFORMED PARTS
(Adapted from 16–19)

Material	Thermoforming (%)	Injection Molding (%)
ABS	0.3 to 0.8	–
SAN	0.5 to 0.6	–
MIPS	0.5 to 0.6	–
PS	0.3 to 0.5	0.2 to 0.6
LDPE	1.6 to 3.0	1.3 to 2.7
HDPE	3.0 to 3.5	2.0 to 4.0
PP	1.5 to 2.2	1.0 to 2.5
RPVC	0.4 to 0.5	–
FPVC	0.8 to 2.5	–
PC	0.6 to 0.8	–
PMMA	0.3 to 0.8	0.3 to 0.5
CAB	0.2 to 0.5	–
PA-66 (nylon)	–	1.0 to 1.7
POM (Acetal)	–	1.0 to 2.7

About 70 to 80% of the dimensional change due to shrinkage occurs as the sheet cools from its forming temperature to its set temperature (or heat distortion temperature at 455 kPa [66 psi]). (17). Stabilization to final dimension can take several hours, however. Most of this change may be due to material relaxation once the forming stresses are removed. Stress relaxation time, λ, at Tg for most polymers is about 1000 s (20). This time usually increases exponentially with decreasing temperature:

$$\lambda = A \exp (\Delta E/RT)$$

ΔE is an energy of activation that can be accurately predicted for amorphous polymers (and some crystalline polymers) for temperatures above Tg (21). Extrapolation to most crystalline polymers and to temperatures below Tg is unwarranted. To illustrate the temperature effect on stress relaxation, let $\Delta E \simeq 40$ kcal/mol K and Tg = 100 C = 373 K. The stress relaxation value at T = 80 C is 20 times that at Tg, or 5.9 hr. For a simple Voigt (linear viscoelastic) stress-strain model, 95% of the strain (or deformation) is recovered in 3 relaxation times, or 18 hr in this case. Strain recovery is one of the major causes of the long times needed to achieve stable part dimensions. *Uneven strain recovery*, caused by nonuniform orientation in the trim area, is a major cause of long-term (days) part distortion and warping (22). In difficult cases, 24 hr annealing at mold temperature (or maximum part use temperature) prior to trimming can reduce warping.

Shrinkage can cause serious part removal problems when forming onto male molds. Draft angles can be estimated from:

$$\theta_{draft} = \tan^{-1} (2 \times \text{shrinkage fraction})$$

For amorphous plastics, the draft angle can be ½° to 1°. For crystalline polymers, it should be 2° to 3°. Textured surfaces require greater draft than smooth surfaces. Female portions of molds require no draft if smooth and ½° if textured.

Drilling

Drilling, slotting and grooving are mechanical operations similar to trimming and are frequently done while the thermoformed shape is still held in the trimming fixture. Plastics are quite difficult to drill without some damage. Friction between the drill flutes and the drilled hole heats and expands the plastic inward, burning it or gumming the drill. Continuous chips from PPS, PC and other high performance plastics can spiral around the drill, binding and stalling it. With olefins, thermal distortion at the hole inlet can cone the hole. For PMMA, PS and SAN, the hole exit can be chipped as the drill tip breaks through. Nevertheless, most plastics can be drilled with conventional two-tooth twist drills (Figure 5.21 (14)).

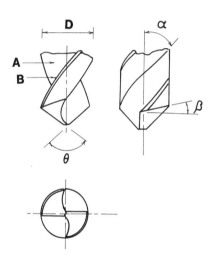

Figure 5.21 Two-Tooth Twist Drill Geometry (14). D: Drill Diameter. A: Flute. B: Margin. θ: Point Angle. α: Helix Angle. β: Relief Angle. Figure used by permission of author.

Single-edged tool cutting guidelines can be used for drilling. The depth of cut per drill tooth, d, is given as:

$$d = (s/n) \sin \theta/2 = (v/n \, N) \sin \theta/2$$

n is the number of teeth on the drill (usually two), N is the rotational drill speed, RPM, v is the axial feed rate, in mm/min, and θ is the point tooth angle, deg. The drill feeding speed, $s = v/n$, is in mm/rev.

A large depth of cut produces cut surface fracture and fracture around the hole as the drill exits. A small depth of cut enhances friction and can result in gumming and hole distortion. As an example, the drill feed rate, v, below which PMMA will gum is given empirically as (14):

$$v_g = 25 \times 10^{-6} \, N^2 \; (\text{mm/min})$$

The feed rate above which PMMA will crack, producing hackle marks in the drilled hole, is:

$$v_c = 0.28\,N - 20 \times 10^{-6}\,N^2\;(mm/min)$$

At $N = 2000$ RPM, the acceptable drilling feed rate range for PMMA is $100 < v < 480$ mm/min [$4 < v < 20$ in/min]. At $N = 4000$ RPM, the range narrows to $400 < v < 800$ mm/min [$16 < v < 32$ in/min]. Above about 6000 RPM, there is no acceptable drill feed rate.

Drilling conditions for many plastics are given in Tables 5.16 and 5.17. For many materials, high elastic deformation and recovery can wear drills, gum drill surfaces and distort the drilled hole. The drills for some plastics such as PS, PVC, and PC should be cooled. Water can be used for PS and PVC. Rapeseed oil produces optimum cooling for PC. An air jet on the drill shank during drilling of most plastics is beneficial (15). Nylons must be moisture-controlled or drilled hole dimensions will change. In crystalline and tough, amorphous polymers, such as HDPE, PP, ABS (high rubber content), nonuniform biaxial orientation in the material may cause the hole to become elliptical. Excess friction during drilling aids in this distortion. In highly elastic plastics, such as HDPE and PTFE, the drilled hole is always smaller than the drill. Tapered, highly polished, widely-spaced flutes are desired. Further, for tough, highly elastic polymers or for critical hole dimensions, holes should first be drilled undersized. Then the hole should be enlarged to the desired diameter.

TABLE 5.16 EFFECT OF DRILL GEOMETRY ON DRILLING CONDITIONS IN PLASTICS
(Adapted from Kobayashi (14), with permission of author)

Drill Parameter	Drilling Condition
Point Angle	Rotational Drill Speed
Rake Angle	Drill Feeding Speed
Relief Angle	Work Temperature
Helix Angle	Cooling Provisions
Shape of Flutes	Nature of the Hole

Table 5.17 see page 152/153.

References see page 154.

TABLE 5.17   DRILLING CONDITIONS FROM PLASTICS
(Adapted from Kobayashi (14), with permission of author)

Material	Point Angle, deg	Helix Angle, deg	Lip Relief angle, deg	Rake Angle, deg	Feeding Speed, mm/rev	Drill Speed RPM***	Wet/ Dry	Flute Condition	Degree of Difficulty** in Drilling	Comments
PE	70–90	10–20	9–15	0	0.18–0.25	2000–4000	Dry OK	3-Point Drill Preferred	0	High Elasticity.
PVC (rigid)	~120	~27	NA	NA	~0.3	2000	Wet pref.	Extra-Large Flutes	6	Inlet Hole Poorer than Exit Hole.
PMMA	55–140	NA	12–20	NA	~0.05	2000	Water/ oil	Polished	3	Some Gummy Inner Surfaces. Extract Drill Frequently. Exit Cracks.
PS	60–90	40–50	12–15	0	(dry) 0.4 (wet) 0.025–0.4	4000	Wet only	Wide, Highly Polished	8 +	Easy to Gum. Inlet Holes can Cone at Low Feed Rates.
ABS-Low Rubber	70–90	10–20	9–15	0	0.025–0.4	500–2000	–	–	–	
Med. Rubber	70–90	10–20	9–15	0	0.025–0.4	500	NA	Polished	4	Can Gum at Inlet.
High Rubber	70–90	10–20	9–15	0	0.05–0.4	500–1000	NA	Polished	4	Can Gum at Inlet.
SAN	70–90	10–20	9–15	0	0.2–0.4	500	Wet pref.	Polished	5	More Elastic than ABS. Hole Smaller than Drill.
PTFE	70–90	10–20	9–15	0	0.025–0.1	500–2000	Dry OK	Deep, Highly Polished	1	Very High Elasticity. Hole Always Smaller than Drill.
PA-6 (nylon)	70–90	*	9–15	*	0.1–0.4	500–2000	Dry OK	Polished	3	Carbide Drills Preferred.
PA-66	70–90	*	9–15	*	0.2–0.4	500–1000	Dry OK	Special Drill Useful	3	Dimensions Can Change if Not Dried Properly.

PA-610	70–90	*	9–15	*	0.2 –0.4	500–4000	Dry OK	Special Drill Useful	3	Pull Drill Out Frequently in Deep Holes.
PC	70–90	10–20	9–15	0	0.05 –0.2	500	Correct wet	NA	2	Some Gumming. Chips Very Tough, Can Bind Drill. Rapeseed Oil.
POM (Acetal)	60–90	NA	10–15	NA	0.05 –0.4	500–4000	Dry OK	Wide, Highly Polished	2	Some Exit Cracks at Low Drill Speeds.
PP	*	*	*	*	0.2 –0.4	500–4000	Dry OK	NA	1	High Elasticity, Gumming at Low Speeds.

*   Conventional Twist Drill Angles.
** 0 = Easy. 9 = Very Difficult
*** On 8.1 mm Dia Drill.

References

1. W. K. McConnell, Jr., Handout, SPE Industrial Thermoforming Symposium and Workshop, Arlington TX, 12–14 March 1985.
2. M. R. Kamal and S. Kenig, "The Injection Molding of Thermoplastics Part II: Experimental Test of the Model", Polym. Eng. Sci., *12*, 1972, pg. 306.
3. J. Schneider, "Conduction", in W. M. Rohsenow and J. P. Hartnett, Eds., *Handbook of Heat Transfer*, McGraw-Hill, 1973, Section 3, pp. 3-14 to 3-16.
4. J. P. Holman, *Heat Transfer*, McGraw-Hill, 1976, pg. 207.
5. R. M. Caddell, *Deformation and Fracture of Solids*, Prentice-Hall, 1980, pg. 209.
6. T. R. Goodman, "Application of Integral Methods to Transient Nonlinear Heat Transfer", in T. F. Irvine, Jr., and J. P. Hartnett, Eds., *Advances in Heat Transfer*, Vol. 1, Academic Press, 1964, pgs. 54, 59.
7. L. E. Nielsen, *Mechanical Properties of Polymers*, Reinhold, 1962, pg. 6.
8. R. W. Hertzberg, *Deformation and Fracture Mechanics of Engineering Materials*, John Wiley & Sons, 1976, pg. 262.
9. A. J. Kinloch and R. J. Young, *Fracture Behaviour of Polymers*, Applied Science, 1983, pg. 87.
10. R. W. Hertzberg and J. A. Manson, *Fatigue of Engineering Plastics*, Academic Press, 1980, pg. 136.
11. P. I. Vincent, "Fracture – Short-Term Phenomena", in N. M. Bikales, Ed., *Mechanical Properties of Polymers*, Wiley-Interscience, 1971, pg. 125.
12. O. M. Griffin, "Thermal Transport in the Contact Melting of Solids", Polym. Eng. Sci., *12*, 1972, pg. 265.
13. J. L. Throne, *Plastics Process Engineering*, Marcel Dekker, 1979, pg. 824.
14. A. Kobayashi, *Machining of Plastics*, McGraw-Hill, 1967, Chapter 1, "Fundamental Considerations".
15. Joel Frados, Ed., *Plastics Engineering Handbook*, 4th Ed., Van Nostrand Reinhold, 1976, pg. 701.
16. A. Höger, *Warmformen von Kunststoffen*, Carl Hanser, 1971, pg. 163.
17. W. K. McConnell, Jr., "Thermoforming Plastic Sheet and Film", from *Tool and Manufacturing Engineers Handbook*, vol. 2, 4th Ed., part of handout at SPE Industrial Thermoforming Symposium and Workshop, Arlington TX, 12–14 March 1985.
18. H. Voigt, *Lehrgang für Thermoformung*, Paul Kiefel GmbH, undated, pg. 1.4.2.
19. I. I. Rubin, *Injection Molding: Theory and Practice*, Wiley-Interscience, 1972, Chapter 2.
20. G. L. F. Ehlers, "Thermal Stability", in E. Baer, Ed., *Engineering Design for Plastics*, Reinhold, 1964, pg. 402.
21. Z. Tadmor and C. G. Gogos, *Principles of Polymer Processing*, John Wiley & Sons, 1979, pg. 163.
22. G. Gruenwald, *Introduction to Thermoforming*, unpublished manuscript, 1983. Copies available from the author, 36 W. 34th St., Erie PA 16508.

6 MOLD DESIGN

Introduction

The thermoforming mold can be as simple as a smoothed block of wood over which a heated sheet is draped or as complicated as an injection mold, with moving elements, articulated sections, and sophisticated means of isolating, stretching, and in-mold trimming of the formed sheet. Selection of suitable mold materials depends to a large degree on the severity and length of service. If a few parts are to be made and the plastic can be deformed at relatively low temperatures with vacuum, the mold materials can be wood or plaster. On the other hand, if thousands of parts are to be made and high temperatures and pressures are needed to achieve final part design, mold materials must be durable. Aluminum and steel are then recommended.

Regardless of the materials used, every mold must have certain features. Provisions must be made for clamping the sheet against the mold surface. Vent or vacuum holes must be provided in those areas into which the sheet is drawn last. The mold surface must remain relatively nonadhesive during sheet contact and static-free after the sheet is removed. The mold surface should also be sufficiently hard to retain its shape and texture for its lifetime. The mold must not change in dimensions either during fabrication (thermal expansion) or during storage (moisture absorption). And the material should be relatively free from chemical and moisture attack. This minimizes swelling, cracking, rusting, corrosion and patina development.

Appropriate mold material selection must include economic considerations as well. Cost is only one factor. Ease of fabrication, repair, maintenance and serviceability, storage requirements, mold weight, availability of mold material, shop personnel familiarity with the material, and material toughness against accidental abuse are intrinsic factors that frequently act to rule out an otherwise acceptable material (18).

Prototype Tooling

Strictly speaking, prototype molds are designed to produce a few parts. These might be used to demonstrate a part design to be production thermoformed or to be injection or blow molded. They can be used for product testing and prototype assembly schemes as well. Frequently, however, prototype molds are used to produce tens or hundreds of parts in a classical production run. Many heavy-gage sheet applications such as signs, displays, swimming pools, containers, bathtubs, and equipment housings are made exclusively on prototype tools.

Wood, plaster, plastic, and zinc or white metal alloys are materials used in prototype tools. Each has many advantages and some serious limitations. A review of each follows.

Wood. Hardwoods are used for prototype and short production runs. The wood must be thoroughly kiln-dried before shaping to minimize stress relief (warping, cracking) during fabrication. Properties of typical hardwoods used in thermoforming are shown in Tables 6.1 and 6.2 (1). Conventional woodworking techniques are used to fabricate the molds. Wood sections are usually assembled with fluted dowels and resorcinol, hot melt, or epoxy adhesives. Hot melt adhesives yield a weaker joint than other adhesives. Standard woodfilling

TABLE 6.1 FINISHING QUALITIES OF SELECTED HARDWOODS USED IN PRO-
TOTYPE THERMOFORM MOLDS (2)

Wood	Planing	Shaping	Drilling	Sanding	Resistance to Splitting
Ash	C	E	A	C	C
Hickory	C	H	A	B	D
Hard Maple	E	C	A	G	E
Red Oak	A	H	A	B	C
Walnut	D	G	A	G	E
White Oak	D	G	A	G	E
Mahogany	C	F	A	E	F

Key: A = 90-100   C = 70- 79   E = 50-59   G = 30-39   J = 10-19
     B = 80- 89   D = 60-69   F = 40-49   H = 20-29   K = 0-9

techniques are used to remove surface defects. Vent holes are usually drilled through the primary surface first, then enlarged by drilling from the back of the mold. Final sanding to 220 grit is usually sufficient for most low-pressure forming techniques.

It is imperative that the assembled wood mold be carefully and thoroughly dried prior to finishing. Rapid, cyclical heating from contact with the hot plastic sheet can pull moisture from improperly dried wood, causing cracking and checking. Wood grain is characterized by alternating hard and soft bands. Occasionally, the softer portions can preferentially shrink causing an unacceptable texture to be transferred to the formed shape.

After thorough drying, the surface can be sealed with temperature-resistant enamel or varnish. Recently, epoxy enamels and varnishes have been developed that protect wood surfaces for hundreds of cycles without refinishing. For low-temperature forming operations (CA's, FPVC, PS foams), polyurethane (PUR) varnishes work satisfactorily. When mold release is needed, paraffin wax, vasoline, or a very light coating of white grease can be used.

Wood can also be used as a component in molds made of more permanent materials. For example, since wood can be shaped rapidly, temporary plugs and web breakers can be formed during early prototype trials to determine optimum material distribution.

Plaster. Most commercial molding plasters are not strong or tough enough to be used in prototype tooling. The properties of the few that are are given in Table 6.3. Plasters are inorganic calcicious materials that hydrolytically react and harden when mixed with water. Molds are formed by casting the newly prepared water-plaster mixture against a part pattern. Since the hydrolytic reaction is exothermic (to about 100 C or so), the pattern should not be fragile. Typically, pattern surfaces are coated with a release agent such as water soluble PVOH (polyvinyl alcohol). Soaps such as Murphy's oil soap, found in leather goods stores, can also be used. Vents should be designed in by placing release-agent-coated wires perpendicular to the pattern surfaces prior to casting. For very thick molds made in multiple pours, soda straws should be placed over the wires after the first pour so that the wires can be easily extracted later. For very thick molds made in a single pour, release-agent-coated tapered pins should always be used.

A very hard void-free surface on the mold can be achieved by "splatting" a thin layer of relatively high water content plaster slurry against the pattern. This should be allowed to harden before further casting continues. This technique is adapted from those developed by artisans working in fine plaster art (2). To ensure adequate dispersion, care must be taken during mixing of plaster into water. Once the plaster and water are thoroughly mixed, the mass should be vibrated for several seconds to dislodge large air bubbles.

TABLE 6.2 MINIMUM MECHANICAL PROPERTIES OF SELECTED HARDWOODS USED IN PROTOTYPE THERMOFORM MOLDS (2)

Property	Wood Type					
	White Ash	Shagbark Hickory	Sugar Maple	Pinoak Red Oak	White Oak	Walnut
Density						
[pcf]	34	40	35	36	37	32
(g/cm^3)	0.55	0.64	0.56	0.58	0.60	0.51
Flex Modulus						
[10^6 psi]	1.44	1.57	1.55	1.32	1.25	1.42
(GPa)	9.93	10.8	10.7	9.10	8.62	9.79
Work to Max Load						
[in-lb$_f$/in^3]	6.6	23.7	13.3	14.0	11.6	14.6
(cm-kg$_f$/cm^3)	1.17	1.67	0.94	0.99	0.82	1.03
Max Crushing Strength Parallel to Grain						
[psi]	3990	4580	4020	3680	3560	4300
(MPa)	27.5	31.6	27.7	25.4	24.5	29.6
Fiber Stress at Proportional Limit						
[psi]	670	840	640	720	670	490
(MPa)	4.62	5.79	4.41	4.96	4.62	3.38
Parallel-to-Perpendicular Compression Ratio	5.96	5.45	6.28	5.11	5.31	8.78
Impact Bending Height to Complete Failure [in]	38	74	40	48	42	37
(m)	0.97	1.88	1.02	1.22	1.07	0.94

During casting, care must be taken to minimize air bubbles and voids. If the plaster viscosity is too high, air is easily entrapped. A high water ratio recipe, on the other hand, produces lower physical properties. Typically, 35 pph water is a useful starting recipe (3).

Cure against the pattern usually takes about 30 min, although slower reacting plasters and those with fillers need as much as 1 h to reach demolding strength (Table 6.3). While casting the primary mold, the moldmaker will usually pour a simple test mold. This is used to judge the level of exotherm and the degree of cure.

TABLE 6.3 MOLDING PLASTERS (3, 4)

Commercial Name	Source	Water Ratio, pph	Setting Time, min	Dry Compressive Strength	
				(MPa)	[psi]
Pattern Shop Hydrocal (Hydrocal A-11)	US Gypsum	54–56	20–25	22.1	3,200
Industrial White Hydrocal	US Gypsum	40–43	20–30	37.9	5,500
Ultracal 30	US Gypsum	35–38	25–35	50.3	7,300
Densite K5	Georgia Pacific	27–34	15–20	65.5	9,500
Super X Hydro-Stone	US Gypsum	21–23	17–20	96.5	14,000

After the pattern has been removed and the vent wires pulled, the mold is set aside in a dry, warm area for several days. This time is needed to develop final properties and stabilize the water content. The mold surface can be finished with open grit paper and epoxy floor varnish if desired. However, plaster molds are usually used for expediency and a fine surface finish is secondary.

Plaster molds are surprisingly durable. They can withstand cyclical forming temperatures of most commerical plastics quite well. Failure is catastrophic however. Broken molds are rarely repaired and so patterns are usually preserved to produce a new mold. Recently moldmakers are using tougher materials such as hydraulic cement or plasters with 3–5% (wt) E-glass fibers or PP chopped tow for reinforcing and strengthening. These materials are 3 to 5 times more expensive than conventional casting plasters however.

Plastic Molds. Great advances have been made in the last few years in formulating thermoset plastic resins for thermoforming molds. In particular, plastic tooling is economically preferred for thick sheet forming, where heat buildup on the mold surface is intermittent, where the tool is rarely heated to facilitate forming, where the part to be formed has a large surface area, where drape or vacuum forming is used, or where relatively few pieces (100 or so) are needed.

For applications where mold *surface* temperatures (not *sheet* temperatures) do not exceed 60 C (140 F) and where drape or vacuum forming is used, thermoset resins such as epoxy and unsaturated polyester resin (UPE), together with glass fibers, are mold materials of choice. The exact manner of tool fabrication depends upon the tool shop, but the general procedure described below is usually followed.

Since thermosetting resins usually cure most efficiently at relatively high temperatures (100 to 125 C), care must be taken to thoroughly dry the pattern before beginning. Thorough air oven drying (50 C for 24 h or more) of plaster and wood patterns is strongly recommended (4). The pattern surfaces should then be sealed with at least two coats of air-sprayed thinned automotive lacquer or industrial polyurethane (PUR). The hard surfaces should then be waxed (twice) with a hard paste wax such as carnuba or Treewax. The surfaces should be power buffed after each application. PVC plastisol is also recommended as a release agent (4). If the patterns have been thoroughly dried, aqueous polyvinyl alcohol (PVOH) can also be used. These release agents should be air-sprayed to ensure uniform coverage. Two coats are recommended.

Generally, epoxy and UPE molds are fabricated in similar ways. For glass fiber-reinforced UPE (GR-UPE) molds, a 0.3 to 0.4 mm layer of special resin known as a *gel-coat* is first sprayed against the prepared pattern. A typical gel-coat recipe is given in Table 6.4. This layer is allowed to air-cure, either at room temperature or under infrared lamps, until tacky. An optional second layer can then be applied. The surface should then be carefully inspected for bubbles or other defects. Care at this point can obviate extensive surface repairs later.

A layer of very fine glass fabric called *C-veil* is then placed against the gel-coat. A thin layer of UPE laminating resin is sprayed over the fabric and carefully squeegeed into it. An alternate method involves dipping the C-veil in catalyzed resin and applying the wet fabric to the gel-coated surface. Since the wet fabric is quite weak and resin drains readily from it, this approach is quite messy and consumes more resin than spraying. This approach leads to far fewer dry pockets between gel-coat and C-veil, however.

Once the C-veil layer has cured to a tacky state, the first layers of reinforcing glass can be layed. The glass fabric normally used is a plain weave with about 4 to 10 threads/cm (10 to 25 tpi) and weighing about 500 g/m² (20 oz/yd²). Plain weave is used because it has good strength in both directions, can be easily oriented and shifted to fit tight curves, has an open

TABLE 6.4 TYPICAL RECIPE FOR UNSATURATED POLYESTER RESIN GEL-COAT FOR PROTOTYPE THERMOFORMING MOLDS

Resin Recipe	Molar Ratio
Isophthalic Acid	1
Maleic Anhydride	1
Neopentyl Glycol (Glycol Excess, 2%)	2.04

Acid No.: ~18. Hydroxyl No.: ~30. Gel Time: ~5 m. Peak Exotherm: ~225 C [~437 F].

Formulation*	Parts by Weight
Polyester (as above)	48
TiO_2 Pigment	20
Styrene (Diluent)	32
Fumed Silica	1.5
Cobalt Octoate (Promoter)	0.3–0.6
MEK Peroxide (Catalyst)	0.2–0.3

* Polystyrene in Polyester at 40%.

0.32 cm [0.125 in] Clear Casting Properties

Flex Strength, MPa [psi]	145	[21,000]
Flex Modulus, GPa [10^6 psi]	3.90	[0.57]
Elongation, %	1.9	
Tensile Strength, MPa [psi]	65.5	[9500]
Heat Distortion Temperature	112 C	[234 F]

TABLE 6.5 TYPICAL RECIPE FOR UNSATURATED POLYESTER RESIN WITH FIBERGLASS MAT REINFORCING FOR PROTOTYPE THERMOFORMING MOLDS

Resin Recipe	Mole Ratio
Isophthalic Acid	1
Maleic Anhydride	1
Propylene Glycol	2.2

Acid No.: ~8. Hydroxyl No.: ~45–50. Gel Time: 8–12 m.
Peak Exotherm Temperature: ~225 C [~437 F].

Formulation*	Parts by Weight
Polyester (as Above)	42
Styrene (Diluent)	28
Glass Mat/Chopped Fiber	30
Cobalt Octoate (Promoter)	0.3
MEK Peroxide (Catalyst)	0.15–0.3

* Polystyrene in Polyester at 40%. Recipe Depends Upon Wet-Out Method, Type of Fabrication (Hand Lay-Up, Spray-Up, etc.).

Typical Physical Properties of FRP

Flex Strength, MPa [psi]	138	[20,000]
Flex Modulus, GPa [10^6 psi]	7.0	[1.0]
Elongation, %	1.0	
Tensile Strength, MPa [psi]	82.8	[12,000]
Heat Distortion Temperature	190 C	[375 F]

weave to minimize air entrapment, and most important, is an inexpensive fabric structure. Strips 50 mm (2 in) by 500 mm (20 in) are cut, hand-dipped in catalyzed resin, hand-applied to the critical high-stress areas of the mold (corners and rim), and hand-rolled to express air and ensure intimate contact with the C-veil layer. Usually the resin bath is catalyzed for a 1 h gel time (that time when the resin becomes stringy and jellylike). The moldmaker must know how much resin can be applied in that time. A typical resin recipe is given in Table 6.5. Since UPE resins exotherm when curing, the thickness of the built-up layer of un-cured resin on the mold must be restricted to about 6 mm (0.25 in). Excessive thickness will cause the resin to crack during curing. Thicker mold sections can be fabricated by building atop the fully cured mold substrate.

Once the critical stress mold areas have been constructed, reinforcing elements such as thor-oughly dried, untreated wood or plaster can be added. Scrap fully cured GR-UPE pieces can also be used. These are held in place with resin and wet woven glass fabric. Automotive body putty (a filled UPE recipe) can be molded into irregular areas as well. These materials are allowed to cure in place.

The rest of the mold surface area can then be built, either by hand dipping squares of fabric in the catalyzed resin bath and hand applying, or by applying dry fabric to the surface and squeegeeing resin into it. These layers are then allowed to cure to tackiness. Once the entire mold surface has been covered with at least one layer of nearly-cured fabric and resin, addi-tional layers can be added in rapid succession. Wet fabric does not stick well to vertical sur-faces and so orientation of the mold during fabrication may dictate the total mold construc-tion time.

After a solid reinforced layer has been built over the entire mold surface to 3 mm (0.125 in) or so, chopped glass and reactive resin can be sprayed onto the surface. Since the sprayed material resembles wet hay, it must be carefully rolled to express air. Rolling is done with special spaced-disk rollers. The reason for restricting spray-up techniques to a supporting role for hand layup is that spray-up laminates have only 70 to 80% of the flexural strength and modulus of hand layup laminates (4). Spray-up techniques are of course less labor in-tensive and so mold costs are reduced by using them in a supporting role.

Once the minimum mold thickness of about 6 mm (0.25 in) or so is reached, the inner mold structure can be constructed. The moldmaker must keep in mind that molds built this way are frequently very large. Even the low pressures used in vacuum forming can generate sub-stantial forces that can buckle an unreinforced plastic mold. A standard inner structure is an egg-crate of 2 to 2.5 cm (¾ to 1 in) thick exterior plywood or laminated wood, with 10 to 15 cm (4 to 6 in) openings. For a female mold, the egg-crate is fashioned into a cradle to sup-port the flat sides and bottom of the tool. The plywood is held in place with reactive resin and glass fiber tape or automotive body putty. The plywood core allows for easy access of vent holes.

For additional reinforcement, aluminum or phenolic-coated paper honeycomb sheet up to 5 cm (2 in) thick is used. This is just layed into the wet resin against the mold back and held until the resin cures. PVC, aluminum or GR-UPE pipe is also used for reinforcing. Pipe sec-tions are joined to each other and to the mold back with resin-wet fabric strips and held un-til the resin is set. If the tool must withstand large buckling *forces* (not necessarily large pres-sures), a lightweight cement can be cast against the mold back. Recently, many cements have been developed where a low density aggregate such as slag or Perlite expanded materi-al is mixed with 5 to 10% (wt) UPE or epoxy resin, then troweled in place. Note that EPS beads can be mixed with low viscosity epoxy resin (but *not* UPE resin) as a low-density backing agent. Care must be taken to ensure adequate vent hole placement and access *be-fore* the mold back is sealed in several cm of cement.

Once the mold has been constructed, it must be allowed to cure thoroughly, preferably at room temperature. Normally 24 to 48 h is needed, particularly if some areas are quite thick. To ensure a hard, thorough cure, the mold and pattern can be placed in a warm air oven at 50 C [125 F] for an additional 24 to 48 h. It is difficult to cure UPE in thin cross sections to a tack-free state at room temperature, however. Oxygen inhibits reactivity on exposed surfaces. One way around this is to spray a thin layer of air-drying, film-forming PVOH solution on the exposed curing UPE surface. The resulting thin film can be stripped from the mold after the UPE is fully cured.

If the pattern has been suitably prepared, it should release easily from the mold. UPEs and epoxies shrink upon curing, and if sufficient taper has not been provided for female molds, the mold and pattern can become locked together. Even with adequate pattern preparation, very large molds can require considerable manpower and time to release from patterns. Mold release is best accomplished with air, water, and weight. Air and water from separate sources are forced between the edges of the mold and the pattern at their interface, while the entire assembly is suspended slightly above the shop floor. In desperate cases, the pattern must be destroyed to recover the mold.

The mold surface must be adequately cleaned, waxed and buffed prior to use. Even though plastic tools can last for hundreds of cycles, surface deterioration can occur. Most common is pinholing, due to collapse of small bubbles trapped in and behind the gel coat during fabrication. Some dimples and dents are caused by problems in applying the release coat to the pattern. Delamination and blistering are also problems. Usually surface repairs are straightforward. The defect area is sanded or ground down to good material and a patch of catalyzed resin containing a filler such as fumed silica is troweled into the defect. Cure is by infrared lamp. A cave-in, break-out or development of star cracks during forming require heroic repair efforts and usually indicate that the tool was improperly reinforced. Fabrication of a new mold should be given serious consideration over attempted repair.

Although this section has focussed on UPE mold fabrication, epoxy molds are fabricated in a similar fashion (4). Most recently, aerospace applications have included forming of high temperature materials. The typical GR-UPE and GR-epoxy tools described above are restricted to about 60 C [140 F] use temperatures. Higher temperature epoxies can be used to produce tools with use temperatures to 150 C [300 F]. Molds of these materials require much higher curing temperatures and much greater care in pattern making and preparation.

One manufacturer (5) recommends graphite cloth with aerospace-type epoxy for fabrication of tools with use temperatures of more than 200 C [390 F]. These tools are used to form reactive reinforced resin sheet at low temperatures with curing of the formed sheet against the hot mold at temperatures of 200 C [390 F] or more. These sophisticated tools include aluminum or copper pipe for oil heating. A tool life of 500 cycles is claimed.

White Metal Prototype Molds. The metal welding industry relies on the establishment of an intensely hot arc that can be drawn between electrically isolated metal surfaces energized with high amperage low voltage DC power. The arc causes most common metals to melt. If high velocity air is blown into the arc, the molten metal is broken into very fine drops. The molten drops can be transported short distances before cooling below their fusion temperature. One system is shown in Figure 6.1 (6). The TAFA system establishes the electrical arc between metal wires that are fed in a controlled fashion into the spray zone. By accurate control of the metal wire speed, a uniformly fine metal spray issues and can be used to coat a surface. Although most metals can be sprayed, zinc and zinc-alloy metals offer a good balance of flexibility in spraying, relatively low molten metal temperatures (thus preserving delicate pattern surfaces), small drop size, and good hardness and strength. Typically, zinc has

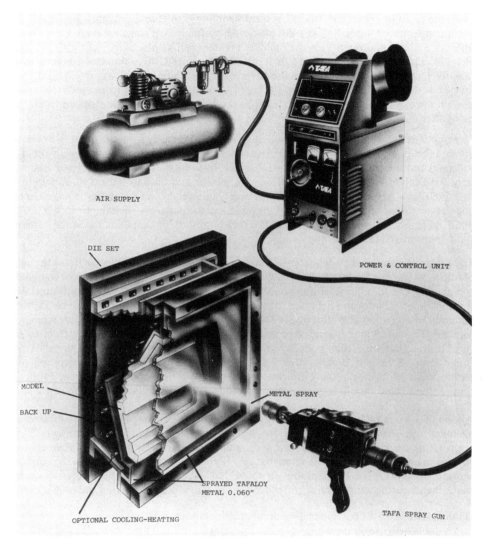

Figure 6.1 Rendering of TAFA Metal Spray Technique for Thermoform Mold Fabrication (By Permission of TAFA Metallisation (16)).

a spraying temperature of 410 C [770 F] and can be dispensed at 5 kg/h [10 lb/h] at a power level of 50 to 150 A, 20 V, 2 kw. A typical surface hardness is 70 Rb. Other physical properties are given in Table 6.6 (4).

The spraying process begins by fastening the pattern, if small, to a turntable and then coating it with aqueous PVOH release agent. Once the pattern is secure and dry, the metal spray unit is activated and an arc established. The spraying rhythm is similar to paint spraying in that the objective is to build up a uniform coat over the entire surface. It is necessary to begin spraying by tying the edges of the metal layer tightly to the edges of the turntable. If this is not done correctly, the air carrier can infiltrate a loose edge, lift the thin metal layer, and catastrophically tear it from the pattern. Then the process must be restarted with pattern preparation. Spraying should be done in a well-ventilated hood, and the operator should wear a breathing helmet.

TABLE 6.6 PROPERTIES OF SPRAYED ZINC (6)

Hardness	70 Rb	
Tensile Strength MPa [psi]	128	[18,500]
Melting Point	410 C	[770 F]
Temperature on Contact with Pattern	340 C	[650 F]
Density, % Theoretical	92–95	
Shrinkage, %	0.1–0.2	
Cost, $/m^2 [$/ft^2]	53.80	[5.00]
Weight, kg/m^2 [lb/ft^2]	24.3	[5.0]
Melt Power, kW/kg [kW/lb]	0.44	[0.2]
Spray Droplet Size, μm	50–150	

If the pattern is made of particularly temperature sensitive material, care must be taken to prevent concentrated spraying in a small area. If the pattern is small and spraying continuous, pattern temperature can easily exceed 100 C [210 F] and may reach 200 C [390 F]. Typically, spraying continues until a uniform layer of metal of at least 1.5 mm [0.060 in] has been deposited. Reinforcing structures, copper water lines, and other features can then be placed on the mold shell and these elements encapsulated by spraying additional metal. For greater metal rigidity, particularly in stress areas (edges, corners, deep recesses), the zinc layer can be built to 6 mm [0.25 in] or more. Epoxy cements are used behind the metal skin to complete mold fabrication. If the mold is to act as a heat exchanger, metal-filled epoxies can be used to 120 C [250 F]. Care must be taken, however, as certain epoxy formulations depolymerize at local temperatures of 200 C [390 F] or more.

Although spray metal molds have been used in production for vacuum forming for years without noticeable wear (4), pressure forming dramatically shortens tool life. In SMC, for example, where pressures to 1.5 MPa [200 psi] and temperatures to 120 C [250 F] are common, tool life is reduced to 100 pieces or so. The primary mode of failure with SMC is surface flaking. In these applications, chrome surface diffusion plating is used to harden the zinc surface. The chrome surface is 0.08 to 0.18 mm [0.003 to 0.007 in] and its hardness is 55 to 65 Rc. Of course, this treatment increases the cost and delivery time of the mold.

Nickel Molds. Another approach to prototype tooling is to use a thin electroformed nickel surface that is reinforced with sprayed zinc metal, cast metal or cast metal-filled epoxy. The nickel used is a very pure electroplating grade (99.95% with a trace of cobalt). The pattern surface must be conductive. For wood, plaster, ceramic and plastic patterns, a coating of PUR varnish is sprayed over the surface. While it is still tacky, a very fine coating of powdered graphite is air-blown onto it. The PUR is then allowed to cure, either at room temperature or more typically in a free convection oven at 50 C [125 F].

The pattern surface is then immersed in a cold plating bath. Nickel is laid down at the rate of 4 μm/h until a uniform layer of about 1.5 mm [0.060 in] thickness has been built onto the pattern surface. At this point, the pattern and nickel layer can be removed for additional backing with sprayed metal or cast plastic. Or it can be immersed in a second plating bath where copper is added to a thickness of 10 mm [0.400 in] or so. Hot plating techniques lay nickel at the rate of 10 to 20 μm/h, but produce a coarse-grained porous surface. Normally this surface is dull and cannot be polished. But it is quite satisfactory for production of non-appearance low-pressure thermoformed parts. The nickel produced by hot plating has about 50% of the toughness of cold plated electroformed nickel.

Production Tooling

Roll-fed sheet forming economics dictate high production rates and long tool life. For this reason, metals that yield low maintenance, good surface hardness, and low wear are selected. Aluminum has been the choice for many years. Aluminum molds wear well, are relatively lightweight, and have excellent strength-to-weight ratio. Lightweight tools do not appreciably increase the inertial factor of mechanically acting forming presses. Aluminum tools can be machined from stock shapes or cast from suitable patterns. More details are given below.

Recently, the increasing interest in high speed forming, matched die forming, in-place die cutting, pressure forming, heated mold forming, and forming of composite sheet has led to selection of tools made from steels that are normally used in injection molding. Such tools are quite expensive and so can be justified only on the basis of extreme or severe service, requirements of faithfulness and accuracy over many, many cycles, and other features, such as sliding action or in-situ die cutting, that could not be achieved in any other tooling medium.

Aluminum Molds. Aluminum is frequently the material of choice for thermoforming molds because it can be easily fabricated, it has a very high thermal conductivity so sensible heat from the formed plastic sheet is rapidly removed, and it is a lightweight, tough metal. Thermoforming tools can be made of either machined plate or cast metal.

Typically, molds are fabricated from plates of either 2024-T4 or 6061-T651 (aircraft grade). These materials contain 1 to 2% Cu, 0.5 to 1% Mg, 0.5% Mn, 4 to 8% Si, 1% (max) Fe, 1% Ni, and traces of Ti and Zn. Typical machined aluminum hardness is 130 Brinell. Since tool steel hardness can be as high as 300 Brinell, care must be taken during mold changing and alignment with steel mold members (rails, guides, platen frames, sheet clamps and hold-downs) to avoid marring or dinging the softer aluminum. Aluminum also has a relatively high thermal expansion coefficient (19×10^{-6} C^{-1}) when compared with steel (11×10^{-6} C^{-1}). Care must be taken when heating large tightly clamped molds to minimize abnormal stress and potential buckling.

Molten aluminum can be cast at 550 to 600 C [1000 to 1100 F] against ceramic, dried and fired gypsum plaster, or foundry sand patterns. Usually atmospheric casting is used to produce prototype or short production-run molds. Atmospheric or foundry casting yields molds that may have surface porosity and nonuniform surface hardness. Porosity can be a problem when pressure forming or if drilled coolant lines pass close to the mold surface. A uniformly high finish is not possible with foundry cast aluminum tools. Pressure casting produces a much denser mold but at a much greater cost. Patterns must be rugged enough to withstand the thermal shock of molten metal *and* 7 MPa [1000 psi]. Fired ceramic patterns are recommended. A casting ceramic of ethyl silicate and quartz powder can be fused into patterns that will withstand pressure casting conditions (7).

Steel Molds. The most severe service of any thermoforming process cannot match, say, typical temperatures, pressures, erosiveness, or number of required parts of a standard injection molding process using filled or reinforced thermoplastics. As a result, thermoforming tools do not need to be constructed of the same tool steel as that specified for injection molding tools. However, mold shops that specialize in injection molding tools are accustomed to working in specific types of steels. They will therefore frequently quote jobs in these materials. Prehardened steels such as AISI P20 are recommended for large molds and molds with low demands on wear resistance. P20 is more difficult to machine and polish than, say, S7 or H13 steels. Since the last two must be air-hardened after machining, the tool shop does not risk tool dimensional change or distortion with P20. Air-hardened H13 is 0.35% C, 5.0% Cr, 1.5% Mo and 1% V, with a hardness of 50 to 54 Rc. P20 is 0.35% C, 1.25% Cr, and 0.4% Mo, with a hardness of only 30 to 36 Rc.

Although sophisticated techniques have been developed for machining and hobbing molds and for hardening steel surfaces, these heroic efforts are not really needed for thermoforming. And similarly investment casting of molten steel against ceramic patterns is also not needed (8).

Other Mold Materials. In injection mold making, beryllium/copper and Kirksite are frequently used for prototype tooling (8, 9). Typically, before extensive repairs are needed, molds of these materials yield more parts than aluminum, sprayed metal and plastic molds. Steel molds yield more parts than all other materials (see Table 6.7). Thermoforming molds see much less severe service and as a result these exotic materials are rarely used. Nevertheless, the service guides given in Table 6.7 hold for thermoforming molds as well, with the mold lifetimes extended by a factor of 10 or more.

TABLE 6.7 GUIDE TO PROTOTYPE TOOLING MATERIALS (9)

Material	Delivery Time, Wks	Number of Parts, × 1000		Repairs[a]	Changes, Texture	Surface Finish[b]
		Inj. Mold	Thermoform			
Epoxy	2– 4	0.1	0.1–10	3	No	C/D
Sprayed Metal	2– 4	0.05	0.1	3	No	C/D
Kirksite	4–20	100	1,000	1	Yes	B
Beryllium/Copper	4–12	500	1,000	2	Yes	A/B
Aluminium						
Cast	3– 8	50	200	2	Yes	A/B
Machined	3–12	100	1,000	2	Yes	B/C
Steel	4–30	1000	10,000	1	Yes	A

[a]: 1 = Easy 3 = Difficult   [b]: A = Diamond   C = 400–600 Grit
                                           B = Buff Polish   D = 350–400 Grit

Vent Holes

As the hot plastic sheet is drawn into the mold, the trapped air must be evacuated. Normally small holes are provided in the mold surface at the point(s) where the last portion of the drawing sheet contacts. The number and diameter of these vent (or vacuum) holes should be determined prior to mold design. If the vent hole diameter is too large, hot plastic will be drawn into it, producing an unsightly bump or nipple on the finished part. If the local drawing is excessive, the sheet can rupture. If too few vent holes are provided or if the vent area is too small, the rate of draw-down will be controlled by the rate of air flowing from the entrapped bubble. If the rate is too slow, the sheet may cool so much that it can no longer be stretched and full mold shape replication may not be achieved.

Mold vent hole diameter depends upon several factors, including the modulus of the hot plastic sheet, sheet thickness over the hole and the allowable draw depth into the vent hole. The maximum deflection y of the sheet of thickness t and modulus E into a hole of diameter d is given as (10):

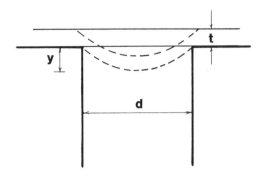

Figure 6.2 Vent-Hole Geometry. t is Initial Sheet Thickness, y is Deflection, d is Hole Diameter.

$$y = \alpha t = (3\ qd^4/16\ Et^3)(5 + v)/(1 - v)$$

q is the applied pressure and v is the polymer Poisson's ratio (Figure 6.2). y is assumed to be proportional to the sheet thickness, with α as the proportionality. For many plastics, the value of v is between 0.35 and 0.5. If $v = 0.5$:

$$\alpha = 0.516(q/E)\ (d/t)^4$$

The maximum acceptable nipple height is usually predetermined by the designer. This establishes an upper limit for α. Rearranging:

$$(d/t) = 1.18\ (\alpha E/q)^{1/4}$$

This is shown in Figure 6.3. As an example, if the temperature-dependent sheet modulus is 10 MPa [1450 psi] and the applied pressure is 0.1 MPa [14.5 psi], a vent hole diameter 3.73 times the local sheet thickness will draw a nipple equal in length to the local sheet thickness. Note the high sensitivity of nipple length to vent hole diameter and sheet thickness. If the vent hole diameter is actually 4.44 times the local sheet thickness (or if the local sheet thickness is actually only 86% of the predicted, design thickness), the nipple length will be *twice* the local sheet thickness. A similar but less dramatic effect is seen if the sheet is hotter than originally predicted. Hotter sheet implies lower elastic modulus and longer nipple length.

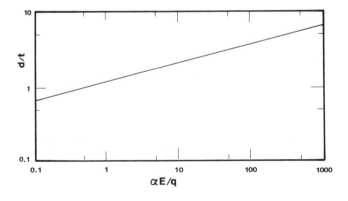

Figure 6.3 Specific Vent Hole Design Parameter (d/t) as Function of Material Modulus E and Applied Pressure q. α is Allowable Specific Sheet Deformation, $= (y/t)$. t is Sheet Thickness.

It is recommended that the vent hole diameter be based on the first common drill size *below* the calculated value. The vent holes should be drilled perpendicular to the plane of the mold. For each vent hole, a 6 mm [0.25 in] diameter hole should be counterbored from the reverse side to within 6 mm [0.25 in] of the primary mold surface.

Number of Vent Holes. Once the size of the vent hole is established, the required number can be easily determined. From very simple measurements, the volume of air captured in the mold cavity the instant the heated sheet seals against the mold rim can be determined. This volume V must be removed from the cavity in a reasonably short period of time θ. Thus the volumetric flow rate of air through the vent holes should equal or exceed the value V/θ. When the ratio of internal to external (vacuum side) pressure exceeds about 0.52, evacuating air speed reaches sonic velocity C, about 335 m/s [1000 ft/s] (11). The vent hole surface area is given as $\pi N d^2/4$, where N is the number of holes. Thus:

$$CN\pi d^2/4 = \beta V/\theta$$

β is a proportionality, representing a safety factor to prevent air escape velocity from limiting draw-down rate. Since the number of holes is to be determined, this can be rewritten as:

$$N = 4\beta V/\theta C\pi d^2$$

If $V = 1000$ cm^3, $\theta = 0.1$ s, $d = 1.59$ mm [0.0625 in] and $\beta = 10$, the number of holes required is $N = 150$. These holes must be placed in regions where last drawdown occurs. Experienced moldmakers avoid providing far too few vent holes of diameters that are far too large. If vent hole diameters are too large, objectionable nipples result, even though the volume of entrapped air is exhausted in reasonable time. Large diameter vent holes force the fabricator to use lower sheet temperature. If stretching forces are limited or the sheet is particularly stiff, poor part replication results.

Other Types of Vents. Porous metal plugs can be used in flat areas in place of multiple vent holes. Sintered powders of bronze, brass or stainless steel of about 50% open area are commercially available. These can be machined to fit an existing vent hole or custom ordered to meet a specific design. A hole large enough to vent the area (usually 6.4 mm [0.250 in] or more) and deep enough to accommodate the plug (usually 6.4 mm [0.250 in] or more) is drilled in the primary mold surface. Exit holes are then drilled from the reverse side to facilitate venting.

Nipples cannot form when porous vent plugs are used. However, the open areas tend to fill with detritus (plastic sander and router dust, atmospheric dust and contamination). Venting efficiency gradually decreases with time, necessitating periodic plug replacement.

Very fine stainless steel, nickel or brass wire screen (–100 mesh) is also commercially available. Open area is usually 35% to 65%. Screen must be supported to minimize bending under sheet draw-down forces. Screen may also leave an undesirable pattern on the part.

Slot vents are used when linear protruding elements occur inside a female mold. Slots are end-milled along the two dimensional corner to a depth of about 6.4 mm [0.25 in]. Exit vent holes are then drilled from the reverse side. The width of the slot vent can be determined in a manner similar to that for round holes. From Figure 6.2, let d be the slot width. The maximum deflection, y, is given as (10; pg. 97):

$$y = \alpha t = (qd^4/4 \ Et^3)$$

Rearranging:

$$(d/t) = 1.414 \, (\alpha E/q)^{1/4}$$

Since this equation is of the same form as that for a circular hole, Figure 6.3 can be used for slot vents if:

$$(d/t)_{slot\ vent} = 1.2 \, (d/t)_{circular\ vent}$$

For the same allowable depth of draw into the vent, slot vent widths can be only 83% of circular vent diameters. For a given dimension, slot vents have 2 to 4 times greater venting area. Reverse side exit holes must be large enough to allow unrestricted air flow from the cavity. And slot vent width must be small enough to minimize part undercutting into the vent.

Surface Treatments

Unlike injection molds, thermoform molds rarely require intermittent topical applications of mold release in areas where the formed shape is particularly difficult to release from the mold surface. There are several reasons for this. The pressures used in thermoforming are modest. The plastic is a rubbery solid rather than a sticky fluid and so polymer adhesion is minimal. The plastic shape is usually quite flexible when stripped from the mold and so vacuum pockets usually do not form. And the mold surfaces are usually vented in precisely those areas where sticking might occur.

Surface treatments on thermoform molds are used for other reasons. When biaxially stretched hot sheet contacts a cold high energy surface such as a metal mold, stretching ceases. Walls of simple vacuum-formed female parts thin with draw depth (See Chapters 4 and 7). In order to avoid excessive drawdown, or to effect preferential drawdown into a specific region, permanent surface treatments are used. The relationship between frictional force F_s and normal force F_n is:

$$F_s = c F_n^{\alpha}$$

c is the kinetic frictional coefficient and α takes the experimental range of $2/3$ to 1. Larger values of α indicate that the deformation of contact area of the plastic is determined by its viscoelastic properties. Values of c between typical smooth-surface metals and solid plastics are in the range of 0.1 to 0.25 (12).

To better understand the surface effect on forming, consider the simple example of draw down of a sheet of initial thickness t_0 and tensile strength τ into a cylindrical female mold of diameter D with a differential pressure P (Figure 6.4). As shown, the sheet already contacts the cylinder to a depth Z and has thinned to a thickness t. The normal forcing holding the sheet against the surface is:

$$F_n = P(\pi D Z)$$

The term in parentheses is the contact area of the sheet on the mold. If the sheet is to slide rather than stick, it must be pulled with a force greater than this, or:

$$F_s > c F_n^{\alpha} = c(P \pi D Z)^{\alpha}$$

The force required to draw the sheet is given as:

$$F_d = \tau A$$

Figure 6.4 Forces Applied to Sheet During Stretching and Sliding. N is Applied Normal Force. Z is Depth of Draw. D is Cylinder Diameter. t_0 is Initial Sheet Thickness. t is Sheet Thickness at Depth Z.

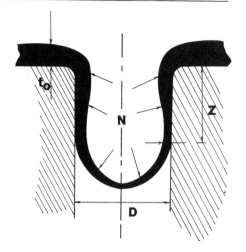

A is the cross sectional area of the sheet at the point where it last contacts the mold. So:

$$F_d = \tau A = \tau \, (\pi D t)$$

If the force needed to slide the sheet exceeds that needed to draw it, the sheet will tend to draw. And vice versa:

$$Fs \lessgtr F_d \quad \rightarrow \quad c(P\pi DZ)^\alpha \lessgtr \tau \pi D t$$

If $\alpha = 1$:

$$cPZ \lessgtr t \quad \text{or} \quad Z \lessgtr t(\tau/cP)$$

Let $\tau = 1$ MPa [150 psi], $P = 0.1$ MPa [15 psi], and $c = 0.25$. If $t = 0.25$ mm [0.010 in], the sheet could slide until it reaches a cylinder depth of 10 mm [0.40 in]. If the molding requires that the sheet slide to a greater depth, the coefficient of friction can be reduced. Baked-on surface treatments of low-friction materials such as PTFE are common. These treatments produce surfaces that are essentially integral parts of the mold surface.

In certain mold designs, the sheet must not slide against the surface. Olefins tend to alternately slip and stick when vacuum formed, causing visible ridges in the part surface. Roughening the mold surface does little to prevent sliding and may aggravate the problem. Roughening may actually reduce contact area (Figure 6.5). A better alternative is to treat the

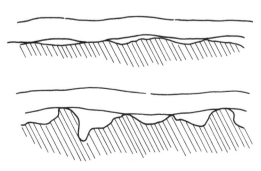

Figure 6.5 Relationship Between Sheet and Mold Surface. Top: Matte Finish. Bottom: Rough Finish.

surface with a high frictional coefficient substance such as a curable polybutadiene or silicone rubber. Also additional forming pressure can be used to minimize sliding.

Typically, plug surfaces are treated with a low frictional coefficient material. As noted in Chapters 1 and 7, the plug is used to aid in uniformly stretching the sheet. Some sheet sliding can be achieved by using PTFE although PA 66 (nylon), graphite-filled PPS and POM can be used to fabricate low frictional coefficient plug tips.

Surface Texture

The primary factor influencing replication of mold surface texture by hot plastic sheet is applied pressure. Very high surface replication is intrinsic to compression and injection molding processes where applied pressures are normally on the order of 100 MPa [14,500 psi].

In low pressure structural foam molding (13), pressures are on the order of 20 MPa [290 psi] and so finer mold surface details (μm in dimension) are not replicated. Typically, these absences are seen as loss in sharpness of detail in product code lettering and boss and rib edges. Parts are therefore designed with larger edge radii and lettering. For low pressure molding, the relationship between applied pressure and molded part surface texture is shown in Figure 6.6.

For thermoforming, the ability to replicate is further reduced by the normally lower applied pressure and the less pliable nature of the polymer. This lack of detail must be recognized during early design (Chapter 7). Further, part appearance depends primarily on the *sheet surface quality prior to contact* with the mold. A poor mold surface can detract from part surface appearance. But excessive mold surface preparation cannot differentially improve part surface appearance (14).

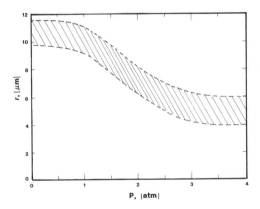

Figure 6.6 RMS Surface Roughness on Plastic Foam Injected Against Gas Back Pressure. r is Roughness in μm. P is pressure in atm. (Used by Permission of Copyright Owner (17)).

Plug Assist Design

On large, simple molds, the plugs are usually wood. They are frequently advanced manually along greased channels or handcranked along rack-and-pinion channels. On small complex or family molds where times for various stages of press action directly influence production rate, plugs must be automatically advanced and retracted. Fortunately, the typical length of plug travel is measured in cm. Thus either mechanical toggle or hydraulic/pneumatic action can be used. Air pressure actuated cylinders are relatively inexpensive and easy to maintain and so are commonly used.

Hardwood is a common plug material for prototype tools. Syntactic foam is also used for plug tips. These foams are made by incorporating sintered or foamed microspheres of fly-ash into a resin matrix which, too, might be foamed. Polyurethanes and phenolics are typical resins for the matrix. These foams are normally available as plank, slabstock or block in density ranges from $0.2 \, \text{g/cm}^3$ [12 lb/ft^3] to $0.8 \, \text{g/cm}^3$ [50 lb/ft^3]. These new materials are finding wide acceptance since they can be easily shaped with woodworking tools and provide insulative tips that do not instantaneously chill the sheet upon contact. Aluminum is a common plug material for thin-gage rollfed forming operations. These materials are easy to machine, are very tough, and are lightweight. The last factor is important since plugs are frequently suspended from actuating mechanisms, which in turn are held in presses on relatively lightweight frames. And for high speed press operation, the plugs should have as low inertial factors as possible.

Plugs can be used in pressure forming as well. The shaft holding the plug is pressure-sealed with O-rings. If the internal pressure is quite high, on the order of 10 MPa [145 psi] or so, special labyrinth seals or hard, nonextrudable O-rings are required.

Plugs are frequently heated or cooled. If the plug is to be heated, electric cartridge heaters are inserted into predrilled holes in the plug tip. The leads are passed up the shaft of the plug to the region where the plug is attached to the cylinder rod. A thermal break, such as a 25 mm [1 in] disk of high temperature plastic such as PA 66 (nylon), should be inserted between the heated plug tip and the main plug body to minimize heat loss to the machine frame and the environment.

It is more difficult to cool a plug. Large diameter water lines remove cross sectional area from the plug and could weaken it. The plug tip can be designed with circular milled grooves so that coolant can flood the back of the tip. This design is similar to that for flat injection mold cores (15). The water lines exiting the plug top must be sufficiently flexible to allow for plug travel.

The decision to heat or cool a plug must be made early in the mold design. If the plug is very cold, the sheet will surely freeze onto it. Drawing will occur between the point where the plug and the sheet separate and the sheet and the mold rim meet. No drawing will occur on the plug surface and very little after the sheet has been stripped from the plug by the stretching forces. In extreme cases, the sheet can shrink onto the plug during stretching. If the plug is very hot, the sheet can preferentially draw down and slide over the plug tip. In the extreme, the plug can simply push through the sheet. Very little drawing will then occur in the sheet area between the plug and the rim.

Figure 6.7 Plug Assist Action in Drawing Sheet. Left: Drawing at Can-Type Plug Outer Ring – Disk Does Not Draw. Center: Tapered Can-Type Plug with Smooth Surface Allows for Drawing of Disk. Right: Smooth Blunt Plug Initiates Drawing at Plug Bottom.

Plug shape can influence final part wall thickness (see Chapter 7). A flat or blunt-nose plug (Figure 6.7) allows sheet drawing in the annulus between the plug and the rim, while freezing the sheet in contact with the plug tip. A part made with this type of plug assist will preferentially have a heavy bottom and thin sidewalls. On the other hand, only a small area of sheet initially contacts a spherical nose plug. Significant sheet stretching can occur as this plug advances, even though the annular area between the rim and the plug decreases.

The can-type plug offers a third alternative. The sheet contacts and freezes against only a small annular ring of plug. Stretching is then similar to that for the blunt nose plug. But the disk in the center of the plug remains sufficiently pliable for additional stretching. Once the plug has fully advanced, the sheet is pushed away from the plug by applied pressure. The disk in the middle can therefore be stretched into the mold cavity. This design has a weakness in that the wall thickness is nonuniform in the region of the frozen ring.

These simple examples serve to illustrate the importance of adequate plug design.

Clamping Mechanism

For large, heavy-gage molding operations and for prototype forming with either single or roll fed sheets, the sheet restraint mechanism must be quite simple. A frame resembling a hinged double picture frame with opening dimensions slightly larger than mold rim clamping dimensions is used. The cold sheet is placed between frame halves and is closed and clamped together using either adjustable C-clamps or toggle clamps. The sheet is then heated and the mold is pushed into the hot restrained sheet until the sheet contacts the mold rim, forming the vacuum or pressure seal (18).

This type of clamping mechanism is not used in high-speed multicavity forming. An alternate type of clamping uses a stationary egg-crate frame above the roll fed sheet, with the molds beneath. After sheet indexing is complete, the molds advance upward, trapping the sheet against the frame. After forming, the molds retract and the sheet drops away from the frame by gravity or with an air burst assist.

On some machines, the frame moves downward to trap the sheet against the immobile mold surface. This design is used if in-mold trimming is required. Here the clamp frame also contains a steel rule die so that the frame simultaneously traps the sheet against the mold and severs it from surrounding material. Since the clamped sheet now does not have supporting material to aid it in resisting the draw-down forces, sufficient contact area between the rim and the clamp must be provided. If not, the sheet will extrude from under the clamp and loss of applied pressure will result. Parts so made usually have a large unformed lip at the rim and so a post-forming treatment is warranted. Drink cups, for example, are normally rim-rolled to add rim stiffness and so in-mold trimming is economically feasible.

Sheet Supports/Sag Bands

Some polymers are quite weak when heated to forming temperatures. Crystalline materials such as HDPE, PP, and PA (nylon) sag quite badly when heated. Certain amorphous materials such as CA and toughened FPVC can also sag when heated to the upper forming temperature. Sheet supports or sag bands are used to minimize catastrophic drooping during the final stages of heating. Sag bands are frequently extended into the molding area and beyond. Provision for them must be included in the overall mold design layout. The presence of sag band slots can seriously restrict arrangement of parts of unequal size in family mold designs. Early consideration must be given to their presence if forming of droopy materials is ever to be considered.

Difficult Molds

Often, seemingly impossible designs are achieved through thoughtful, mature mold design. Since thermoforming is classified as a process using modest applied pressure against a rubbery solid sheet rather than a sticky fluid, mold designs can become quite innovative. So long as a portion of the sheet remains rubbery, in theory it can be stretched. As a result, secondary in-mold forming steps are used, such as moving male plugs that press into a sheet already formed into a female mold. In this way, bosses and ribs can be formed of material having a thickness different than that of the main surface (19). Molds, particularly large prototype molds, can be made in sections that move in different directions. In this way, parts with severe undercuts can be fabricated.

For some severe undercuts, the trapped mold section can be built like an interlocking wooden puzzle. A key section is removed first to allow the remaining segments to unlock and fall free. These are then reassembled and the key section reinserted to lock the segments in place for the next forming operation. This is not an uncommon technique but it requires great ingenuity by the mold designer.

For some parts, the undercut is so severe that even this approach is infeasible. If alternate methods such as post-forming assembly are also infeasible, forming around a disposable mold section can be considered. A very soft grade of plaster is used. It is shaped and hardened in the traditional fashion described above and held in the mold with alignment pins. The sheet is then formed around it. The disposable section is then adequately softened with very hot water and removed in chunks. In order to minimize gas trapping and part distortion around the disposable insert, its surface is covered with a thin layer of cheesecloth, held in place with daubs of water-thinned plaster.

Inserts are usually restricted to captured stiffening agents such as rods and angles. One thermoformed industrial single-deck shipping pallet has four edges reinforced and stiffened with hollow aluminum pipes. Forming around this superstructure is surprisingly straightforward. Care must be taken in the design of this part to allow for the about ten-to-one difference in thermal expansion coefficients for plastic and metal materials. If the metal structure is too rigid, the plastic will crack upon cooling.

References

1. Anon., *Wood Handbook: Wood as an Engineering Material*, Forest Products Lab., Madison WI, USDA Agriculture Handbook 72, Aug. 1974.
2. R. M. Miller, *Figure Sculpture in Wax and Plaster*, Watson-Guptill, 1971, pg. 11.
3. C. Chaney and S. Skee, *Plaster Mold and Mold Making*, Van Nostrand Reinhold, 1974, pp. 114-120.
4. W. P. Benjamin, *Plastic Tooling*, McGraw-Hill, 1972, pg. 20.
5. Anon., "Toolrite Composite Tooling Materials System", Fiberite Corp., 501 W. Third St., Winona MN 55987, undated.
6. M. E. Thorp, "Progress Report: Sprayed Metal Faced Plastic Tooling", 35th Annual Conf., RP/C, New Orleans LA, 4 Feb 1980.
7. J. Worbye, "Steels for Molds", SPE Tech. Papers, *30*, 1984, pg. 948.
8. J. L. Throne, *Plastics Process Engineering*, Marcel Dekker, 1979, pg. 530.

9. D. A. Schrage, "Prototype Molds: Getting Out of Them What You Need", Plast. Mach. Equip., *13:* 6, 1984, pg. 35.

10. R. J. Roark and W. C. Young, *Formulas for Stress and Strain,* 5th Ed., McGraw-Hill, 1975, pg. 363.

11. A. H. Shapiro, *The Dynamics and Thermodynamics of Compressible Fluid Flow,* Vol. 1, Ronald Press, 1953, pg. 47.

12. H. Chang and R. A. Daane, "Coefficients of Friction for Solid Polymers in Various Forms", SPE Tech. Papers, *20,* 1974, pg. 335.

13. J. L. Throne, "Principles of Thermoplastic Structural Foam Molding", in N. P. Suh and N. H. Sung Eds., *Science and Technology of Polymer Processing,* MIT Press, 1979, pg. 77.

14. Anon., "Thermoforming Lustran ABS, Lustrex Polystyrene, and Cadon Engineering Thermoplastics", Monsanto Bulletin # 6547, Undated.

15. R. G. W. Pye, *Injection Mould Design,* 2nd Ed., George Godwin, 1978, pg. 174.

16. TAFA Metallisation, Inc., Dow Rd., P. O. Box 1157, Bow (Concord) NH 03301.

17. S. Semerdjiev, *Introduction to Structural Foams,* Soc. Plastics Engrs., 1982, pg. 52.

18. L. Sors, *Plastic Mould Engineering,* Pergamon, 1967, pg. 108.

19. J. L. Throne, "Thermoforming – A Look Forward", SPE Tech. Papers, *29,* 1983, pg. 464.

7 PART DESIGN

Introduction

With so many variations on the basic stretching process and so many potential materials to choose from, design of thermoformed parts must of necessity follow careful protocol. In this chapter, the elements of parts design are outlined first. For example, what constraints are placed on the part by the application? Prototyping is considered briefly. Prototyping or production processing rarely succeeds without problems. Many typical processing problems and possible courses of action are detailed. Some general do's and don'ts are also given.

There are several ways of defining draw ratio. Areal and linear draw ratios and depths of draw are defined for several simple geometries, and rim draw down is also accounted for arithmetically.

Draw ratios are gross and imperfect measures of the amount of stretching a sheet must endure in order to replicate the mold and produce a perfect part. As will be seen, material is stretched least just below the mold rim and most as it is drawn into three-dimensional corners. Material must have sufficient elongation at the drawing temperature and applied pressure or it will either fail to replicate the mold details or split. Overall draw ratios fail to accurately predict potential stretching of the sheet to ultimate elongation. Differential draw ratios yield more relevant information. Accurate prediction of local wall thicknesses yields the most useful information.

Part wall thickness is a function of the depth of draw and the geometry of the part. The arithmetic for conical and prismatic shapes is presented. Frequently the sheet is prestretched by inflation or with plug assist with obvious improvement in part wall thickness distribution. Advanced finite element methods are currently being developed for wall thickness prediction of more complex shapes. Designers will soon be using computer-assisted thermoforming programs for their toughest designs.

As with other chapters, the material in this chapter progresses from descriptive to technically advanced concepts. Regardless of the degree of technology needed to achieve adequate designs on today's parts, the designer should be comforted to know that there is technical support for the tough designs of the future.

Elements of Parts Design

Regardless of the nature and depth of prior experiences of designer, mold maker, thermoformer, or customer, no plastics fabrication should be attempted without strict, formal *written* protocol on parts design. All parties should clearly understand the project objective and ancillary part performance standards. Guidelines must be carefully written and agreed upon, *in writing*, by all principals. This should be done with all principals present, just prior to issuance of purchase orders for materials, molds and forming time. Processes, applications and materials continue to grow in sophistication. As a result, the parts designer is destined to play an increasingly important role as project coordinator. It is incumbent upon him to ensure correct protocol, particularly in this increasingly litigious era.

Plastic parts fail in use for several fundamental reasons. The most common is customer "misuse", in that the device is used under conditions beyond the designer's original intent. It is impossible to design against all levels of stupidity. However, safety factors and sources of inherent product weakness must always be considered in critical parts design. Whenever possible, parts should always be designed to fail safely when used beyond design conditions.

A proper design approach establishes a formal *design check list*. Environmental conditions (nominal and extreme), materials specifications, part mechanical behavior (and tolerance) under environmental conditions, dimensional tolerances, and others are typical items for such a check list. Table 7.1 lists some additional items that require round-table agreement on definitions. From this master list, secondary check lists can then be written (Tables 7.2 to 7.7).

Once the overall design concepts are well understood by all parties, initial parts designs, materials specifications, process elements (Chapter 1) and cycle parameters can be estimated. These should be kept quite preliminary and should focus on general fitting of proper materials and process elements to the application. The object is to make an early test of concept feasibility. At this point, no prototype has been authorized. Designers should be working from quality sketches. Not every potential application will result in a thermoformed part. The application may require materials that cannot be successfully extruded into sheet or drawn to the requisite depth. Or the forces required to stretch the material may exceed the available process conditions. The part may be too large or too small. Or the design may waste too much material. Or the web material may be unprocessable as regrind, resulting in prohibitive processing cost. The design may require structural materials or materials that are reinforced or highly filled. Or tolerances and draft angles may require exotic mold designs. Or more simply, the design may require parts with uniform wall thicknesses. Or competitive processes may be more economic.

Once it is apparent (to all!) that thermoforming offers a technically feasible, economically viable process to make a part of a material needed to meet the application constraints, the pencil process can be fine-tuned. Techniques for determining part wall thickness are described in detail below. In general, fine-tuning should focus on optimizing material distribution across the part to achieve the greatest local part strength at the lowest material usage. And every fine tuning should concentrate on minimizing scrap.

Scrap minimization begins by minimizing web area through intelligent mold design and careful sheet size selection. Proper part design can minimize unnecessary trim scrap, particularly in rim areas. Conservative parts designs usually generate less out-of-specification parts than exotic designs. Exotic, multi-step, and/or relatively new processes usually produce more scrap than simple, one-step processes such as vacuum or drape forming. Materials that are drawn close to their extensional limit will usually cause higher scrap levels. Process equipment that is not in good operating condition or that has inadequate or inferior automatic cycle control can generate off-specification parts. Workers who are not fully trained in the nuances of the requisite forming and trimming process, materials of choice and/or part design aspects produce higher-than-expected scrap percentage.

TABLE 7.1 FIRST-LEVEL DESIGN ELEMENTS FOR THERMOFORMED PARTS
(See Also Campbell (27)) (Examples in Parentheses) (More Detail Given in Noted Tables)

* Field of Application [Table 7.2]
    (Food Packaging, Materials Handling, Disposable, Permanent)

* Part Function [Table 7.3]
    (Decorative, Protective, Container (Liquid, Solid), Structural)

* Environment [Table 7.4]
    (Temperature, Nature (Corrosive, Liquid, Solid), Nature of Load (Static, Cyclical))

* Appearance [Table 7.5]
    (Surface Quality (Class A), Nonappearance, Trim Line Appearance)

* Cost [Table 7.6]
    (Balanced Against Material Requirements, Number of Parts Required)

* Competitive Processes [Table 7.6, Chapter 8]
    (Injection Molding, Blow Molding, Rotational Molding)

* Part Design Limitations [Table 7.7]
    (Strength, Load Characteristics, Potential Abuse)

* Governmental Regulations
    (Standards (FDA, FM, EPA), Biodegradability)

* Interaction with Other Elements [Table 7.3]
    (Assembly Requirements, Metal-to-Plastic Concerns)

TABLE 7.2 CHECK LIST FOR THERMOFORM PARTS DESIGN

Application

* General Field
    Packaging
    Leisure
    Transportation
    Military
    Medical

* Sub-Catagory (Such as Packaging)
    Food
        Disposable
        Storage
        Cook-in
        Barrier
    Animal Feed
    Cosmetics
    Pharmaceuticals
    Chemicals
    Electronics
    Display Items
    And So On

* Part Life
    Permanent (Such as Swimming Pool)
    Part of a Permanent Assembly (Computer Housing)
    Limited Life (Celery Boxes)
    Disposable (Blister Packs, Unit Servings)

TABLE 7.3 CHECK LIST FOR THERMOFORM PARTS DESIGN

Part Function

* Container
    Single-Use
    Continuous
    Solids
    Liquids (Corrosive Nature)
    Convenience

* Protective
    Shipping
    Food Packaging
    Blister Pack

* Decorative
    Architectural
    Interior Decoration
    Cosmetic

* Structural
    Total Load Bearing
    Temporary Support
    Compression Load Function (Foams)

* Interaction with Other Elements
    Stand-Alone
    Covering, Edge Contact/Interlocking Only
    Elements Assembled into Formed Shapes
    Formed Shape Incorporated into Others
    Plastic/Plastic Assembly
    Plastic/Nonplastic Assembly

TABLE 7.4 CHECK LIST FOR THERMOFORM PARTS DESIGN

Environmental Conditions

* Use Temperature Range
* Design Temperature Range (Maximum and Minimum)
* Extreme Temperature Range (Maximum and Minimum)
* Limitations on Part Shape Deformation (Under Expected Load, at Use Temperature)
* Extreme Chemical Environment (Under Load, at Temperature)
* UV Environment (Outdoor, Fluorescent)
* Nature of Load
    ** Static (Expected and Maximum)
    ** Vibrational or Periodic (Expected and Maximum)
* Interface with User (Casual, Continuous, Leisurely, in Crisis Situation)

TABLE 7.5 CHECK LIST FOR THERMOFORM PARTS DESIGN

Appearance

* Quality
        Class-A (Automotive)
        Plating Substrate

* Optical
        Aircraft
        Automotive/RV
        Furniture
        Cosmetics
        Blister Pack
        Food Containers

* Decorative
        Deckled
        Textured
        Painting Substrate
        Replication of Letters/Logos/Symbols

* Nonappearance

* Trim Line Appearance
        Secondary Finishing
        Buffing
        Location of Trim Line

TABLE 7.6 CHECK LIST FOR THERMOFORM PARTS DESIGN

Cost and Competitive Processes

* Target Part Cost

* Materials Cost
        Quality of Extrusion
        Level of Regrind
        Property Requirements (Price, Property, Performance)
        Quantity of Material Needed (Price Break)

* Prototype Cost
        Tooling
        Parts Fabrication
        Peformance Evaluation

* Allowable Cost of Fabrication, Tooling

* Tooling Quality
        Run Length
        Tolerance
        Cycle Times
        Maintenance

* Alternate/Competitive Process Cost
        Injection Molding
        Rotational Molding
        Stamping from Hot Sheet
        Blow Molding
        Metals/Ceramics (Nonpolymer) Processing

TABLE 7.7 CHECK LIST FOR THERMOFORM PARTS DESIGN

Part Design Limitations

* Intrinsic Material Properties
    At Nominal Use Conditions
    At Extreme Conditions

* Process/Material Interaction
    Draw Ratio
    Strength of Thinned Material
    Strain-Induced Brittleness
    Recycle Property Loss

* Allowable Corner/Lip Designs

* Allowable Part Tolerance/Dimensional Variation/Draft Angle

* Part Appearance
    Warp, Racking
    Optical Distortion
    Draw Lines/Stretch Marks
    Trim Edge Appearance
    Mold Detail Replication (Texture, Letters)

* Interaction with Nonplastics
    Nature of Interface
        Slip-Fit
        Adhesive
        Mechanical Assembly
    Strain Under Temperature Extremes
    Strain During/After Assembly

Prototyping

In the plastics industry, prototype parts are produced primarily to check part design and appearance. Frequently, thermoforming is used to produce prototype parts for other processes such as injection, rotational, and blow molding. Prototype thermoformed parts are required when materials are relatively unproven, when one aspect of the design is particularly critical or when the part is to fit with other components. Prototyping can serve as an important *early warning* to future processing problems, such as narrow processing windows, badly sagging sheet, or sheet orientation problems (Chapter 8). It can be used to identify possible post-forming problems, such as warping and distortion, trimming problems, long-term dimensional change (particularly with ABS, CPET and olefins), assembly problems and so on. Mold materials can be evaluated and trimming fixtures developed during prototyping. And of course, prototype thermoformed parts are excellent visual aids when promoting a new concept or application.

Fine-Tuning the Process

Regardless of the care taken to design out those material and process elements that interfere with production of quality parts, process problems still occur during start-up and any normal process run. McConnell (1) has identified many reoccurring problems and grouped them into 22 classes (Table 7.8). He has carefully assessed the probable cause(s) of each of these problem classes and has suggested appropriate courses of action to correct or eliminate the problem (Table 7.9). Some of these problem classes are characteristic of heavy-gage sheet and some pertain only to thin-gage sheet or blister film.

TABLE 7.8 THERMOFORMED PART PROCESS/PRODUCT PROBLEMS
(from McConnell (1)) (By Permission of Copyright Owner)

* Blisters or Bubbles
* Incomplete Forming or Poor Detail
* Sheet Scorching
* Blushing or Change in Color Intensity
* Sheet Whitening
* Webbing, Bridging, Wrinkling
* Nipples on Mold Side of Formed Part
* Excessive Sag
* Sag Variation between Sheet Blanks
* Chill Marks or "Mark-Off" Lines on Part
* Bad Surface Markings
* Shiny Streaks
* Excessive Post Shrinkage or Distortion After Part Removal from Mold
* Warpage
* Poor Wall Thickness Distribution/Excessive Local Thinning
* Nonuniform or Bulging Prestretch Bubble
* Shrink Marks on Part, Particularly in Corners (Inside Radius of Molds)
* Deep Draw Corners Too Thin
* Part Sticking to Mold
* Sheet Sticking to Plug Assist
* Part Tears During Forming
* Cracking in Corners During Use

TABLE 7.9 TROUBLE-SHOOTING GUIDE TO THERMOFORMING
(Adapted from McConnell (1)) (Used by Permission of the Copyright Owner)

Problem: BLISTERS

Probable Cause	*Suggested Course of Action*
Heating Too Rapidly	Lower Heater Temperature
	Use Slower Heating
	Increase Distance Between Heater(s) and Sheet
	Blow Air Across Sheet Surface During Heating
Excess Moisture	Predry Sheet
	Preheat Sheet
	Heat from Both Sides
	Do Not Remove Moisture Barrier Film
	Until Ready to Use
	Require Supplier to Provide Dry Sheet
Uneven Heating	Check Heater Output, Power Consumption
	Use Pattern Heating
Wrong Sheet Type or Formulation	Order Correct Formulation

Problem: INCOMPLETE FORMING, POOR DETAIL

Probable Cause	*Suggested Course of Action*
Sheet Too Cold	Heat Sheet Longer
	Raise Heater Temperatures
	Use More Heaters
	Change to More Efficient Heater Design
	If Problem is Localized, Check Heater Bank for Problems

(continued on page 182)

TABLE 7.9 TROUBLE-SHOOTING GUIDE TO THERMOFORMING (continued)

Clamp Frame Cold Prior To Sheet Insertion	Preheat Frame
Insufficient Vacuum	Check Vacuum Holes for Obstruction Increase Number of Vacuum Holes Increase Diameter of Vacuum Holes
Vacuum Not Applied Rapidly Enough	Use Vacuum Slots Rather than Holes Surge Tank/Pump Too Small Vacuum Line/Valves Too Small Too Many Bends in Vacuum Line Vacuum Leaks
Applied Pressure Too Low	Increase Air Pressure Use Plug, Silicone Slab Rubber, or Bladder as Pressure Assist

Problem: SCORCHED SHEET

Probable Cause	*Suggested Course of Action*
Sheet Surface Too Hot	Shorten Heat Cycle Use Slower, Soaking Heat Consider Convection Heating

Problem: BLUSHING OR COLOR INTENSITY CHANGE

Probable Cause	*Suggested Course of Action*
Insufficient Heating	Lengthen Heating Cycle Raise Heater Temperature Change to More Efficient Heaters
Excess Heating	Reduce Heater Temperature Shorten Heater Cycle If Localized, Check Heater Efficiencies Consider Convection Heating/Surface Cooling
Mold Too Cold	Warm Mold
Assist Too Cold	Heat Assist
Sheet is Stretched Too Far	Try Heavier Gage Sheet Try More Elastic Formulation Change Mold Design
Sheet Cools Before Fully Formed	Transfer Sheet Faster Increase Forming Rate Increase Mold, Plug Temperature
Poor Mold Design	Reduce Draw Ratio Increase Draft Angles Increase Corner Radius
Material Not Suitable	Change Sheet Formulation Change Materials
Excessive, Poor Use of Regrind	Retest Regrind for Problems Check Percentage of Regrind

(continued on page 183 to 188)

TABLE 7.9 TROUBLE-SHOOTING GUIDE TO THERMOFORMING (continued)

Problem: WHITENING

Probable Cause	Suggested Course of Action
Stretching Below Forming Temperature	Increase Sheet Temperature Increase Forming Speed
Sheet Dry-Colored	Poor Extrusion Material Unsuitable for Pigmentation Local Blemishes Removed with Hot Air Gun

Problem: WEBBING, BRIDGING, WRINKLING

Probable Cause	Suggested Course of Action
Sheet Too Hot (Drape into Forming Area)	Shorten Heating Cycle Increase Heater Distance Lower Heater Temperature Air Cool Just Before Forming
Resin Melt Strength Too Low (Sheet Sags)	Change to Lower MI Olefin Increase Orientation Use Very Low Heater Temperature
Orientation Mismatch	Increase or Decrease Orientation
Insufficient Vacuum	Check Vacuum System Add More Vacuum Holes
Preferential Bridging	Rotate Sheet 90°
Excess Draw Ratio/ Poor Mold Design/Layout	Redesign Mold Use Plug/Ring Assist Use Female Mold Rather Than Male Use Assist Blocks to Pull Out Wrinkles Increase Radii/Draft Angles For Many Parts on a Mold, Move Them Apart For Multi-Part Molds, use Part Isolators Speed up Assist and/or Mold Travel Redesign Grid/Plug/Ring Assists

Problem: NIPPLES ON FORMED PART

Probable Cause	Suggested Course of Action
Sheet Too Hot	Reduce Heating Cycle Reduce Heater Temperature
Vacuum Holes Too Large	Plug Holes/Redrill

Problem: EXCESSIVE SAG

Probable Cause	Suggested Course of Action
Sheet Too Hot	Reduce Heating Cycle Reduce Heater Temperature
Melt Index Too High	Use Lower MI Olefin Change Resins Increase Sheet Orientation
Sheet Area Excessive	Pattern Heat to Reduce Temperature of Sheet Center Add Sag Bands

TABLE 7.9 TROUBLE-SHOOTING GUIDE TO THERMOFORMING (continued)

Problem: CHILL MARKS/STRIATIONS

Probable Cause	*Suggested Course of Action*
Plug Assist Temperature Too Low	Increase Plug Temperature Use Wood/Synthetic Plug Cover Plug with Wool/Felt/Fabric
Mold Temperature Too Low	Increase Mold Temperature
Poor Mold Temperature Control	Reconfigure Cooling/Heating Channels Add More Coolant Channels Increase Coolant Flow Rate Increase Coolant Channel Diameter Inspect Flow Path for Debris, Plugging, Rust
Sheet Too Hot	Reduce Heating Cycle Cool Sheet Surface with Air Prior to Forming Change Forming Rate
Wrong Forming Technique	Change Forming Technique
Wrong Resin	Change to Higher Tensile Strength Resin, Lower MI Olefin Resin
Ghosts in Details, Rim (Rollfed)	Matched Die Mold Misaligned Mold Hesitates in Travel, Check Guides, Alignment

Problem: SURFACE BLEMISHES

Probable Cause	*Suggested Course of Action*
Indentations	Mold Surface Too Smooth, Roughen Increase Vacuum Hole Area Sheet Cast Against Smooth Roll, Air Trapping
Poor Vacuum	Increase Vacuum Hole Area If Local, Check for Plugged Vacuum Holes
Plasticizer Accumulation	Clean Mold Periodically Reduce Mold Temperature Regulate Mold Temperature Do Not Allow Mold To "See" Heaters Shorten Heating Cycle
Mold Too Hot	Reduce Mold Temperature
Mold Too Cold	Increase Mold Temperature
Improper Mold Composition	Change Mold Materials, Offgassing Blocking Try Aluminum Molds
Rough Mold Surface	Polish Mold Use Aluminum Molds
Dirt	Clean Mold, Sheet
Atmospheric Dust	Clean Thermoforming Area Enclose Former, Used Filtered Air
Contaminated Materials	Dirty Regrind is Source Check Resin, Sheet Supplier
Scratched Sheet	Inspect Handling Procedures Require Surface Paper Protection Polish Sheet

TABLE 7.9 TROUBLE-SHOOTING GUIDE TO THERMOFORMING (continued)

Drag Marks (Rollfed)	Sag Bands to Keep Sheet From Touching Mold Edge Open Mold Daylight

Problem: SHINY STREAKS

Probable Cause	*Suggested Course of Action*
Local Overheating	Check Heater Temperatures Pattern Heat Air-Cool Locally Reduce Heating Cycle Increase Heater-to-Sheet Distance

Problem: POST-FORMING SHRINKAGE/DISTORTION

Probable Cause	*Suggested Course of Action*
Time On Mold Too Short	Increase Cooling Time Decrease Coolant Temperature Use Free-Surface Cooling Change Free-Surface Cooling to Water Spray Check for Restricted Coolant Flow Use Cooling Fixtures
Mold Too Hot	Reduce Mold Temperature Increase Coolant Flow Rate

Problem: WARPED PARTS

Probable Cause	*Suggested Course of Action*
Uneven Part Cooling	Change Coolant Channel Configuration Check for Blocked Coolant Channels Direct Free-Surface Cooling to Warped Area
Poor Material Distribution in Part Wall	Use Prestretching or Plug Assist Poor Temperature Uniformity Out-of-Spec Sheet Thickness Vacuum Holes in Wrong Place
Poor Mold Design	Increase Vacuum Hole Area Redesign Rim Area to Stiffen Add Moat to Mold at Trim Line Plugged Vacuum Holes
Poor Part Design	Large Flat Areas Should Include Ribs/Corrugations Crown Large Radius Areas
Mold Temperature Too Low	Increase Mold Temperature to Just Below Material Set Temperature
Part Removed Too Early	Part Must be Below Set Temperature
Part Cold Formed	Increase Sheet Temperature Increase Hold-Down Pressure Increase Vacuum Hole Area and Rate of Forming

Problem: POOR MATERIAL ALLOCATION

Probable Cause	*Suggested Course of Action*
Improper Sheet Sag	Try Mounting Mold on Top Platen Try Vacuum Snap-Back Try Sag Bands

TABLE 7.9 TROUBLE-SHOOTING GUIDE TO THERMOFORMING (continued)

	Use Sheet With Higher Orientation
	Increase Speed of Forming
	Use Resin with Different MI
Sheet Thickness Variation	Gauge All Sheet, Contact Sheet Supplier
	Set Guidelines with Sheet Supplier
Hot/Cold Spots	Check Heater Elements
	Pattern Heating
Periodic Drafts	Enclose Forming Area
Excessive Sag	Increase Sheet Orientation
	Reduce Sheet Temperature
	Use More Elastic Resin
	Use Sag Bands
	Pattern Heating
Cold Mold	Increase Mold Temperature
	Change Coolant Channel Configuration
	Check for Plugging
Sheet Pulls From Rails	Air-Cool Rails Prior to Heater
	Move Rails in to Grasp More Sheet
	Use Drag Bands at Rail Edge
	Increase Rail Tooth Bite
Sheet Slips From Frame	Adjust Frame Alignment
	Increase Frame Clamp Pressure
	Sheet Gage Variation
	Heat Frames Prior to Inserting Sheet
	If Retainer Springs Are Used,
	Change to High Temper Springs

Problem: NONUNIFORM PRESTRETCH BUBBLE

Probable Cause	*Suggested Course of Action*
Uneven Sheet Thickness	Check with Sheet Supplier
	Tighten Quality Control
	Heat Sheet Slowly, in Hot Air
Uneven Heating	Check Heater Efficiency
	Change to More Efficient Heaters
	Improve Heater Temperature Control
	Pattern Heat
Periodic Drafts	Enclose Entire Forming Area
Non-Uniform Air Inflation	Check Air Flow
	Install Baffles if Necessary
	Preheat Air if Necessary

Problem: SHRINK MARKS

Probable Cause	*Suggested Course of Action*
Inadequate Vacuum	Vacuum Leaks
	Vacuum Surge Tank/Pump Inadequate
	Plugged Vacuum Holes
	Vacuum Hole Area Inadequate
Mold Surface Too Smooth	Roughen Mold Surface
	Change to Lower Conductivity Mold Material

TABLE 7.9 TROUBLE-SHOOTING GUIDE TO THERMOFORMING (continued)

Part Shrinking During Forming	Increase Forming Pressure
	Increase Mold Temperature
	Change to Less Elastic Material
	Reduce Free-Surface Cooling
Inadequate Air Pressure	Increase Air Flow Rate
	Increase Air Pressure
	Increase Cycle Time Under Pressure

Problem: VERY THIN CORNERS

Probable Cause	*Suggested Course of Action*
Incorrect Forming Technique	Try Plug Assist
Sheet Too Thin	Increase Sheet Thickness
Sheet Temperature Variation	Check Material Allocation
	Pattern Heating
	Increase Rate of Forming
Variation in Mold Temperature	Change Coolant Line Configuration
	Check Free-Surface Cooling
Incorrect Material	Use Stiffer Resin
	Use More Elastic Resin

Problem: PARTS STICK IN MOLD

Probable Cause	*Suggested Course of Action*
Part Temperature Too High	Increase Cooling Cycle
	Lower Mold Temperature
	Reduce Heating Cycle Time
Inadequate Draft	Rework Mold for More Draft
	Use Female Mold
	Remove Part Early, Then Fixture Until Cool
Mold Undercuts	Remove Part Early, Then Fixture Until Cool
	Consider More Sophisticated Ejection System
	Use Stripping, Breakaway Frame
Sticking in One Spot	Uneven Mold Temperature
	Uneven Sheet Temperature Prior to Forming
	Vacuum Break Inadequate
Wooden Mold	Lubricate with Dry Mold Release
Rough Mold Surface	Polish, Especially Corners
	Use Dry Mold Release
Very Smooth Surface (Olefins)	Add Anti-Block to Resin
	Roughen Mold Surface Slightly
	Inadequate Vacuum Break
	Try Female Mold, Excessive Shrinkage

Problem: SHEET STICKS TO ASSIST

Probable Cause	*Suggested Course of Action*
Assist Temperature Too High	Reduce Plug Temperature
	Use Dry Mold Release
	Use Felt/Cloth/Fabric Cover

TABLE 7.9 TROUBLE-SHOOTING GUIDE TO THERMOFORMING (continued)

Wooden Plug	Coat with Lubricant
	Use Felt/Cloth/Fabric Cover
Assist Speed Too High	Reduce Plug Penetration Rate
	Increase Air Pressure Behind Plug
	Decrease Air Pressure Ahead of Plug

Problem: SHEET TEARS WHILE FORMING

Probable Cause	*Suggested Course of Action*
Mold Design	Increase Corner Radius
Sheet is Too Hot	Decrease Sheet Temperature
	Preheat Sheet, Then Bring to Forming Temperature Slowly
	Sheet Thickness May Not be Uniform
Sheet Too Cold	Increase Heating Time
	Preheat Sheet
Improper Material	Depth of Draw Excessive for Material, See Resin Supplier
	Change Forming Technique
Forming Conditions Improper	Decrease Assist Penetration Rate
	Increase Inflation Rate
	Increase Draw-Down Rate

Problem: CORNER CRACKING IN SERVICE

Probable Cause	*Suggested Course of Action*
Stress Concentration	Increase Radii
	Corner Too Cold During Forming
	Increase Mold Temperature
	Increase Sheet Temperature
	Increase Forming Rate
	Prestretch Sheet
	Decrease Free-Surface Cooling
	Decrease Assist Rate of Penetration
	Change to ESCR Resin
Under-Designed	Re-evaluate Design

Most major problems identified in Tables 7.8 and 7.9 are the direct result of inadequate process control. Improper sheet temperature at the time of forming is a primary source of problems. Poor draw-down control, inadequate monitoring of inflated bubble elevation, and inadequate cooling are also typical causes. Part appearance problems are usually the result of inadequate moisture control, improper temperature conditioning, out-of-specification sheet or improper handling of the hot sheet in the forming step.

If the part design has been thoroughly reviewed by all principals, improper mold design or unsuitable material choice should not be the causes of unacceptable parts. Unfortunately, in real life, improper mold design and poor choice of materials still remain the major causes of product failure in the marketplace. For novel designs or experimental processes, extensive development and prototyping should be done in advance of production manufacturing. Again, if everyone has reviewed all details, very few processing problems should be attributed to improper mold design or choice of materials. Reality indicates that most product problems are related to these two areas, however.

In addition to guidelines and steps to correct processing problems, certain do's and don'ts are sufficiently general to be considered as guidelines to thermoforming. In many cases, the items in the list that follows are helpful to the designer. But designs that violate some of these items can also be successful.

Most common plastics are formed in a temperature range of 100 C to 175 C [210 F to 350 F].

Sheet thicker than about 1 cm [0.400 in] is best heated in forced convection air ovens.

The distance between heater elements should be less than the distance between the element plane and the sheet.

The extent of sheet sag during heating is a useful (and sometimes the only) way of determining material formability.

In vacuum forming, the surge tank volume should be 6 to 20 times the free cavity volume.

In vacuum forming, vacuum should never drop below 500 mm Hg [20 in Hg] and 710 to 725 mm Hg [28 to 28.5 in Hg] is standard.

The faster the vacuum is applied, the better the draw-down becomes (to a point). Excessive draw-down rate can lead to excessive webbing.

Slow vacuum draw-down requires hot molds for mold replication.

The hotter the mold, the greater the final shape shrinkage.

If an excess of blowing air is used, it should be preheated to within 5 to 10 C [10 to 20 F] of the sheet temperature to minimize premature chilling of the sheet. If small amounts of air are used for prestretching, the air does not need to be heated.

Metal plug temperatures should be within 10 to 20 C [15 to 30 F] of the sheet temperature to minimize chill marks on the sheet. Syntactic foam and plastic-surfaced plugs do not necessarily need to be heated.

Plugs with good surface slip reduce the need for close temperature control.

Aluminum window screen is an effective screen for pattern heating.

If the formed shape is for an optical application, the hot sheet should not touch a cold surface during forming.

In pressure forming, the mold and the pressure box should be mechanically or hydraulically locked together during forming.

Bayonet locking, V-groove locking, and overlap joints are typical ways of positively positioning pressure box and mold during pressure forming. A flexible gasket is usually required for adequate seal.

Pressure forming is most economical for 5,000 to 20,000 parts.

Pressure forming competes with injection molding at 10 to 20% mold cost and ¼ to ½ the lead time.

Although air pressures to 3.4 MPa [500 psi] have been used in pressure forming, current practice uses 0.34 to 0.68 MPa [50 to 100 psi] air pressure.

A typical prestretch depth equals half the narrowest unformed sheet dimension. Thus for a 100 mm × 500 mm rectangle, 50 mm is a good prestretch depth.

In snap-back forming, an optimum bubble height is ⅔ the draw ratio (or H:d = 2:3).

Snap-back forming should actuate when the bubble top intersects a photocell beam.

Matched die molding is needed when the sheet is normally too stiff at forming temperature to be easily vacuum drawn. Typical materials are PS foam, CPET, HDPE, PP, and short-fiber or mineral filled materials.

Typical matched die mold clamping pressures are 0.34 to 0.68 MPa [50 to 100 psi].

Matched die molding is used if details are needed on both sides of the part or if abrupt changes in wall thickness or direction are required.

Female molds produce parts with thick rims and thin bottoms.

Male molds are cheaper to make but require greater draft angles than female molds.

Typical female mold draft angles are ½ deg to 5 deg, with the average of about 1 to 2 deg.

Typical male mold draft angles are 2 deg to 8 deg, with the average of about 4 to 6 deg.

50% to 75% of part shrinkage occurs before the part temperature has fallen to its heat-distortion value.

Typical part shrinkage is on the order of 0.5% on male molds and 1.0% on female molds.

For textured details to be sharp, their depth should be greater than the local sheet thickness.

As with injection molding, draft angles must be increased to compensate for texturing on perpendicular surfaces. Typically, 1 deg of draft angle is allowed for each 0.005 mm [0.0002 in] depth of texture.

Vacuum hole diameter should be less than the local sheet thickness to prevent nipples.

Chill marks are usually an indication of rapid local thickness change. However they can also be caused by slow vacuum or a cold mold.

The extent to which a plastic sheet can be stretched is a strong function of its hot strength. Typically, however, areal draw ratios are usually less than 5, linear draw ratios less than 3 and H:d draw ratios less than about 1.

When notch-sensitive plastics such as PA (nylon), PC, and PS are drawn into sharp corners, parts may fail because of the inherent brittleness of the material.

Parts with angles less than 90 deg can be notch-sensitive regardless of the material.

Polarized filters aid in detecting highly stressed regions in transparent PS, PC, PMMA parts.

Stiffening ribs, corrugations, flutes, and multiple cones are typical ways of stiffening thermoformed parts.

Dimensional tolerances are rarely specified on free or non-tool surfaces.

Typical dimensional tolerances are 1% (such as $\pm$ 0.020 in on a 2 in dimension) on small parts, 0.2% (such as $\pm$ 0.050 in on a 25 in dimension) on large parts. Material thickness tolerance is about 5% on medium and heavy gage sheet. This tolerance must be doubled and added to dimensional tolerance for inside dimensions on parts formed in female molds.

In the sections that follow, emphasis is on fundamental design tools. Full understanding of these tools is not always required to design thermoformed parts. However, these tools will be used to meet increasingly stringent design standards. Beall notes that overall final piece part inaccuracies today are caused by tooling-associated inaccuracies, "sheet-to-sheet and run-to-run variations, female versus male tooling, piece part geometry, specifics of the vendors' manufacturing processes, operator skill and training, tooling maintenance procedures, etc."(2). He further recommends that the customer should carefully select "a vendor with proven capabilities to meet the designer's tolerance requirements." The tools discribed below will enable all parties to better minimize final part inaccuracies.

Draw Ratios

Regardless of the stretching process used to produce the formed shape, a sheet of plastic initially of thickness t_0 and surface area A_0 is stretched to provide a part having a surface area A (A > A_0) and an *average* thickness t_a (t_a < t_0). As noted in Chapter 4, the plastic volume V is essentially constant. Thus:

$$V = t_0\,A_0 = \int t\ dA = t_a A$$

The simplest measure of stretch is the *areal draw ratio*, Ra = A/A_0. Ra is also the thickness ratio based on the average part thickness, Ra = t_0/t_a. The areal draw ratio is considered to be a measure of the biaxial orientation of the sheet. It is an *artificial concept*, since it depends upon an average sheet thickness (3). Most thermoforming processes do not yield parts having uniform wall thicknesses.

The areal draw ratio of a parallel-sided female part (Figure 7.1) is:

$$Ra = \frac{A_{sidewall} + A_{bottom}}{A_0} = \frac{\pi ds + \pi d^2/4}{\pi d^2/4} = (4s/d) + 1$$

s is the part height and d is its diameter. A *reduced areal draw ratio*, Ra* = Ra $-$ 1, is also used (3). The areal draw ratio is sometimes called the stretch ratio (4), stretching ratio (17), stretch factor (5), or areal elongation (6). Areal draw ratios for other simple geometries are given in Table 7.10.

Areal draw ratios for complex shapes can be easily obtained. Consider a female straight-walled cylinder of diameter d and height s, with a *solid* center rod of diameter d/2 and height s/2 in its center (Figure 7.2). The overall areal draw ratio is:

$$Ra = (6s/d) + 1$$

If the solid rod is replaced with a straight-walled *hollow* cylinder of the same dimensions but zero wall thickness (Figure 7.3), the overall areal draw ratio is:

$$Ra = (8s/d) + 1$$

TABLE 7.10 AREAL DRAW RATIOS FOR REGULAR SHAPES

Shape	Figure	Area	Areal Draw Ratio, Ra
Hemisphere		$2\pi R$	2
Right Cylinder		$\pi R^2 + 2\pi Rh$	$1 + 2\,(h/R)$
Right Cone		$\pi R (R^2 + h^2)^{\frac{1}{2}}$	$[1 + (h/R)^2]^{\frac{1}{2}}$
Truncated Cone		$\pi R^{*2} + \pi (R + R^*) \times$ $[(R - R^*)^2 + h^2]^{\frac{1}{2}}$	$(R^*/R)^2 + (1 + R^*/R) \times$ $[(1 - R^*/R)^2 + (h/R)^2]^{\frac{1}{2}}$
Square (side a)		$5a$	5
Right Rectangle $(a \times b \times h)$		$2ah + 2bh + 2ab$	$2(1 + h/b + h/a)$
Wedge $(a \times b \times h)$		$ah + 2b(h^2 + (a/2)^2)^{\frac{1}{2}}$	$(h/b) + [1 + (2h/a)^2]^{\frac{1}{2}}$
Pyramid $(a \times b \times h)$		$(ab/e)[1 + (2h/b)^2]^{\frac{1}{2}} +$ $(ab/2)[1 + (2h/a)^2]^{\frac{1}{2}}$	$(\tfrac{1}{2})[1 + (2h/b)^2]^{\frac{1}{2}} +$ $(\tfrac{1}{2})[1 + (2h/a)^2]^{\frac{1}{2}}$
Frustrum of Pyramid $(a \times b \times h$ and $a^* \times b^*)$		$a^*b^* + (a - a^*) \times$ $[(b/2 - b^*/2)^2$ $+ h^2]^{\frac{1}{2}} + (b - b^*) \times$ $[(a/2 - a^*/2)^2 + h^2]^{\frac{1}{2}}$	$(a^*b^*/ab) + (\tfrac{1}{2})(1 - a^*/a) \times$ $(1 - b^*/b) \times$ $(\{1 + [2h/(1 - b^*/b)]^2\}^{\frac{1}{2}}$ $+ 1 + \{[2h/(1 - a^*/a)]^2\}^{\frac{1}{2}})$

If the inner surface of the inner cylinder is drawn *only* from the disk of material formerly on the top of the cylinder, the areal draw ratio for this (only) is:

$$Ra' = (4s/d) + 1$$

Note that this material has already been drawn. If the material touching the rim has been drawn into a hemisphere of area, $A = \pi d^2/2$, it has seen a draw ratio of:

$$Ra'' = (\pi d^2/2)/(\pi d^2/4) = 2$$

The total average areal draw ratio of the material inside the inner cylinder is thus:

$$Ra = Ra''\, Ra' = 2[(4s/d) + 1]$$

For the case where $s = d$ (a very deep draw), the overall areal draw ratio is $Ra = 9$ but that inside the inner cylinder is $Ra = 10$.

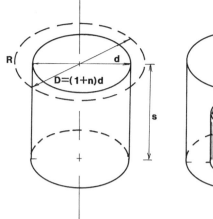

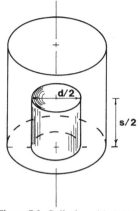

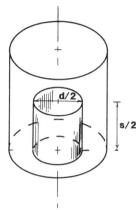

Figure 7.1 Dimensions for Straight-Walled Right Cylinder. R = Rim Material. d = Diameter. s = Depth or Distance Down Wall. D = Diameter of Rim.

Figure 7.2 Cylinder with Solid Inner Cylinder. d/2 = Its Diameter. s/2 = Its Height.

Figure 7.3 Cylinder with Hollow Inner Cylinder.

The average areal draw ratio value is insensitive to local drawing. The average areal draw ratio of a rounded bottom cylinder with a corner radius, $r' = d/8$ (Figure 7.4), is:

$$Ra_1 = (4s/d) + [(\tfrac{3}{4})^2 + (\pi/4) - (\tfrac{1}{2})] = (4s/d) + 0.848$$

For a square-bottom cylinder ($r' = 0$), it is:

$$Ra = (4s/d) + 1$$

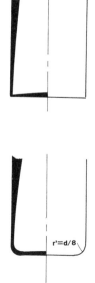

Figure 7.4 Draw-Down into Square-Bottom Cylinder (Top) and Radius-Bottom ($r' = d/8$) Cylinder (Bottom).

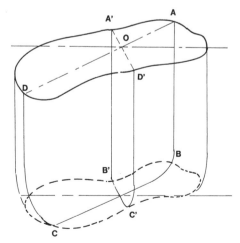

Figure 7.5 Linear Draw-Down - Irregular Shape. RL(1) = ABCD/AOD. RL(2) = A'B'C'D'/A'OD'.

For $s = d$, Ra_1 is 97% of Ra. Yet, for the square-bottom cylinder, the last material to be drawn into the sharp corner must be infinitely elongated. This is more apparent when a linear draw ratio is used.

The *linear draw ratio*, RL, is the ratio of the length of a line projected onto a part surface, to its length on the unformed flat sheet (Figure 7.5). RL reflects uniaxial stress-strain behavior of a material. The linear draw ratio for a parallel-sided cylinder is:

$$RL = (2s + d)/d = (2s/d) + 1$$

RL is also called the depth of draw ratio (2). A *reduced linear draw ratio* is written as $RL^* = RL - 1$. Except in simple geometric cases, there is no relationship between the areal and linear draw ratios. As with Ra, RL is an artificial concept, since the local draw-down can differ substantially from the average.

For complex shapes, RL is difficult to define unambiguously. Consider a five-sided box, $a \times b \times c$ in dimension. Three values for RL can be obtained:

$$RL(a\ side) = (2c/b) + 1$$

$$RL(b\ side) = (2c/a) + 1$$

$$RL(diagonal) = 2c/(a^2 + b^2)^{1/2} + 1$$

Traditionally, the largest value of RL is used.

Consider the concentric cylinder part (Figure 7.2), with a solid inner cylinder core:

$$RL = (3s/d) + 1$$

With a hollow inner cylinder (Figure 7.3), the *average* value is:

$$RL = (4s/d) + 1$$

The linear draw ratio of the material *outside* the inner cylinder is:

$$RL = (6s/d) + 1$$

while that *inside* is:

$$RL' = (2s/d) + 1$$

Prior to being drawn inside, however, the material that makes up the inner cylinder has been linearly elongated an amount:

$$RL'' = \pi/2$$

so that the actual linear draw ratio for the inside material is:

$$RL = (\pi/2)(2s/d + 1)$$

For a $s = d$ cylinder, the average, outside and inside linear draw ratios are 5, 7, and $3\pi/2 = 4.7$, respectively.

Another form of linear draw ratio is the ratio of depth of draw to mold opening at the rim, H:d (7) or H:D. Except for simple shapes, it too is difficult to define unambiguously. For a simple parallel-side cylindrical part:

$$RL = 2(H:d) + 1$$

$$H:d = RL*/2$$

For unformed sheet, H:d, RL* and Ra are zero.

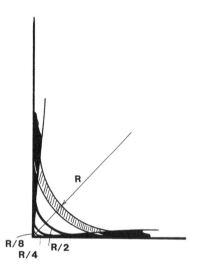

Figure 7.6 Progressive Draw-Down into Two-Dimensional Corner.

As noted, average draw ratios are artificial and insensitive to localized drawing. Consider progressive draw-down of a sheet into a two-dimensional corner (Figure 7.6). The initial sheet length is $\pi R/2$. At $r = nR$, the sheet length is $\pi r/2 + 2(R - r)$. The linear draw ratio is:

$$RL = 4(1 - n)/\pi + n$$

When $n = 1$, $RL = 1$. When $n = 0$, $RL = 4/\pi = 1.27$. This is the *average linear draw ratio into a two-dimensional right angle corner*.

Consider progressive drawing steps, as follows. Let $r = R/2$. Now $RL_1 = (4/\pi + 1)/2 = 1.14$. When the sheet is drawn from $r = R/2$ to $R/4$, only the sheet *not in contact* with the surface is drawn. Thus $RL_2 = (4/\pi + 1)/2$. But in going from $r = R$ to $r = R/2$, this sheet has already been drawn an amount $RL_1 = (4/\pi + 1)/2$. Thus the free sheet is drawn:

$$RL_2 = (4/\pi + 1)^2/2^2 = 1.292 \qquad (R/4 < r < R/2)$$

If the free portion is again drawn, from $r = R/4$ to $R/8$, its draw ratio is:

$$RL_3 = (4/\pi + 1)^3/2^3 = 1.47 \qquad (R/8 < r < R/4)$$

It is apparent that for the mth step, the free portion of sheet is drawn:

$$RL_m = (4/\pi + 1)^m/2^m = (1.14)^m \qquad (R/2^m < r < R/2^{m-1})$$

In the limit as r→0, RL_m→∞. Thus the last infinitesmal amount of sheet is drawn an infinite amount. The average draw ratio remains at RL=1.27, however.

Rim and Lip Material

It has been observed (8, 9) that the volume of material in formed parts is greater than that in the material free of the mold surface prior to forming. The amount varies from 15% to 35% or so. This additional material is drawn from the lip or rim region into the mold cavity during draw-down (Figure 7.7). To account for the excess material, Gheen (5) recommends that the calculated areal draw ratio values be increased by a factor of 50% of the sheet surface area between the lip and the clamping ring.

Consider forming a parallel-sided cylinder of depth s and diameter d, clamped at diameter $D=(1+n)d$, as shown in Figure 7.7. The areal draw ratio with *no* rim material included is:

$$Ra=(4s/d)+1$$

If *all* the rim material is included in the draw ratio:

$$Ra=\frac{A_{sidewall}+A_{bottom}+A_{rim}}{A_0+A_{rim}} = \frac{4s}{d(1+n)^2} +1$$

And if only *a fraction*, g, of rim material is included:

$$Ra=(4s/d)[(1-g)+g(1+n)^2]+1$$

The term in brackets represents a rim factor. Consider the case where $D=1.2d$, $n=0.2$ and $s=d$. For $g=0$, $Ra=5$. For $g=0.5$ (Gheen's suggestion), $Ra=4.28$, and for $g=1$, $Ra=3.78$. The effect of rim material inclusion on reduced areal draw ratio is shown in Figure 7.8. For the experimental observations of 15 to 35% greater volume, $n=0.07$ to 0.16 for this simple case.

A more formal analysis examines the relationship between the forces required to stretch the sheet and those needed to slide it along the mold surface. A simple force balance illustrates this. The stretching force can be written as:

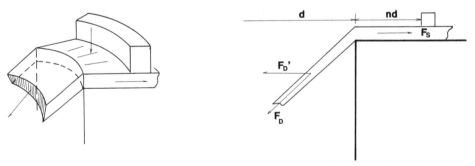

Figure 7.7 Schematic of Rim Area Coordinates. d=Diameter. nd=Rim Width. Fs=Sliding Force. Fd=Stretching Force. Fd'=Component of Stretching Force Perpendicular to Cylinder Axis.

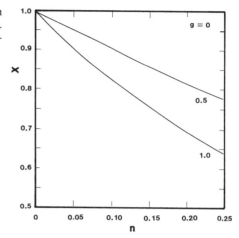

Figure 7.8 Effect of Rim Material Contribution on Areal Draw Ratio. n = Rim Fraction of Diameter. d = diameter. s = depth. g = Fraction of Rim Material Included in Draw-Down. X = (Ra − 1)/(4s/d).

$$F_d = TA'$$

T is the strength of the sheet at forming temperature and A' is its cross-sectional area, at the edge of the cavity (Figure 7.7). The sliding force, F_s, is written as:

$$F_s = CN^\alpha = C\ (PA)^\alpha$$

N is the normal force, P is the pressure applied to the free-to-deform rim material and A is the contact area between the clamp and the rim. C is the kinetic coefficient of friction between the polymer and the mold surface (10, 11). The experimental value of α is 0.67 to 1 (12).

The force required to slide the sheet along the rim is vectored *perpendicular* to the draw axis. The deformation force, F_d, may be vectored in the sliding force direction initially, but as the sheet draws, F_d^*, the component of F_d in the F_s direction, diminishes rapidly. $F_d^* = 0$ when the material touches the wall of a parallel-sided female cylinder mold, for example. F_d^* is given as:

$$F_d^* = F_d \cos \beta = T\ t_0\ \pi d \cos \beta$$

β is the sheet angle to the horizontal. If the rim is clamped at $D = (1 + n)d$, the force needed to slide this area of the sheet, F_s, is:

$$F_s = C\ P^\alpha \{d^2 \pi[(1 + n)^2 - 1]/4\}^\alpha$$

The sheet stops sliding when $F_d^* < F_s$. For $\alpha = 1$:

$$P \rightarrow 4T\ t_0 \cos \beta / Cd[(1 + n)^2 - 1]$$

This assumes that the material on the rim is sliding, not stretching. P then is the amount of pressure that must be applied to force the free material against the rim to prevent it from sliding. It is proportional to the tensile strength of the hot sheet and to the initial sheet thickness. It is inversely proportional to the coefficient of friction (as expected) and to the amount of material on the rim (n). If T = 0.7 MPa [100 psi], t_0 = 0.25 mm [0.010 in], $\beta = 0°$,

C = 0.25, d = 2.5 cm [1 in], and n = 0.1, P > 0.52 MPa [76 psi]. In vacuum forming, P < 0.1 MPa [14 psi]. so the sheet could preferentially begin to slide. In this example, it would continue until $\beta > 78°$ or so. If the mold is a parallel-sided cylinder, the sheet stops sliding and begins stretching before contact is made. For a 60° cone, contact occurs first.

In processes that blow a bubble prior to forming, the dimensions of the expanding sheet differ from the mold dimensions. An appropriate factor must be included in the rim-included draw ratio definitions to account for this form of prestretching.

Average draw ratios are used primarily to screen candidate materials. For example, CAB, PS, PETG and HIPS can be bubble-blown into greater than hemispherical bubbles (13), whereas PVC/PMMA, PVC, PMMA, and PC cannot. Low-density PS foam cannot be drawn greater than about H:d = 1:1 (14) unless coated with an unfoamed capsheet. Cross-linked polyethylene foam cannot be drawn greater than about H:d = 0.6:1 to 0.8:1 (15). Practical temperature-dependent H:d draw ratios for several materials and several initial sheet thicknesses for simple vacuum forming into a parallel-sided female mold are seen in Figure 7.9. Plug assist can be used to prestretch sheet in applications where a material would otherwise be only marginally acceptable. But plug-assist forming is primarily used to redistribute material along the part wall. Wall thickness distribution via simple vacuum forming into a near-parallel-sided cylindrical mold with H:d = 1:3 (RL = 1.667, Ra = 2.33) is given in Figure 7.10 for several polymers (16). The plug assist (Figure 7.11) for 0.040 cm [0.016 in] MIPS at H:d = 1:3 and H:d = 1:1 (RL = 3, Ra = 5) acts to distribute material from the side and bottom of the part to the corner.

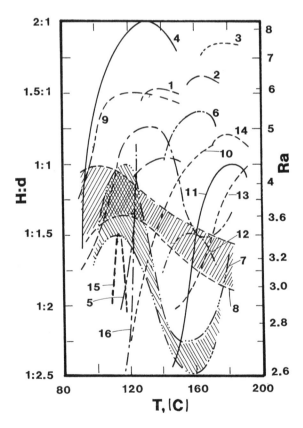

Figure 7.9 H:d Draw Down Ratios for Several Materials. Sheet Thickness = 0.5 mm [0.020 in] Unless Otherwise Noted. ((16); Figure 60). Curve 1: LDPE (0.4 mm). 2: HDPE. 3: PP (0.4). 4: HIPS (0.3). 5: OPS (0.25). 6: ABS. 7: RPVC (0.3). 8: FPVC (0.3). 9: PVC Copolym. 10: CA (0.3). 11: PC (0.2). 12: PMMA (3 mm). 13: CAB. 14: CAP. 15: Hostalit Z. 16: PS Foam. T = Average Sheet Temperature. Ra = Areal Draw Ratio for Tapered Cylindrical Female Mold. Figure used by permission from Carl Hanser Verlag.

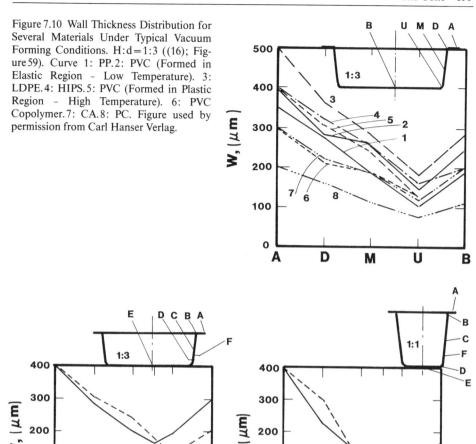

Figure 7.10 Wall Thickness Distribution for Several Materials Under Typical Vacuum Forming Conditions. H:d=1:3 ((16); Figure 59). Curve 1: PP. 2: PVC (Formed in Elastic Region - Low Temperature). 3: LDPE. 4: HIPS. 5: PVC (Formed in Plastic Region - High Temperature). 6: PVC Copolymer. 7: CA. 8: PC. Figure used by permission from Carl Hanser Verlag.

Figure 7.11 Effect of Plug Assist on Wall Distribution for 0.4 mm [0.016 in] MIPS for H:d=1:3 and H:d=1:1 Draw Ratios. (7). Solid Line: Vacuum With Plug Assist. Broken Line: Vacuum Only. W = Thickness (mm). Figure Used by kind permission of Paul Kiefel GmbH.

The Cone

The relationship between draw ratios and local sheet thickness in a formed part is best illustrated by forming sheet into a conical female mold (Figure 7.12). At time θ, the sheet of initial thickness to has been drawn into the mold of angle β to a depth h_1. The sheet is in contact with the mold surface for a diagonal distance (or slant height) s. That portion of the sheet not in contact with the mold forms a spherical cap of radius R. The thickness, t, of material in the cap is uniform. The cap area is:

$$A_c = 2 \pi R^2 (1 - \cos \beta)$$

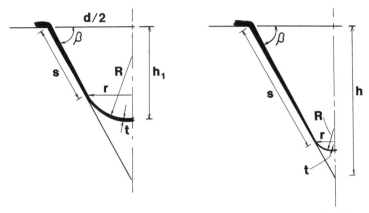

Figure 7.12 Geometry and Coordinates for Progressive Draw-Down into Female Cone.

At time $\theta + d\theta$, a differential amount of material from the rim of the cap has been deposited on the cone surface. The cap material has been differentially stretched so that it is differentially thinner. A material balance (17) gives:

$$(At)_{(\theta)} = (At)_{(\theta + d\theta)} + (A_{cone}\, t)$$

$$2\, \pi R^2 (1 - \cos \beta)\, t = 2\, \pi\, (R + dR)^2 (1 - \cos \beta)(t + dt) + (2\, \pi rt)\sin \beta\; ds$$

R is written in terms of h, s and β as:

$$R = (h - s \sin \beta)/\sin \beta \tan \beta$$

and $dR = -ds/\tan \beta$. The differential material balance is then written:

$$dt/t = (2 - \tan \beta \sin \beta/(1 - \cos \beta))(\sin \beta/(h - s \sin B))\, ds$$

This is integrated as:

$$t/t^* = (1 - s \sin \beta/h)^{(\sec \beta - 1)}$$

$t = t^*$ when $s = 0$. Note that the sheet initially does not touch the cone side as it sags into the cavity. It touches when $A_0 t_0 = A_{cap} t^*$ $(s = 0)$. Since $R = d/2 \sin \beta$:

$$t^* = (t_0/2)(1 + \cos \beta)$$

The sheet thickness ratio is given in terms of initial sheet thickness as:

$$t/t_0 = [(1 + \cos \beta)/2]\,(1 - (2s/d) \cos \beta)^{(\sec \beta - 1)}$$

$h = (d/2) \tan \beta$ and $\sec \beta = 1/\cos \beta$. For $\beta = 60°$, $(t/t_0) = (\tfrac{3}{4})(1 - s/d)$. Thickness decreases linearly with distance down the cone side. When $s = d$ (at the cone tip for $\beta = 60°$), $t/t_0 = 0$.

The surface area for material being drawn into the cone at any time is the sum of the area of material in the cone frustrum and that in the cap. The areal draw ratio is given in Appendix 7.I. For $\beta = 60°$, the ratio is:

$$Ra = (2s/d) + (\tfrac{4}{3})(1 - s/d)^2$$

TABLE 7.11 SHEET WALL THICKNESS FOR VACUUM DRAW-DOWN INTO 121 C [250 F] 60° CONE MATERIAL IS ANNEALED PAI (POLYAMIDE-IMIDE) (Theory Assumes 0% Rim Material in Draw) (t/t_{Theo} Given in Brackets Below Actual Value)

Item No.	Sheet Temp (C)	Sheet Thickness (mm) at Slant Height (mm)						End Cap*
		12.7	25.4	38.1	50.8	63.5	76.2	
Initial Sheet Thickness (0.635 mm) [0.025 in]:								
Theo.	–	0.406	0.335	0.267	0.196	0.127	0.056	0
32.1	371	0.58 [1.44]	0.46 [1.36]	0.36+ [1.33]	–	–	–	0.28 (0.200) [1.39]
32.2	343	0.53 [1.31]	0.43 [1.29]	0.25 [0.95]	0.15+ [0.78]	0.15 [1.20]	–	0.15 (0.127) [1.20]
32.3	366	0.48 [1.19]	0.41 [1.21]	0.28 [1.05]	0.18 [0.91]	0.13+ [1.00]	–	0.10 (0.094) [1.08]
32.4	332	0.48 [1.19]	0.36 [1.06]	0.28 [1.05]	0.18+ [0.91]	0.13 [1.00]	–	0.13 (0.127) [1.00]
32.5	373	0.48 [1.19]	0.36 [1.06]	0.33+ [1.24]	–	–	–	0.30 (0.200) [1.52]
Initial Sheet Thickness (0.356 mm) [0.014 in]:								
Theo.	–	0.229	0.188	0.150	0.109	0.071	0.030	
32.6	373	0.25 [1.11]	0.15 [0.81]	0.10+ [0.68]	0.10 [0.93]	–	–	0.10 (0.112) [0.91]

* The End Cap value in parens is calculated assuming that the material thickness is uniform and 75% of the thickness of the part where it no longer contacts the funnel wall.
+ The point where the material releases from the cone wall.

For full draw down into the cone tip, $s = (d/2) \cos \beta$. For $\beta = 60°$, $s = d$ and $Ra = 2$.

The linear draw ratio is also given in Appendix 7.I. For the $\beta = 60°$ cone:

$$RL = (2s/d) + (\pi/3\sqrt{3})(1 - s/d)$$

For full draw down, $s = d$ and $RL = 2$. Note the expected relationship between reduced thickness and areal draw ratio when $s = 0$ at the point where the sheet just touches the cone surface. $Ra = \frac{4}{3}$ and $t/t_0 = \frac{3}{4} = 1/Ra$. Once the plastic sheet touches the mold surface, there is no further relationship between local sheet thickness and any form of draw ratio.

The thickness equation for a cone has been experimentally verified for low-temperature amorphous sheet (8, 17). As seen in Table 7.11, thickness values for high-temperature amorphous PAI (polyamide-imide) polymer, vacuum drawn into a heated 60° cone, are essentially linear with depth of draw. However the experimental values are on the average 35% greater in value than predicted. This indicates that rim material is being drawn into the cavity.

The above derivation of local wall thickness ratio depends only on the part geometry. No material properties are required. Therefore initial sheet thickness and material temperature should affect only depth of draw and not material distribution in the part. This is seen in Table 7.11 for PAI and reported for PVB (17).

To sum, average draw ratios cannot characterize local part wall thickness. For the simple 60° cone, the last amount of sheet drawn into the cone tip is infinitely extended. Yet the linear and areal draw ratios each have a maximum value of 2.

Thickness Equations for Other Shapes

Geometers have recently cataloged wall thickness equations for several other simple female mold shapes. These include truncated cones (17, 18), long triangular concave and prismatic shapes (8) and trapezoidal (trapezical) molds (18). These designs are shown in Figure 7.13. The thickness equations given in Table 7.12 are quite complicated and are best solved numerically.

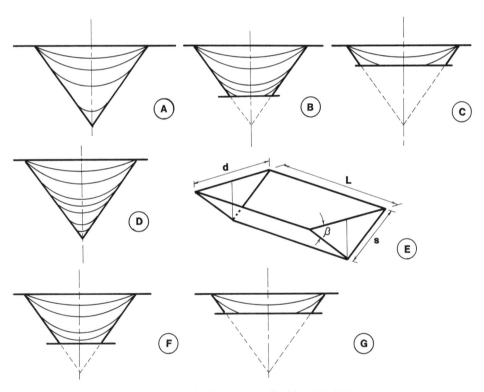

Figure 7.13 Geometry and Coordinates for Shapes Described in Table 7.12.

Truncated designs are segmented into shallow and deep parts. If the freely expanding sheet touches the mold bottom before it touches the mold sides, the part is shallow (Figure 7.13 C). If it touches the sides first, it is deep (Figure 7.13 B). For a truncated cone to be deep:

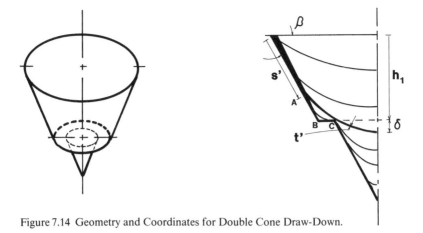

Figure 7.14 Geometry and Coordinates for Double Cone Draw-Down.

$$h > (d/2)(1 - \cos \beta)/\sin \beta$$

For $\beta = 60°$, $h > (d/2)\sqrt{3} = 0.289$ d. For a parallel-side can, $\beta = 90°$ and $h > d/2$.

With care, combinations of these equations can be used to get approximate part wall thicknesses in more complex parts. Consider two concentric truncated cones (Figure 7.14). The thickness, t', of the cap sheet at the point where it just touches the rim of the second cone, is obtained from Table 7.12:

$$t'/t_0 = (1 + \cos \beta)/2 \, (1 - s' \sin \beta/h)^{(\sec \beta - 1)}$$

$$s' = h'(1 + \cos \beta)/\sin \beta - d/2$$

$h' = h_1 + \delta$, the depth of the sheet below the rim of the second cone. The part wall thickness distribution for the second cone can be obtained from Table 7.12 for a truncated cone, with t' substituted for t_0. The thickness of the material drawn into the corner of the first cone (Figure 7.14, A-B-C) is approximated from the truncated cone equations of Table 7.12.

Truncated cone equations are quite difficult to solve without a computer. Approximate wall thickness equations have been proposed that are much easier to manipulate (17). For deep truncated cones, the cap sheet thickness at the point where it just touches the bottom is given by:

$$t/t_0 = \sin^2 \beta/2 \, (1 - \cos \beta)$$

For shallow truncated cones:

$$t/t_0 = d^2/(d^2 + h^2)$$

In general, $t/t_0 = G$, where G is a geometric factor. Experimentally, the sheet thickness, t_c, in a corner of a drawn part of PVB, PVC, and PS is a simple function of the amount of stretching (Figure 7.15 (17)):

$$t_c/t_0 = 1/Ra^2$$

TABLE 7.12 THICKNESS EQUATIONS-CONICAL

Geometry	Configuration	Figure No.	Step I	
			Criterion	Thickness Equation
Cone	Full	7.13A	Bubble Touches Side	$\dfrac{t}{t_0} = \dfrac{(1+\cos\beta)}{2}$
	Deep Truncated $h > \dfrac{d}{2}\dfrac{\cos\beta}{(1+\cos\beta)}$	7.13B	Bubble Touches Side First	$\dfrac{t}{t_0} = \dfrac{(1+\cos\beta)}{2}$
	Shallow Truncated $h > \dfrac{d}{2}\dfrac{\cos\beta}{(1+\cos\beta)}$	7.13C	Bubble Touches Bottom First $(x=0)$	$\dfrac{t}{t_0} = \dfrac{(1+\cos\beta)}{2}$
Triangle (Wedge)	Full $d \ll L$ (L = Length)	7.13D	Bubble Touches Side	$\dfrac{t}{t_0} = \dfrac{\sin\beta}{\beta}$
	Full $d < L$ $k < 1.0$ (k is Correction Ratio for Corner Draw Down)	7.13E	Bubble Touches Side	$\dfrac{t}{t_0} = \dfrac{\sin\beta}{\beta}$
Triangle (Wedge)	Deep Truncated $d \ll L$ $h > \dfrac{d}{2}\dfrac{\sin\beta}{(1+\cos\beta)}$	7.13F	Bubble Touches Side First	$\dfrac{t}{t_0} = \dfrac{\sin\beta}{\beta}$
	Shallow Truncated $d \ll L$ $h < \dfrac{d}{2}\dfrac{\sin\beta}{(1+\cos\beta)}$	7.13G	Bubble Touches Bottom First $(x=0)$	$\dfrac{t}{t_0} = \dfrac{\sin\beta}{\beta}$

$$F_x = \left| \frac{as^2 + bs + c}{as^{*2} + bs^* + c} \right|^A \left| \frac{(2as + b - g)(2as^* + b + g)}{(2as + b - g)(2as + b + g)} \right|^B$$

$A = f\sin\beta / [2a\,(2-f)]$ $\qquad\qquad$ $B = \sin\beta\,(d' - fb/2a)/[g(2-f)]$

$a = \sin\beta - \beta$
$b = \beta\,(h/\sin\beta + s^*) - 2h$
$c = (h - s^*\beta)h/\sin\beta$
$d' = (d/2) - h(1/\tan\beta - \cos\beta)$
$f = 1 - \cos\beta$
$g = \beta\,(h/\tan\beta - d/2)$

AND TRAPEZOIDAL SHAPES (From (18)), with permission from Society of Plastics Engineers

	Step II			Step III		
	Criterion	Thickness Equation	Supplemental Terms	Criterion	Thickness Equation	Supplemental Terms
	Bubble Touches Bottom	$\dfrac{t}{t_l}=\left[1-\dfrac{s}{h}\sin\beta\right]^{(1/\cos\beta-1)}$				
	Bubble Touches Bottom Next	$\dfrac{t}{t_l}=\left[1-\dfrac{s^*}{h^*}\sin\beta\right]^{(1/\cos\beta-1)}$	$h^*=(d/2)\tan\beta$ $s^*=\dfrac{h(1+\cos\beta)}{\sin\beta}-\dfrac{d}{2}$	Bottom and Sides Touching	$\dfrac{t}{t_{II}}=\dfrac{S_I}{SF_x}$	$S_I=2\pi(1+\cos\beta)\times$ $(h/\sin\beta-s^*)^2$ $S=(2\pi)(h-s\sin\beta)\times$ $[(s-s^*)\beta+(h-$ $s\sin\beta)]/(1-\cos\beta)$ $(F_x$ given below)
	Bubble Covers Bottom $0>x>x^*$	$\dfrac{t}{t_l}=\dfrac{S_I}{SF_{x_1}}$	$R=\dfrac{(d/2-h)^2}{2h}+\dfrac{h}{2}$ $S_I=[(d/2)^2+h^2]$ $\dfrac{t_I}{t_0}=\dfrac{d^2}{d^2+(2h)^2}$ $x^*\dfrac{d}{2}-\dfrac{h(1+\cos\beta)}{\sin\beta}$ $S=2\pi R$ $\times[\pi/2-\sin^{-1}(1-h/R)]+h$ $F_{x_1}=\exp[2\pi\displaystyle\int_0^x(x/s)\,dx]$	Bubble Covering Both Sides and Bottom	$\dfrac{t}{t_{II}}=\dfrac{S_I}{SF_{x_2}}$ t_{II} given by substituting x^* into Step II thickness equation	$S_I=2\pi h(x^*\beta+h)/$ $(1-\cos\beta)$ $S=2\pi R[x\beta+(d/2-$ $h/\tan\beta-x)\sin\beta^*(d/2-$ $h/\tan\beta-x)/\tan\beta$ $(F_{x_2}$ given below)
	Bubble Touches Bottom	$\dfrac{t}{t_l}=\left[1-\dfrac{s}{h}\sin\beta\right]^{(\tan\beta/\beta-1)}$				
	Bubble Touches Bottom	$\dfrac{t}{t_l}=\Bigl[1-$ $\dfrac{s}{h}\sin\beta\Bigr]^{[\tan\beta/\beta)(1+kW/L)-1]}$				
	Bubble Touches Bottom Next	$\dfrac{t}{t_l}=\left[1-\dfrac{s^*}{h^*}\sin\beta\right]^{(\tan\beta/\beta-1)}$	$s^*=\dfrac{h(1+\cos\beta)}{\sin\beta}-\dfrac{d}{2}$ $h^*=\dfrac{d}{2}\dfrac{\sin\beta}{(1+\cos\beta)}$	Bubble Covering Both Sides And Bottom	$\dfrac{t}{t_{II}}=\left[\dfrac{h/\sin\beta-s}{d/2-h/\tan\beta}\right]^{[2\tan(\beta/2)/\beta-1]}$	
	Bubble Covers Bottom $0<x<x^*$	$\dfrac{t}{t_l}=\dfrac{R_I\,\theta_I}{R\theta Fx_1}$	$R_I=d^2/8h+h/2$ $\theta=\tan^{-1}[(d-2x)/$ $2(R-h)]$ $\theta_I=\tan^{-1}[d/2(R_I-h)]$ $R=(d/2-x)^2/2h$ $+h/2$ $x^*=d/$ $2-h(\cos\beta-1)/\sin\beta$ $F_{x_1}=\exp[\displaystyle\int_0^x dx/R\theta]$	Bubble Covering Both Sides And Bottom	$\dfrac{t}{t_{II}}=\left[h^{**}\times\right.$ $\left.\dfrac{-x^{**}\sin(\beta/2)}{h^{**}}\right]^{[2\tan(\beta/2/\beta-1]}$	$x^{**}=x-x^*$ $h^{**}=h/2\cos(\beta/2)$ t_{II} Given by Substituting $x=x^*$ into Step II Thickness Equation

$$F_{x2}=\left|\dfrac{(ax^2+bx+c)}{ax^{*2}+bx^*+c}\right|^A\left|\dfrac{(2ax+b-g)(2ax^*+b+g)}{(2ax+b-g)(2ax+b+g)}\right|^B$$

$A=f\sin\beta/[2a(2-f)]$ $B=\sin\beta(d'-$
$fb/2a)/[g(2-f)]$

$a=\sin\beta-\beta$
$b=\beta(h/\sin\beta+x^*)$
$-2(h+x^*\sin\beta)$
$c=(h/\sin\beta-$
$x^*)^2\sin\beta$
$d'=(d/2)+x^*\cos\beta$
$f=1-\cos\beta$
$g=\beta(h/\sin\beta+x^*)$

Ra is the areal draw ratio, the formed sheet surface area to the initial sheet area. Further, the sheet thickness in a corner can be approximated by:

$$t = (h_1/h)(t_c - t_0) + t_0$$

For any truncated cone:

$$t/t_0 = G \{(h_1/h)(1/GRa^2 - 1) + 1\}$$

Ra is determined by part design, G depends upon geometry, and $h_1 = f(h)$, as given in Appendix 7.I. The experimental results and computed values agree to within 15%. The error is attributed to rim material being stretched into the cavity.

Prestretching and Material Properties

The analyses above concentrate on the geometric prediction of part wall thickness during simple female mold forming. Many forming processes described in Chapter 1 depend upon prestretching to improve material distribution. Inflation and plug assist are common prestretching methods.

Consider *inflation* (Figure 7.16). In the analysis on draw-down into the corner of a truncated cone, the sheet thickness ratio, t/t_0, was experimentally found to be inversely proportional to the square of the areal draw ratio (Figure 7.15). For inflation of an unformed sheet, experiments show that the sheet thickness (away from the rim) is a function only of the inflation height, δ (Figure 7.17 (9)). For very large inflation ratios (exceeding hemispherical), the sheet thickness is constant only in the polar region (13). If the material in the cap is assumed to have a uniform overall thickness (19):

$$t/t_0 = 1/[1 + (\delta/a)^2] = 1/Ra$$

For purely elastic sheet (9,13), the relationship between inflation height, δ, and inflation pressure, P, is:

$$Pa/2t_0p_0 = \ln[1 + (\delta/a)^2](2\,\delta/a)/[1 + (\delta/a)^2]^2$$

p_0 is obtained from the material elastic stress-strain model, $\sigma = p_0\varepsilon$. As seen in Figure 7.17 for HIPS and PMMA, there is a distinct offset in the thickness ratio relation to δ/a. An approximate relationship is:

$$t/t_0 = (\%)/[1 + (\delta/a)^2]$$

The material thickness near the rim is much greater than the average, resulting in the offset.

The extent of inflation depends upon the ability of the material to inflate without bursting (see Chapter 4) and on the extent of prestretching needed to achieve the desired wall thickness uniformity. If the inflated cap is to be snapped into a female mold, the cap surface should not quite touch the mold bottom upon eversion (Figure 7.18). At that point, the sheet thickness can be considered uniform (with a possible correction near the rim for the offset described above). For further drawing into the final shape, the thickness distributions in Table 7.12 can be used, with t_I (the second-step initial thickness) replaced with the appropriate thickness value from above. A similar adjustment can be made in the approximate analysis given earlier.

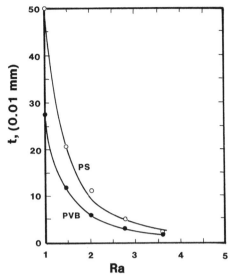

Figure 7.15 Experimental Sheet Thickness as Function of Areal Draw Ratio for Draw-Down into Truncated Cone Bottom Corner. PS = Polystyrene. PVB = Polyvinyl Butyral. t = Thickness in 0.01 mm [0.0004 in]. Ra = Areal Draw Ratio. (17).

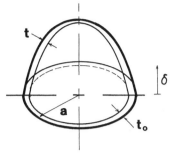

Figure 7.16 Schematic of Bubble Inflation. a = Radius. t_0 = Initial Sheet Thickness. t = Local Sheet Thickness. δ = Inflation Height.

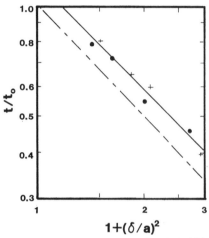

$$1+(\delta/a)^2$$

Figure 7.17 Experimental Inflated Bubble Thickness, t/t_0. (δ/a) is Reduced Inflation Height. Solid Dot = PMMA. + = HIPS. Broken Line: Williams (19) Theory; $t/t_0 = 1/[1+(\delta/a)^2] = 1/Ra$. Solid Line: Best Fit; $t/t_0 = (⅚)/[1+(\delta/a)^2] = (⅚)/Ra$. Data from Williams used by permission from Ellis Harwood, Ltd.

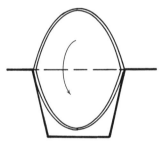

Figure 7.18 Schematic of Bubble Eversion.

Emphasis has been on prestretching for female molding. A similar analysis can be made for insertion of a male mold into the inflated sheet cap. This is discussed as an aspect of *plug assist forming*.

Sheet can also be prestretched by forcing a plunger into the sheet center (Figure 7.19). The plug usually moves along the center axis of a female mold. The plug design parameters include the shape of the plug tip, the plug penetration depth (relative to the cavity depth) and the plug diameter (relative to the cavity diameter). The plug surface temperature and coefficient of friction (between the plug surface and the stretching sheet) are also considered design factors.

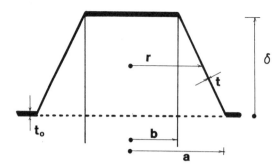

Figure 7.19 Schematic of Blunt-Nose Plug Assist Penetration. a = Clamp Radius. b = Plug Radius. r = Sheet Radius, b < r < a. δ = Plug Penetration Depth. t_0 = Initial Sheet Thickness. t = Sheet Thickness at r.

Consider the flat plunger of Figure 7.19, with radius b and penetration depth δ, stretching a sheet of radius a. The thickness ratio is:

$$t/t_0 = 1/\sqrt{(1+(\delta/r \ln (a/b))^2)}$$

r is the sheet radius, b < r < a (19; 5.122). The sheet thickness on the plunger surface is t_0. At large values of δ/a (greater than 0.4 or so), the thickness ratio from b to a is about equal to the radius ratio, b/a. For b/a = 0.8, at δ/a = 1, for example, t/t_0 at r/a = 0.8 is 81% of the value at r/a = 1. An overall material balance illustrates this. The initial material volume, V, is $\pi a^2 t_0$. That material is distributed unstretched to the plunger top and stretched in the truncated cone of sheet between the plunger edge and the mold rim. The material volume on the plunger tip is $V_p = \pi b^2 t_0$. The material volume in the stretched sheet is:

$$V_s = \int_b^a \delta \cdot t(r) \cdot 2\,\pi\,dr$$

This can be approximated by $V_s \simeq \delta \cdot t_{avg} \cdot 2\pi(a+b)/2$. Since $V = V_p + V_s$:

$$t_{avg}/t_0 = (1-b/a)/(\delta/a)$$

At b/a = 0.8, δ/a = 1, t_{avg}/t_0 = 0.1. This value brackets the t/t_0 values at r/a = 0.9 to 1.0 to within 6%. This approximation fails as b/a decreases in value. Nevertheless, it is important to account for all material in any calculation. A simple test such as this can save extensive computer time.

The plug tip shape can aid somewhat in stretching the sheet, as noted in Chapter 6. The effect of plug surface curvature can be approximated by using an effective value of b, the plunger radius. Consider a spherical plug tip (Figure 7.20) of radius b penetrating a sheet of radius a. Let b' be the effective plug radius. When the plug tip just touches the sheet, b' = 0. When the plug has penetrated to a depth δ = b, the sheet touches it at (b'/a) = (b/a)². And when it has penetrated to a depth δ = 2b, the effective reduced radius, b'/a = 1 − cos (2α), where α = tan⁻¹ (b/a). If the sheet on the plug surface does not slide, a conservative estimate of the sheet thickness at any plug depth, δ/a, can be obtained by using the effective radius b' in the thickness equation. As expected, draw-down at the same δ/a is less with a spherical plug than with a blunt one.

The force required to stretch the sheet to a given penetration depth δ with the flat plunger is given as (20):

$$F = 2 \pi\delta\varphi t_0/\ln(a/b)$$

Figure 7.20 Spherical Nose Plug Assist Penetration. b = Nose Radius. a = Clamp Radius. t_0 = Initial Sheet Thickness. t = Sheet Thickness ar r. δ = Plug Penetration Depth. B = Locus of Tangent Points Defining b′, the Effective Plug Radius.

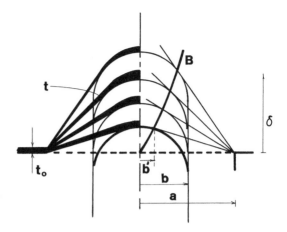

φ is the temperature-dependent material parameter (Chapter 4). As expected, the force is directly proportional to the penetration depth and the initial sheet thickness. For example, 115 kg-f [253 lb-f] is required to extend a flat plug b = 2.03 cm [0.8 in] into a plastic sheet, t_0 = 0.127 cm [0.050 in] by a = 2.54 cm [1.0 in], to a depth δ = 2.54 cm [1 in]. The material parameter value φ = 1.24 MPa [180 psi]. The applied pressure on the plug face is 0.87 MPa [126 psi]. A similar relationship for a rounded plug shows the same relationship except that b is replaced with the effective plug radius, b′.

The extent of sheet stretching over a plug tip can be estimated using the force balance for analysis of rim material draw-down described above. To obtain an appropriate thickness ratio relationship for stretching over a curved plug tip, a differential force balance must be integrated over the length of plug travel. The force holding the sheet against the plug tip increases with increasing penetration. The component of tensile force stretching or sliding the sheet on the plug tip also decreases with increasing plug penetration. Thus, any biaxial extension of the sheet in contact with the plug probably occurs just as the plug penetrates the sheet. In practice, stretching of the free sheet dominates throughout the plug motion.

For large molds, the plug-to-cavity radius ratio, b/a, should be 0.8 to 0.9 (20; 306). The plug-to-cavity depth ratio, δ/h, should be 0.7 to 0.9. Experience shows that for simple shapes, δ/h of 0.7 to 0.85 yields the best ratio of bottom to wall thickness. If the material against the plug tip requires no further stretching, the plug penetration depth can be within 1 to 2 cm [0.40 to 0.80 in] of the cavity bottom.

If the sheet is to be freely stretched between the plug tip and the mold rim, the pressure on each side of the sheet must be the same. If the cavity pressure is allowed to build, the sheet will be forced against the plug. This will result in a part that is thin in the rim area. If the cavity pressure is low, the sheet will be pulled against the mold wall. This reduces the effectiveness of the plug and results in parts that are thin in corners. Control of sheet position becomes much more difficult as b/a approaches unity. A tapered plug penetrating into a mold having the same sidewall taper helps overcome lack of control.

A blunt plug with generously rounded edges, a compromise between a flat plug and a hemispherical one, is the best basic design (Figure 7.21). The plug is usually kept warm (to within 20 C [40 F] of the set temperature of the plastic) or insulated to minimize conduction heat loss. Heated plugs are needed whenever the material in contact with the plug must be drawn further in the next forming step. Plug materials are discussed in Chapter 6.

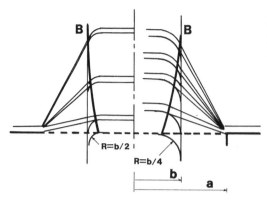

Figure 7.21 Schematic of Blunt Plug Assists with Rounded Corners. Left: $R = b/4$. Right: $R = b/2$. $B = $ Locus of Tangent Points Defining b', the Effective Plug Radius.

Finite Element Method

The complex analytical schemes given in Table 7.12 are best solved with computers for even relatively simple geometries. Approximate thickness values for complex geometries can be obtained by assuming that the actual shape can be approximated by a simple geometry (or series of geometries). Finite element analysis is a more practical scheme for determining wall thickness of well-behaved stretched elastic membranes. The *finite element method* (FEM) divides the continuous sheet into many discrete elements, usually two-dimensional triangles (Figure 7.22). Each triangle has three nodes. Each node is positioned by coordinates in three-dimensional space. The initial coordinates are found from geometry (21).

The sheet is then numerically differentially deformed by applying known external forces. This causes a change in the total strain energy of the sheet. The individual elements are strained, resulting in differential changes in their nodal coordinates. This is given for all elements as:

$$\{F^L\} = VE\ \{(\partial W/\partial u)^L\}$$

F is the local nodal force, VE is the initial elemental volume, W is the strain energy function of the materials (see Chapter 4) and u is the elemental nodal coordinate. L refers to the local element.

The strain energy function, W, can be expressed in terms of interpolation functions for each of the individual elements. The nodal values then become the new functions and these must be matched to adjacent elements to affect a solution.

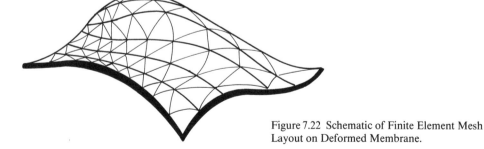

Figure 7.22 Schematic of Finite Element Mesh Layout on Deformed Membrane.

The interpolation functions are chosen to allow continuity across the elemental boundaries at the nodes. Recent computer work has found the weighted residuals method most efficient in finding appropriate values for these functions. The Galerkin weighted residual method is a good way of obtaining the requisite functions (21).

The descretization of the initial value elastic membrane problem results in a set of matrix equations. The size of the matrices depends upon the number of elements. Accuracy to the continuous equation demands fine mesh size or many elements. Accuracy is required when the sheet surface topography is very complex (a highly detailed part with several levels and relatively sharp corners and angles). Therefore large matrices are quite common. For linear equations, solution to matrix equations is relatively straightforward and requires only moderate computational skills, computer memory and time. For very nonlinear equations, solutions can require reliable trial-and-error techniques, elaborate tests for convergence, patience, large computer memory, long run times, and consummate computer skills.

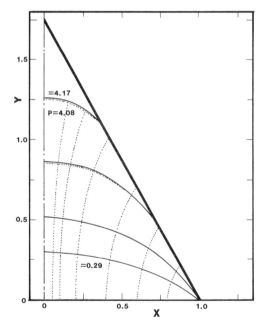

Figure 7.23 Theoretical Draw-Down into 60° Cone. P = Reduced Forming Pressure. X = Reduced Cone Radius. Y = Reduced Cone Height. Dashed Line: No Slip at Wall. Solid Line: Total Slip at Wall (22, 23).

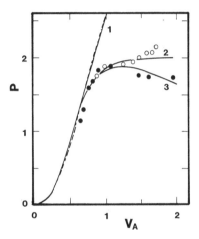

Figure 7.24 Theoretical and Experimental Expansion into Symmetric Shapes. Curve 1: 60° Cone. 2: Right Circular Cylinder. 3: Unconstrained Deformation. Squares, Circles: Data on HIPS. P = Reduced Forming Pressure. VA = Reduced Apex Height.

Since the thermoforming process can be approximated as one in which the sheet is undergoing only isothermal, planar-isotropic biaxial membrane stretching, FEM should be directly applicable. Two academic programs are focussing on FEM for thermoforming. McGill (22, 23) proposes direct, mainframe computer solution of the basic elastic stress-strain equation using triangular two-dimensional planar elements. The McGill model includes a slip boundary condition at the sheet-mold interface. As seen in Figures 7.23 and 7.24 for draw-down into a 60° full cone, there is little apparent difference in either the shape (or thickness) of the sheet or the (dimensionless) pressure required to stretch the sheet to a given depth. To date, this approach has been restricted to simple shapes (cone, parallel-sided cylinder, free circular expansion, free elliptical expansion, expansion against a horizontal flat plate). Technically, the approach should work for any part shape. Complex parts and those with great detail will require variable mesh size schemes in order to minimize computer time and memory.

Louisville (24–26) has approached draw-down into female molds in a more pragmatic fashion. It was noted that for the conical and triangular molds (Figure 7.13 and Table 7.12), the differential relationship between local sheet thickness, t, and slant height or distance down the mold wall, s, is always of the form:

$$dt/ds = At/(B - Cs)$$

A, B, and C are geometric constants that depend upon the mold wall angle, β, the ratio of actual to full projected depth, and so on.

The solution of a single differential equation can be achieved by one-dimensional finite elements, again using a Galerkin weighted residual method. The method is simple enough to allow programming in BASIC on a limited-memory personal computer with run times in seconds (26). The results are quite accurate for relatively few elements (Figure 7.25). In fact, the method compensates for the functional discontinuity given in the analytical solution for the shallow truncated cone (Table 7.12) (See Figure 7.26).

In addition to computer models that descretize the deformation behavior of an elastic sheet, McGill is also analyzing viscoelastic sheet behavior (23). The analysis follows the concept of the inflation of a viscoelastic fluid (see Chapter 4) and results in the solution of the isothermal equation of motion with an appropriate constitutive equation of state. The method of analysis is *finite difference*. For a viscous-only fluid (n, the power-law index, $= 0.492$), draw down into a 60° full cone mold yields wall thickness values that are unchanged from either a Newtonian fluid or a fully elastic solid. As expected however, the draw-down rate decreases with increasing nonNewtonianness (Figure 7.27). Draw-down is rate-independent for an elastic solid.

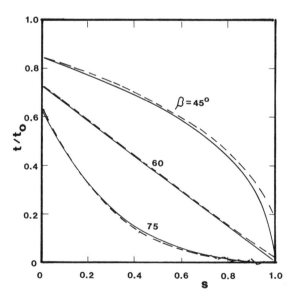

Figure 7.25 Finite Element and Exact Solutions for Draw-down into a Full Cone. Reduced Wall Thickness (t/t_0) as Function of Reduced Slant Height (s) and Cone Angle (β, in deg). Solid Lines: Exact Solutions (See Table 7.12). Broken Lines: 20 Element Galerkin Weighted Residuals FEM. (25), by permission of author.

Figure 7.26 Finite Element and Exact Solutions for Draw-down into a Shallow Truncated Cone. Reduced Wall Thickness (t/t_0) as Function of Reduced Slant Height (s). Cone Angle $\beta = 45°$. Solid Line: Exact Solution (See Table 7.12). Broken Line: 10 Element Galerkin Weighted Residual FEM (26), by permission of author.

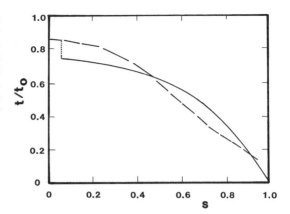

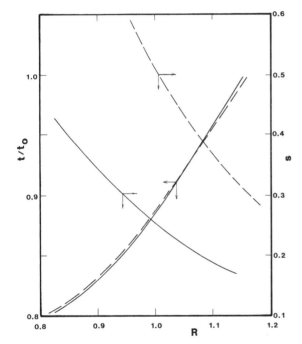

Figure 7.27 The Sheet as a Viscous-Only Fluid, Drawn into a Full 60° Cone. Variation of Wall Thickness (t/t_0) and Contact Length (s) with Radius of Curvature of Deforming Spherical Cap (R). Solid Lines: Newtonian Fluid. Broken Lines: Power-Law Fluid, $n = 0.492$.

None of these approaches allows the thermoformed part designer the freedom, flexibility, accuracy and ease of design currently being used by designers of plastic parts in other areas. The finite element method (FEM) has reached a high level of sophistication in injection molding and blow molding and undoubtedly will form the basis for computer-aided design (CAD) of thermoformed parts in the very near future.

Computer-Aided Design in Thermoforming

There are several reasons for computerizing the entire thermoforming process. Consider the following process generalizations:

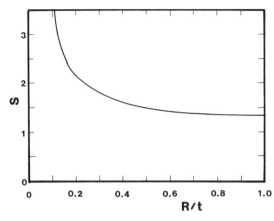

Figure 7.28 Stress Concentration Factor (S) as Function of Radius per Unit Local Sheet Thickness (R/t).

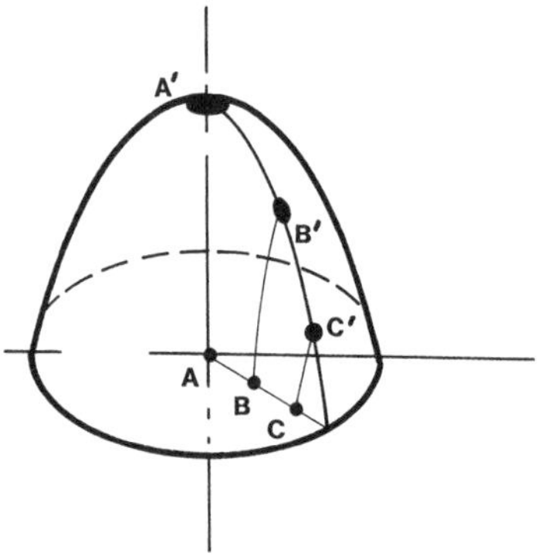

Figure 7.29 Concept of Material Allocation. Translation from Flat Sheet (A, B, C) to Inflated Bubble (A′,B′,C′).

1. Production of sheet from pellets or powders is a process expense that most other technologies do not incur. The added costs range from US$0.11/kg to US$0.44/kg ($0.05/lb to $0.20/lb).

2. Most thermoforming operations convert only 50 to 75% of the ready-to-be-formed sheet into product (formed parts). The rest (web, edge, cut-outs, trim) must be reprocessed at additional cost with some loss in properties. In some cases, the web material cannot be reused.

3. Despite technological advances in processing equipment, thermoforming is an energy intensive process, adding to the processing costs.

4. The nature of the thermoforming process is biaxial deformation and thinning of a rubbery elastic sheet. Thus, the *average* final part thickness is (substantially) less than the initial part thickness.

5. As a first approximation, plastic sheet draws only when free of a solid surface. This leads to parts of nonuniform wall thickness. In one-step natural drawing (vacuum forming, pressure forming, drape forming), parts are thin in two-dimensional corners and thinnest in three-dimensional corners.

6. The nature of the process dictates that the material in the thinnest areas is stretched the most. This material is therefore closest to its ultimate strength. Part performance under load therefore depends upon the method of stretching the sheet and upon the thinnest section under load. The stress in a corner is strongly dependent on the radius to local wall thickness ratio. As seen (Figure 7.28), the stress concentration factor exceeds 2 when $r < t/4$. A strong corner design has $r \geqslant 3t/4$.

7. Conversely, many regions of the formed part are relatively unoriented, are weaker or thicker than desired, and thus wasteful of material.

8. Computer-aided engineering (CAE) of the thermoforming process encompasses control of the sheet temperature prior to forming, the applied forming forces (including necessary sequencing of pressure to allow inflation and/or plug assist prestretching), and proper sheet cooling techniques to ensure optimum overall cycle time or optimum energy efficiency.

9. Computer-aided part design (CAD) is only one facet of CAE. It depends upon material allocation. For a given processing history and a given mold configuration, a specific element in the unformed sheet will always transform into a specific deformed element on the formed part (Figure 7.29). The controllable CAE parameters (local sheet temperature, pressure or stretching sequence and so on) only differentially alter the relative location, differential area and thickness of that element.

10. The easiest approach to material allocation is to assume large-scale isothermal biaxial stretching of an isotropic rubbery elastic sheet.

11. This assumption allows two-dimensional finite element analysis to be used to determine wall thickness for one-step formed shapes. With proper selection of the initial deformation matrix, prestretching may be (but has not yet been) added as a preliminary step.

12. As a further simplifying assumption, the material allocation algorithm can include a non-slip condition. Thus only the material free of a solid surface can stretch under applied force.

13. Two further aspects of free surface stretching can be included in model-building. The volume of free material that continues to stretch is simply the difference between the initial volume of material (that in the unformed sheet) and that already deposited on the mold wall. And the free material thickness tends to be uniform across its surface at any time during the stretching process.

14. *Computer-assisted thermoforming* may be of greatest value when multi-layer rigid barrier containers become economically viable. Thermoforming will then meet a specific product need as the packaging industry (in particular) moves toward products requiring precise wall thickness control.

References

1. W. K. McConnell, Jr., Material Presented, Distributed at SPE Industrial Thermoforming Symposium & Workshop, 12–14 March 1985. Material Copyrighted by Author.
2. G. Beall, *Design Guide to Pressure Formed Plastic Parts*, ARREM Plastics Inc., Addison IL, 1985. pg. 17.
3. L. R. Schmidt and J. F. Carley, "Biaxial Stretching of Heat Softened Plastic Sheets Using an Inflation Technique", Int. J. Engng. Sci., *13*, 1975, pg. 563.
4. Crawford and Lui (17) call areal draw ratio "stretching ratio" or "stretch ratio".
5. W. Lloyd Gheen, "Computer Aids to Thermoforming: Stretch Factor and Average Formed Thickness", SPE Tech. Papers, *30*, 1984, pg. 748.
6. L. R. Schmidt and J. F. Carley, "Biaxial Stretching of Heat-Softened Plastic Sheets: Experiments and Results", Polym. Eng. Sci., *15*, 1975, pg. 51, especially footnote, pg. 60.
7. H. Voigt, "Lehrgang für Thermoformung", Paul Kiefel GmbH, 8228 Freilassing, Industriestraße 19, undated, pg. 3.4.1.
8. N. Rosenzweig, M. Narkis, and Z. Tadmor, "Wall Thickness Distribution in Thermoforming", Polym. Eng. Sci., *19*, 1979, pg. 946.
9. M. O. Lai and D. L. Holt, "The Extensional Flow of Poly(methyl Methacrylate) and High-Impact Polystyrene at Thermoforming Temperatures", J. Appl. Polym. Sci., *19*, 1975, pg. 1209.
10. A. Kobayashi, *Machining of Plastics*, McGraw-Hill Book Co., 1967, Table 2.1, pg. 44.
11. H. Chang and R. A. Daane, "Coefficients of Friction for Solid Polymers in Various Forms", SPE Tech. Papers, *20*, 1974, pg. 335.
12. A. S. Lodge and H. G. Howell, Proc. Phys. Soc., *76B*, 1974.
13. L. R. Schmidt, "Biaxial Stretching of Heat-Softened Plastic Sheets", Ph. D. Thesis, U. Colorado, Boulder CO 1972, pg. 129.

14. C.J. Benning, *Plastic Foams*, Vol. 1, Wiley-Interscience, 1969, pg. 86.
15. Anon., "Volara Vacuum Forming Guide", Voltek, Div. Sekisui America Corp., Lawrence MA, Jan. 1984.
16. A. Höger, *Warmformen von Kunststoffen*, Carl Hanser, 1971, pg. 61.
17. R.J. Crawford and S.K.L. Lui, "Prediction of Wall Thickness Distribution in Thermoformed Mouldings", Eur. Polym. J., *18*, 1982, pg. 699.
18. N. Rosenzweig, "Wall Thickness Distribution in Thermoforming", SPE Tech. Papers, *29*, 1983, pg. 478.
19. J.G. Williams, *Stress Analysis of Polymers*, 2nd Ed., Ellis Harwood Ltd: Halsted Press, 1980, pg. 240.
20. J. Frados, Ed., *Plastics Engineering Handbook*, 4th Ed., Van Nostrand Reinhold, pg. 306.
21. K.H. Huebner, *The Finite Element Method for Engineers*, John Wiley, 1980, pg. 6.
22. R.L. Wu, "Finite Element and Experimental Analyses of the Inflation of Membranes in Relation to Thermoforming", M. Eng. Thesis, McGill University, Montreal Quebec CAN, 1984.
23. R. Allard, J.-M. Charrier, A. Ghosh, M. Marangou, M.E. Ryan, S. Shrivastara, R. Wu., "An Engineering Study of the Thermoforming Process: Experimental and Theoretical Considerations", paper presented at First Annual Meeting, Polym. Proc. Soc., Akron OH, April 1985.
24. R.C. Campbell, "A Finite Element Model for Thermoforming: Small Deformation of Nonlinear Materials", M. Eng. Thesis, Dept. Chem. Eng., U. Louisville, Louisville KY, 1983.
25. D.S. Garrett, "Polymer Process Modeling: Thermoforming Via Finite Elements", M. Eng. Thesis, Dept. Chem. Eng., U. Louisville, Louisville KY, 1984.
26. J.M. Wooldridge, "Polymer Process Modeling: Thermoforming of Simple Objects Via Finite Element Analysis", M. Eng. Thesis, Dept. Chem. Eng., U. Louisville, Louisville KY, 1985.
27. C.M. Campbell, "Designing for Thermoforming", Materials Presented, Distributed at SPE Thermoforming Symposium & Workshop, 20 March 1984, Arlington TX.

Appendix 7.I

DRAW RATIOS FOR TRUNCATED CONE

Areal Draw Ratio

As shown in Figure 7.30, a sheet that is partially drawn into a cone of slant height s, depth h, diameter d and cone angle β can be divided into a frustrum of a cone and a spherical cap. If $R = d/2$, the cone radius at the rim and r is an indeterminate radius at the bottom of the frustrum, the frustrum area is:

$$A_f = \pi (R + r)[(R - r)^2 + h_1^2]^{1/2}$$

h_1 is related to h by $h_1 = h(1 - r/R)$ and $h = R \tan \beta$. The area of a spherical cap is:

$$A_c = 2 \pi a \delta$$

But $r^2 + \delta^2 = 2 a \delta$. So:

$$A_c = \pi (\delta^2 + r^2)$$

Now $r = a \cos \beta$ and $\delta = a(1 - \sin \beta)$, and:

$$A_c = 2 \pi r^2 [1 - \sin \beta]/\cos^2 \beta$$

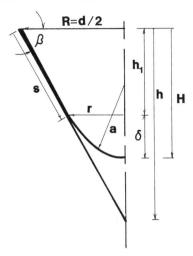

Figure 7.30 Geometry for Draw-Down into Full Right Cone of Angle β.

The total area in terms of r is:

$$A_t = \pi R^2/\cos \beta - (\pi r^2/\cos \beta)[1 - 2(1 - \sin \beta)/\cos \beta]$$

The areal draw ratio is:

$$Ra = A_t/\pi R^2 = (1/\cos \beta)[1 - (r/R)^2[1 - 2(1 - \sin \beta)/\cos \beta]]$$

For full draw-down into $\beta = 60°$ cone, $Ra = 2$.

The relationship between r and H, the depth of the formed part $(H \leqslant h)$ is:

$$r = (h - H) \cos \beta/(2 \sin \beta - 1)$$

The areal draw ratio in terms of measured depth of draw (H:d) is:

$$Ra = (1/\cos \beta)[1 - (\tan \beta - 2(H:d))^2\{\cos \beta/(2\sin \beta - 1)\}^2 \times$$

$$[1 - 2(1 - \sin \beta)/\cos \beta]]$$

For a 60° cone:

$$Ra = 2[1 - 0.2165(1.732 - 2(H:d))^2]$$

Linear Draw Ratio

The slant height s down the cone frustrum is given as:

$$s^2 = (R - r)^2 + h_1^2 = (R - r)^2 + R^2 \tan^2 \beta (1 - r/R)^2$$

$$s = (R - r)/\cos \beta$$

The distance across the cap is:

$$s^* = a\alpha/2$$

where α is the base half-angle in radians, $\alpha = \pi/2 - \beta^*$. In terms of r:

$$s^* = r\alpha/2 \cos \beta$$

The linear draw ratio then is:

$$RL = [2(R-r)/\cos \beta + r\alpha/2 \cos \beta]/2R$$
$$RL = (1/\cos \beta)[1 - (r/R)(1 - (\pi/2 - \beta^*)/4)]$$

For a $\beta = 60°$ cone, $RL = 2[1 - 0.869(r/R)]$ and $RL = 2$ for full draw into this cone. In terms of measured depth of draw (H:d), RL is:

$$RL = (1/\cos\beta)[1 - (1 - (\pi/2 - \beta^*)/4)(\tan\beta - 2(H:d))\cos\beta/(2\sin\beta - 1)]$$

For a 60° cone:

$$RL = 2[1 - 0.594(1.732 - 2(H:d))]$$

8 THE ECONOMICS OF THERMOFORMING

Introduction

The business of doing business depends upon several fundamental concepts. Modern machines are designed to produce parts, repetitively, day in and day out, with relatively little maintenance or attention. Businesses require that these machines make money. Profitable businesses require that the machines make quality parts, that can be sold at values greater than their total manufacturing costs. Profit is the expected return on investment for taking the risk of being in business. The keys to business success are quality and accountability. To make products from sheet, the interaction of the sheet with the process parameters must first be thoroughly understood. The quality of the products depends upon the skill of the operator, the selection of quality raw materials, and an adequate quality control of all incoming and outgoing materials (Figure 8.1). Since energy consumption is an important factor in thermoforming, accountability of energy should be made (Figure 8.2). Money can also be treated in this fashion, as cash flow (Figure 8.3).

Several elements of the thermoforming business are considered here. Good finished parts cannot be made from imperfect sheet material. Incoming raw material quality and the condition of regrind materials for reprocessing into additional sheet require management awareness and dedication. An understanding of current non-thermoforming (extrusion, calendering, milling, casting) processing practices is necessary to establish meaningful quality standards. Accountability has become immeasurably easier with the successful development of 16-bit (and now 32-bit) office computers and the attendant accounting software. Even the smallest business can now have very sophisticated payroll, inventory control, accounts receivable and payable, and other accounting techniques. The thermoformer must still have a basic understanding of the various elements of his specific business that make up cash balances and annual operating costs.

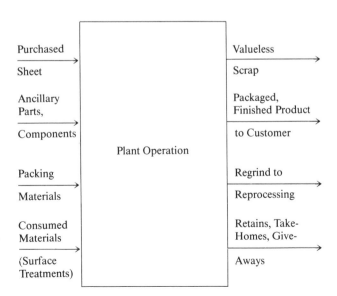

Figure 8.1
Steady State Material
Balance - Thermoforming.

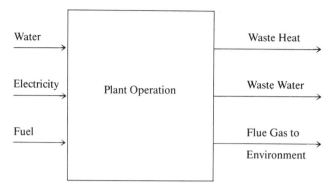

Figure 8.2 Steady State Energy Balance – Thermoforming.

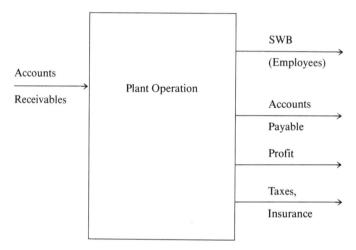

Figure 8.3 Steady State Cash-Flow – Thermoforming.

The thermoformer is usually concerned with three general catagories of business: existing, incremental, and isolated new venture. *Existing business* deals with the costs required to produce another (or similar) article when the costs of producing the last one are known. An *incremental business* is the addition of a new product line to an existing business. And an *isolated new business* focusses on the ground-up costs of beginning a new business in a location remote from current business efforts. Some important elements in each of these business catagories are shown in Table 8.1.

Existing product business is treated as fitting into an on-going effort whose costs are essentially time-independent (or steady-state). The isolated new business venture requires the most analysis, since not only is the value of the product initially unknown, but long-term effects of money and energy costs and inflation are also unknown. Isolated ventures require careful analysis of competitive processes as well. For these reasons, major emphasis is placed on understanding the elements of the isolated venture. The incremental product/process combines elements of both steady-state production costs and new venture costs, and being more complex, is considered last.

TABLE 8.1 NEW THERMOFORMING PRODUCT NATRUE

	Existing	Incremental	Isolated New Venture
Nature of Business	Existing	New Product on Existing	New
Effect on General Operation	None-Steady State	Existing-Expansion	New-Expansion
Effect on Equipment	None	New or Modification	New
Effect on Site	None	Existing Expansion	New Expansion
Effect on Labor	None	Expansion	New Hires
Effect on Sales/Service	None	Expansion, Retraining	New Hires
Effect on Mangement	None	None	New, Training
Effect on R & D	None	None	Little
Effect on Facilities	None	Expansion	New, Groundup
Nature of Materials	New or Well-known	New	New
Debugging			
Machine	None	Some	Significant
Materials	Some	Some	Significant
Facilities	None	Moderate	Significant
Molds	Moderate	Moderate	Significant
Debugging Time	Immediate to a Week	Week to Month	Months to Year
Start-up Costs	None to Slight	Moderate	Significant
Accuracy of Cost Analysis	±5%	±15%	±25% (or more)

Material Quality – Some Definitions

Many thermoformers purchase sheetstock. As a result, they must depend upon extruders to provide them with a quality product at a fair price. It is imperative that both the supplier and his customers agree on a set of standards and definitions, to minimize misinterpretation and engender good will. Some classical definitions follow:

Virgin. Virgin means "unprocessed". Virgin resin is that supplied to the extruder by the resin supplier. Virgin sheet, therefore, should be defined as sheet made only from virgin resin. All other materials, such as factory regrind of virgin sheet, or scrap regrind returns from a specific source or multiple sources, should be considered *regrind*. This does not imply that regrind should not be used. Sheet containing regrind is frequently much less expensive than virgin sheet. Keep in mind, however, that extended time at melt temperature can be quite detrimental to many plastics, leading to loss in mechanical properties such as tensile strength and elongation at break and to change in color, such as yellowing. The thermoformer should specify to the extruder the type and extent of regrind used in the sheet.

For example, consider a thermoforming plant that is regrinding 40% of its throughput as web and returning the regrind to its extruder. If the sheet order specifies "Sheet from virgin resin *plus* web regrind from this unit (only).", the plant will be getting sheet containing 40% regrind. On the other hand, if the order specifies "Sheet from virgin resin *plus no more than* 10% web regrind from this unit (only).", the plant will pay a premium since not all of its web regrind can be recycled into new sheet by the extrusion operation.

Dimensions. When plastic sheet is stretched, it becomes thinner. A sheet that is already thin yields parts that can be substantially thinner than desired. Thick sheet, on the other hand, yields parts that are overdesigned and thus more costly than expected. Although significant improvements have been made in recent years in controlling the thickness of extruded sheet, some tolerance must still be given. The extruder and thermoformer usually compromise on overall sheet thickness (or gage). It appears that with today's technology, sheet thickness variation can be held to less than 5% in sheet thinner than 3 mm [0.120 in] and to within 0.2 mm [0.005 in] in thicker sheet. Sheet thickness variation across the sheet width can be held to within 2% of the nominal sheet thickness dimension.

Orientation. During the extrusion process, sheet can become preferentially oriented in the machine direction [MD]. While this is not a serious problem in roll fed thermoforming processes that usually use thin gage sheet, it can lead to significant processing problems with cut-sheet thermoforming. The most serious problem occurs when the residual strain in the clamped sheet is relieved during oven heating. If the orientation is excessive, the sheet can be physically pulled from the clamp frame. A simple oven test has been used for some time as a quality control method (1). Strips (either 250 mm × 50 mm [10 in × 2 in] or 250 mm × 250 mm [10 in × 10 in]) are cut from as-received sheet. It is recommended that these strips be cut in a fixed pattern every time the test is run. Preferably, strips should be cut from the edges and the center of the sheet. These strips are placed on screens in the radiant heating zone of the thermoformer for a time typical of the heating time needed during thermoforming. The samples are cooled, then measured to determine the degree of orientation. The degree of orientation is the change in sheet dimension in a given direction (machine direction [MD] or transverse direction [TD]) upon heating, divided by the initial dimension. For example, if a 250 mm × 250 mm HIPS sheet is heated to 200 C [390 F] and has cooled dimensions of 125 mm [MD] × 200 mm [TD], the sheet orientation is 50% [MD] × 20% [TD].

Uniformity of orientation is also important. Sheet-fed frames can be adjusted for a given sheet orientation. Wide variation can lead to pull-out or excessive sheet sagging. It is recommended that orientation uniformity be controlled to within 5% (for the example above, 47-52% [MD] and 18-23% [TD]). The shape of the heated strip can also give information about the internal stresses in the sheet. As noted in Chapters 2 and 3, plastics heat and cool quite slowly when compared with other materials. In thick sheets (greater than 5 mm [0.200 in]), heating relieves or "anneals" out cooling stresses, resulting in a (very slight) increase in sheet thickness and a measurable necking-in and/or bowing-out all along the sheet edge. Poor processing skills such as low processing temperature, high nip roll pressure, or excessive roll stack cooling, can lead to heated sheet edge deformation.

Cut sheet dimension is also of concern. Thick gage sheet is frequently cut to within 3 mm [0.125 in] in length and width, in order to minimize scrap held in the clamping frames. Out-of-square sheet frequently cannot be clamped. One quality sheet extruder recommends cross diagonal dimensions to within 5%. Another recommends that corners be right angles to within 1/4 degree (or 89-3/4 to 90-1/4 degree). Sheet bowing or warping can also lead to clamping problems. The flatness of a sheet is determined by clamping three corners on a flat surface and measuring the height of the fourth above the surface plane. Out-of-flatness of 2% (based on the diagonal dimension) can probably be tolerated. Very thick sheet may need to be oven-annealed prior to forming in order to flatten the sheet enough to close the clamp frame.

Moisture. Many plastics such as polycarbonate, acrylic (PMMA), polyethylene terephthalate (PET), and ABS, are hygroscopic. The extent to which a given material absorbs water depends upon the nature of the polymer and the time that sheet has been exposed to the environment. Water absorption is a diffusion process, in that the water molecules move from the moist environment (the air) into and through the entangled polymer molecules that make up the dry plastic sheet. The rate of diffusion depends upon the concentration driving force (how much water is in the air) and the nature of the plastic. Some plastics, such as nylon and PET, have strong affinities to water, through hydrogen bonding along the polymer backbone. As a result, these materials absorb water readily and to a relatively high extent. It is thought that the water molecules cluster in void regions between molecular chains or bundles. When wet sheet is rapidly heated (as in thermoforming), these microscopic clusters expand to produce microvoids. Additional water molecules diffuse to these voids to produce visible bubbles. In mild cases, a transparent sheet appears hazy. In extreme cases, the sheet appears translucent, opaque white or blistered. Typically, moisture-sensitive sheet should be sealed in polyethylene (an excellent moisture barrier film) by the sheet producer. Moisture-sensitive thin-gage roll-stock should be sealed for moisture protection in the same way. Quality control samples should be taken by the thermoformer at the time of shipment receipt. A visual inspection for moisture can be made at the time the degree-of-orientation evaluation is being made, and again prior to forming. In order to ensure dry sheet, however, resin suppliers recommend that specific materials be thoroughly dried immediately prior to using. Some guidelines on specific materials are given in Table 8.2. Note that materials are usually dried at temperatures a few degrees below their typical glass transition temperatures, Tg. If a material that is not listed in the table is to be dried, it is recommended that a drying temperature of $(Tg - 20)C$ for at least 2 hours per mm of sheet thickness be used.

TABLE 8.2 DRYING TIMES FOR VARIOUS TYPES OF PLASTICS
(Times are per 1 mm [0.040 in] sheet thickness) (Adapted from (10)) (Air Dew Point Unknown)

Material	Glass Transition Temperature, Tg, C	Oven Temperature T_0, C	Time hr
ABS	100	90	2
PMMA	105	95	2
PET	70	65	3–4
PA6 (nylon 6)	50	50	3–4
PA66 (nylon 66)	50	50	3–4
PVC	90	70	2
Acetate	100*	90	1.5

* Cellulose triacetate also shows a possible Tg at 70C.

Cap Sheet. Multilayer sheet and film are used in many ways, as noted earlier. As examples, UV-barrier films are applied over materials such as PS and ABS so that the formed parts can be used outside for signs, pools, camper tops and the like. 0.2 mm layers of PS-type plastics are applied to one or both sides of low-density (0.064 g/cm^3 [4 lb/ft^3]) PS foam to increase depth of draw and improve final product stiffness. In order to process crystallizing PET (CPET) to proper stiffness without causing brittleness, two layers of PET are coextruded, one of which contains a crystallizing agent. Certain polymers do not adhere and so "tie layers" such as ethylene vinyl acetate are used to form a functional bond. The laminated structure can be formed in a number of ways, depending upon the compatability of the materials.

Coextrusion today means that (at least) two polymers are brought together in the melt state in a special die and extruded as a single extrudate. *Hot melt lamination* brings two (or more) molten layers of polymer together outside the dies, usually at a nip roll or at the top roll of a roll stack. Cap sheet lamination (or *coating*, if the layer is very thin) implies that a polymer melt is being cast or laminated onto an already-formed sheet. The surface of the substrate may have to be treated to ensure good adhesion. Typical surface treatments include corona discharge, flame treating, coating with tie layer polymers, or simply reheating. Adequate adhesion is ensured by passing the laminate through a series of cold nip rolls. In addition to material property monitoring and control of each of the layers, care must be taken to monitor laminate layer thickness and thickness distribution across the sheet. This can be done by sectioning the sheet and optically measuring thicknesses of the various layers. Warping and cupping during heating of multilayer sheet can become quite severe if the thermal expansion coefficients of the various layers are not carefully matched, or if dissimilar materials are used on opposite sides of the laminate centerline. The typical screening test for laminates is the same oven test described above for measuring the degree of orientation.

Another important concern to the thermoformer is interlayer delamination during heating and forming. This appears as "swarms" of bubbles or blisters in the finished part. In the extreme, two layers can separate completely. The primary cause for process delamination is inadequate adhesion during the sheet fabrication process. However, excessive or uncontrolled heating during thermoforming can severely reduce the interfacial adhesion forces, a transparent surface layer can allow radiant energy to penetrate to the interface, resulting in a loss of adhesion, a mismatch in thermal expansion coefficients of materials in different layers can cause one layer to separate from another, a gassy or wet layer can evolve moisture at the innerlayer, and so on. Thus the cause of delamination is not always apparent.

Sheet Appearance. In most applications, there are specific requirements on various aspects of sheet quality. These are called here simply "sheet appearance". Since these requirements vary from application to application, no general set of criteria can be established. The following serve merely as a check-list:

> *Linear Surface Marks.* Die lines, polish roll or calender roll marks typically are in the sheet direction and are straight linear lines. Some of these surface defects can be minor and can disappear when the sheet is heated. Die lines can be quite noticeable. Since they occur when the sheet is hot and being formed, they cannot be annealed out. Wavy linear lines can appear in some materials such as PET if the material is extruded at an excessively high extrusion melt temperature or if insufficient back pressure is applied to the die lips during extrusion. Wavy lines are frequently the downstream image of the tip of the rotating screw.

> *Holes, Pits and Lumps.* These are discrete, isolated, random occurrences in the sheet which do not disappear when the sheet is heated. On the contrary, these defects can lead to sheet splitting during forming, and so their frequency must be carefully monitored. There are three major sources of these defects: contaminated virgin resin, contaminated (or "damaged") regrind, and moisture in the extruder feed. Of these, contaminated or thermally damaged regrind is usually the most suspicious. Thermally sensitive resins can degrade during reprocessing and this off-spec polymer can form gel particles. *Gels* are usually resinous, thermally crosslinked polymer that cannot be remelted. Gel particles are a prominent source of defects. Off-spec virgin resin can contain such gel particles. Moisture can be eliminated as a source of defects by proper processing techniques.

Color Quality. Advanced color computer matching techniques have minimized the problems in obtaining good color matching. Nevertheless, it is incumbent upon the thermoformer to make certain that batch to batch color uniformity is met. The pigments used to produce the colors must be permanent, and must not change tint during typical processing operations. Color intensity across the sheet must of course also be quite uniform. In highly oriented thin-gage sheet and film such as oriented PS (OPS), light and dark regions can be produced if the orientation is not uniform. Obviously, the problem is more apparent with darker colors.

Surface Appearance. Gloss and embossing-retention represent extremes in sheet surface appearance. The degree of *gloss* can be regulated to some degree by the surface temperature of the finishing rolls, and to some degree by the extrudate temperature and the temperature and speed of the first roll the extrudate contacts. Usually the free surface of any extruded sheet has a higher gloss than the contact surface. Materials such as ABS or HIPS usually yield intrinsically semi-glossy sheet owing to their two-phase nature. High gloss can be obtained by high melt extrusion temperatures, slow extrusion speeds and high polish roll temperatures. On the other hand, *embossed design details* are best retained when the sheet temperature is quite low, the embossing roll is cold, and the material has very low elastic memory. The last point was discussed in Chapter 4 and is quite important. Keep in mind that embossing can be thought of as a form of thermoforming. If the pattern is empressed into a material that has excellent memory retention, that pattern will be lost when the sheet is reheated prior to forming. Thus the quality of the image retention from the embossing roll is less important than an initially correct selection of material to be embossed.

Processing Economics "Rules-of-Thumb"

The largest element in the price of any plastic article is the cost of the plastic. Graf (2) notes that injection molded parts costs were less than 2.75 times the material costs for 98% of the cases studied, and less than 1.8 to 2.1 times for 50% of the cases. The range of 1.5 to 10 times is considered to include all materials and all processes. The "factor of two" rule evolved from this observation. It states that a first approximation of the manufacturing cost can be obtained by doubling the material cost. It is well known that more expensive resins require more labor to produce a useful product (3). Although labor costs increase with increasing unit polymer cost, they do not increase in direct proportion to the resin cost. Therefore the multiplier for more expensive resins should be less than that for inexpensive ones. For thermoforming, the fixed and variable burden should also be less sensitive to resin costs. External costs, on the other hand, should increase with the most expensive materials, as seen in Table 8.3. The ratio here is *Selling Price per Unit Material Cost*, and so the ratio is substantially greater than 2.

The nature of the conversion from raw material to finished goods also has an influence on the selling price range (Table 8.4). Typically, injection molding and blow molding are more highly automated and energy efficient and less labor intensive than other conversion processes. The thermoforming raw material cost includes a cost for conversion to sheet. Graf's most probable thermoforming ratio range of 3 to 4 agrees well with the general ratio range of 2.8 to 4 in Table 8.3. These ratios should be used only to get an approximate cost for a conceptual part and not for comparative process analysis. More detailed comparisons are given below.

TABLE 8.3 THERMOFORMED PART SELLING PRICE RANGE

Material	Material Cost	+Labor Cost	+F/V Burden	=Mfg Cost	+External Charges	=Selling Price
LDPE, GPS, HDPE, PP, PVC	1	0.65–1	1.5	3.13–3.5	0.5	3.65–4
PET, ABS, PPS, Cellulosics	1	0.4 –0.75	1.25	2.65–3	0.4	3.05–3.4
PA6, PA66, PC, POM, PMMA	1	0.3 –0.5	1.0	2.3 –2.5	0.5	2.8 –3.0
(Engineering), PI, PES, PEEK	1	0.25–0.4	1.0	2.25–2.4	0.6	2.85–3.0

TABLE 8.4 COMPARATIVE PLASTICS PROCESS SELLING PRICE RANGE (2)
(Material Cost Factor = 1)

Process	Range	Average Part Range
Compression Molding	2 –10	3–5
Injection Molding	1.5– 5	2–3
Blow Molding	1.5– 5	2–3
Extrusion	2 – 5	3–4
Thermoforming	2 –10	3–5
Reinforced Construction	2 – 5	3–4

Global Production Costs

For the simplest case where an existing business is producing a single product, the unit cost for that product is obtained by dividing the average *Global Cost* of the business in a given unit of time by the average number of products produced in that time:

Product Cost = Business Expenses/Number of Products

Approximate costs for several products can be obtained this way with proper proportioning of business expenses. The items that make up typical *Manufacturing Plant Operating Costs* are given in Table 8.5. Plant operation is considered "steady state" when supplemental orders for currently manufactured goods are quoted. When new products similar to currently manufactured goods are quoted upon, the operation can also be considered "steady state", even though additional personnel and/or operational costs are incurred *but only so long as* the unit manufacturing time to produce the new product is a small fraction (3–8%) of the total product manufacturing time.

For a "steady state" operation, the unit time global cost can be obtained as shown in Table 8.6. Some items need definition:

> *Raw Materials* are all elements that go into the final product, such as sheet, additives and admixtures (such as surface-applied antistats or finishing and decorating materials), purchased components (such as inserts, decorations), and so on.

> Direct wages are paid to *Direct Laborers*. These are the people who contact the ma-

TABLE 8.5 MANUFACTURING PLANT OPERATING COSTS

Operating Labor
Maintenance Labor
Supervision
Top Management
Overhead Employees (Guards, Cafeteria)
Technical Support
Clerical Support (Secretaries, Computers)
Payroll Benefits
Utilities
    Fuel
    Steam
    Electricity
    Water Cooling/Treatment
Polymeric Materials
Additives and Admixtures
Molds, Cutters, Jigs, Fixtures
Supplies
Maintenance Materials
Overhead Materials
Local Taxes
Insurance
Contract Services (Cleaning People, Consultants)
Demurrage
Containers/Cartons/Pallets

TABLE 8.6 EXISTING BUSINESS THERMOFORMED PART BALANCE SHEET

Inventory of Raw Materials, Month X	–	
Additional Purchases, Month X	–	
Inventory of Raw Materials, Month X-1	(–)	
Cost of Raw Materials Consumed, Month X	–	
Direct Wages, Month X	–	
Direct Utilities, Month X	–	
Other Direct Expenses, Month X	–	
Direct Manufacturing Expense, Month X	=	=
Payroll Overhead, Month X	–	
Plant Overhead, Month X	–	
Other Indirect Expenses, Month X	–	
Indirect Manufacturing Expense, Month X	–	
Depreciation, Month X	(–)	
Indirect Costs, Month X	=	=
Net Cost of Work In Progress, Month X		=
Production Costs, Month X		=
Inventory of Finished Goods, Month X	–	
Inventory of Finished Goods, Month X-1	(–)	
Net Inventory Cost, Month X	=	=
Gross Profit, Month X		=
Sales, Month X		=

terial during processing. Direct laborers include dock and warehouse workers, quality control inspectors, thermoform machine operators, trimmers, packers, *and their immediate supervisors.*

Since it is hard to separate direct and indirect *utilities* (to proportion the amount of power required to operate thermoformers from that required to power the buildings and grounds), utilities are usually considered to be only direct utilities.

Note that the *direct manufacturing cost* simply represents the material and direct labor costs. Indirect costs deal specifically with the benefit package to direct laborers and the specific cost of the facility to house them, and with depreciation of the processing and ancillary equipment.

The *plant overhead* specifically *excludes* the cost of indirect labor people (such as management, technical staff, sales, clerical and support staff). The cost of their salaries, wages and benefits (SWB) is to be subtracted from the *gross profit.*

The net cost of work in progress is usually a small but potentially significant fraction of the total manufacturing cost. *Work in progress* is material that has been moved from inventory to the work stations, already formed, trimmed, inspected, or packed and not yet in finished product inventory. It can be assumed that these goods have values not much greater than raw material value. Occasionally, finished products are awaiting "rework", and so have values only slightly less than finished goods value. Many cost reduction efforts focus on minimizing the net cost of work in progress.

TABLE 8.7 THERMOFORMED PART BALANCE SHEET FOR NET PROFIT

Sales, Month X		=
Net Inventory, Month X		(-)
Production Costs, Month X		(-)
Gross Profit, Month X		=
Administration	(-)	
Sales/Marketing	(-)	
Shipping	(-)	
Advertising	(-)	
Technical Service	(-)	
R & D	(-)	
SAR, Month X	(=)	(=)
Net Profit Before Taxes, Month X		=

The *gross profit* is the sales revenue less production costs and increases in inventory value (Table 8.7). The *net profit* (before taxes) is the gross profit less SAR. Note that *SAR* includes the total cost (SWB) of *all* indirect labor, including top management.

If a single product is produced, the unit production cost and net profit can be obtained by simply dividing by the number of *good* or *saleable* pieces produced. Further, if all forming machines are the same and produce parts at the same throughput rate (for the same number of clock hours at the same efficiency), an accurate value for *machine hour cost* can be obtained:

$$M = \text{Machine Hour Cost} = \frac{\text{Production Cost}}{(\text{No. Machine} \times \text{No. h per Machine})}$$

For example, if 4 identical machines each operated 500 h/month at a steady state monthly production cost of $100,000, the average machine hour cost would be $50/h. In general, machine hour cost is the sum total annualized cost to operate a given machine, not including SAR:

$$\text{Total Annual Production Cost} = \sum M_i C_i$$

Today, computerized accounting procedures allow accurate record keeping on individual machines, and so such innacurate estimates are no longer used for final cost analyses.

Manufacturing Efficiencies

Overall *product efficiency* is the actual number of good or saleable parts divided by the ideal number that can be obtained from a given amount of material. *Process efficiency* is the actual number of parts produced in a given period of time, divided by the ideal number that can be produced in that same time period. Individual efficiencies make up these efficiencies. Care must be taken in applying efficiency factors, for they strongly influence part production cost and can penalize it if not applied correctly. *Not all efficiency factors are multiplicative.*

Although thermoforming machines are designed to operate continuously, they rarely do (Table 8.8). The industry average is about 70% or 6100 h/yr (500 h/mo). Machine efficiency depends upon the start-up condition of the thermoformer. Start-up times for forming new products on new tools with new materials are substantially longer than for momentary shutdowns (at break for example) (Table 8.9).

Operators are required for all times except maintenance, mold changeover or lack of business. Industry average is about 75% or 6600 h/yr. Operator efficiency is about 80% (although slightly lower on evening shifts and 10 h days). Thus, supervision is required to man machines for at least $[(0.70)/(0.80 \times 0.75)] - 1 = 17\%$ or 1060 h/yr, or approximately ½-man-

TABLE 8.8 THERMOFORMER MACHINE EFFICIENCY

Nature of Time	Clock Time	Percent of Total Time
Scheduled Maintenance		3
Emergency Maintenance		1
Shut-down – No Business or Mold Changeover		20
On – Idle, Not Running	X	2
Running – Startup, Setup, Shutdown – No Product (See Table 8.9 for Specific Start-up Times)	X	2
Running – Off-Spec Product	X	2
Running – Quality Product	X	70

TABLE 8.9 THERMOFORMER START-UP TIMES (Cycle = Time on Mold)

Stock Nature	Start-up Condition	Time
Roll Sheet	Restart after momentary stop (minutes)	4–10 cycles 1– 2 cycles
Roll Sheet	After extended shutdown (hours)	10 cycles–1 h 2– 4 cycles
Both	Cold start-old tool, known material (wks)	1– 2 h
Both	Cold start-new tool, known material	4–20 h
Both	Cold start-old tool, new material (homologous to old material)	2– 4 h
Both	Cold start-old tool, new material	4–20 h
Both	Cold start-new tool, new material	20–40 h

shift/yr. Industry standard range is 20–30%. For those parts where process cycle time controls production cycle time, labor efficiency does not usually affect the number of good parts produced. It serves to directly affect the production costs on each good part. If production rate is labor-controlled, as might be the case where extensive finishing and post-forming operations are required, labor efficiency can contribute directly to the overall manufacturing efficiency.

TABLE 8.10 THERMOFORMED PART EFFICIENCY

Nature of Loss	Percent	Comment on Types of Failure
Damage in Shipment	–	Sheet supplier's responsibility – return for credit
Fails Material Inspection	–	Blemishes, off-color. Same as above.
Damage in Warehouse	0– 1	Corner damage, crushed roll cores.
Damage during Drying	1	Handling, blistering, marring of soft surfaces.
Damage in transit to machine, during loading	0– 1	Cracks in edges of britle materials, scuffing.
Thermal loss	0– 1	Overheating, grain wash, discoloration. Thermally sensitive materials – PVC, ABS
Poorly formed	3– 5	Too thin, uneven wall thickness, blisters, webs. Can be serious if part dimensions are critical, extreme drawdown, low temperature.
Mold Stripping Damage	1– 2	Chill marks, blemishes. Low mold, sheet temperature.
Trimming Damage	1– 2	Dull saws, knives cause splits, surface melting produces, threads.
Reject by Final Inspection (Material Flaws)	1	Sheet imperfections (gels, draw lines) become more apparent *after* heating and forming.
Packing Damage	0– 1	Awkward, Bulky parts difficult to handle.
Damage in Warehouse, Miscellaneous causes	1– 2	Long-term inventory more susceptible. Also samples, cut-aparts, take-homes, and so on.
Customer Returns	2– 3	
	10–20	

Although the machine efficiency allows good parts to run about 70% of the year, there are product losses due to the inherent nature of the process itself (Table 8.10). The most significant of these are forming defects, but for certain products such as transparent optical goods, surface blemishes and distortion can become major reasons for product losses. Thus, product efficiency is 80–90%, but depends strongly upon the end-use of the product.

"Steady-State" Example

Consider a quotation on 2000 VCR covers of smoky PMMA (acrylic) by an on-going thermoforming operation:

1. Materials

> Unit Size: mm [in] $400 \times 300 \times 100$ dp.   [$18 \times 12 \times 4$ dp.]
> Avg. Thickness: mm [in] 2.5   [0.100]
>
> Areal Draw Ratio: $\dfrac{(400 \times 300 + 2 \times 100 \times 300 + 2 \times 100 \times 400)}{(400 \times 300)} = 2.11$
>
> Initial Thickness, mm [in]:$2.5 \times 2.11 = 5.4$ [$0.100 \times 2.11 = 0.211$]
> Material in Part: $40 \times 30 \times 0.54 = 648$ cm^3 [0.0264 ft^3]
> Supplied Sheet Dimensions, mm [in]:$600 \times 400 \times 5.4$ [$24 \times 16 \times 0.21$]
>
> Material Cost: $2.65/kg   [$1.20/lb]
> (Based on $0.90/lb + $0.30/lb conversion costs)
>
> PMMA [acrylic] specific gravity: 1.2 g/cm^3 [75 lb/ft^3]
>
> Finished Part Weight: $1.2 \times 648 = 778$ g   [$0.0264 \times 75 = 1.98$ lb]*
>
> *Inaccurate owing to round-off errors. Economics continue in metric units only.

2. Machine Cost/Efficiency:

> Machine Hour Cost: $40/h
> (Assumes labor, overhead,
> SWB, excludes profit)
>
> Steady-State Cycle Time: 3 min
> (Based on about 30 s/mm)
>
> Process Efficiency: 90%
>
> Set-up Time: 2 h (+ 10 Scrap Parts)
>
> Down-time: 10% of Run-time (+ 12 Scrap Parts)
>
> QC Retains: 100 Good Parts
>
> Time to Produce Good Parts: $(2000 + 100)/(0.9 \times 20) = 117$ h

3. Material Balance:

Good Parts Shipped:	2000
Good Parts Retained:	100
Bad Parts: $2 \times 117 =$	234
Set-up Scrap:	10
Down-Time Scrap:	12
Total Production:	2356

4. Material Costs

Purchased Sheet Wt: $2356 \times (60 \times 40 \times 0.54) \times 1.2 =$	3664 kg
Purchased Sheet Cost: $\$2.65 \times 3664 =$	$9710

Shipped Product Wt: $2000 \times 0.778 = 1556$ kg
Material Cost in Shipped Product: $\$2.65 \times 1556 =$ $4123

Scrap Value: $0.45/kg [$0.20/lb]
Scrap Value (Credit): $\$0.45 \times (3664 - 1556) =$ $950

Net Material Cost: $9710 - $950 = $8760

5. Unit Cost:

Net Material Cost:	$8760
Machine Hour Cost: $\$40/h \times 131\ h =$ $(117 + 2 + 12)$	5240
Finishing (routering, flame polishing edges, packaging ($8/h \times 131\ h$ – efficiency included)	1048
Appliques, Metallic Tape, Packaging $0.85/Good Unit:	1700
Manufacturing Cost:	$16748

Cost/Good Unit: $16748/2000 = \$8.37$

Cost/kg per Good Unit: $\$8.37/0.778$ kg $= \$10.76$

Material Cost Efficiency: $\$4123/\$8760 = 47\%$
Material Weight Efficiency: $1556/3664 = 42.5\%$

[The above example illustrates the interaction of manufacturing efficiencies and is not meant to illustrate a proper cost analysis. Machine hour costs should always be calculated from overall material and energy balances and raw materials should always include purchase prices of assembly components.]

Learning Curves

Efficiencies in the production of new products tend to be lower than those for established products (Table 8.9). As production continues, learned skills and shortcuts help to reduce the manufacturing cost per piece. This is referred to as the *Learning Curve* (Figure 8.4). Learning curve arithmetic can be used to predict the cost of future parts, as follows:

Let Y = cumulative-average cost (production time, manufacturing cost, whatever) per unit
X = cumulative production, units

Then $Y = KX^n$

where K = effective cost of the first unit
n = slope of the learning curve; $-1 < n < 0$

If Y_1 = cost of the first run of X_1 units, then the average unit cost of the *second* run is

$$\bar{Y} = \frac{Y_1[(X_2/X_1)^{n+1} - 1]}{[(X_2/X_1) - 1]}$$

where X_2 is number of units of the second run.

Further, C_x, the cost of the last unit in the production of X units, is given by:

$$C_x = K[X^{n+1} - (X-1)^{n+1}]$$

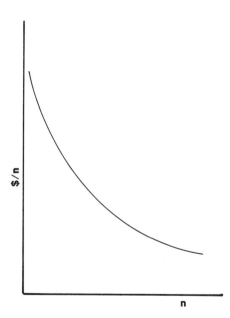

Figure 8.4 Learning Curve Schematic.
Abscissa: Number of Units.
Ordinate: Cost per Unit.

An example illustrates the learning curve. Consider the previous example where 2000 units were quoted on. Assume that this was the third order of identical units. The *actual* production costs of the first two orders were:

$$X_1 = 1000 \quad Y_1 = US\$12.15$$
$$X_2 = 1800 \quad Y_2 = \quad 10.15$$

The projected cost of a third order, $X_3 = 2000$ units, is found as follows. The first two lots $(1000 + 1800 = 2800)$ were manufactured at a cumulative unit cost of $(12.15 \times 1000 + 10.15 \times 1800)/2800 = \$10.864$. Thus:

$$\ln Y = \ln K + n \ln X$$

$$\ln 12.15 = \ln K + n \ln 1000$$
$$\underline{\ln 10.864 = \ln K + n \ln 2800}$$

$$n = -0.1086$$
$$K = 25.736 \text{ (unit cost of first piece)}$$

$$\hat{Y} = \frac{(10.864)[(4800/2800)^{0.891} - 1]}{[(4800/2800) - 1]} = \$9.38$$

Thus, the *average* unit cost for each of the next 2000 units should be \$9.38. The cost of the last unit made in the second run ($\#2800$) can be obtained as well:

$$C_x = 25.736[(2800)^{0.891} - (2799)^{0.891}] = \$9.68$$

The slope of the learning curve can be used as a guide to production efficiencies. The *Learning Curve Characteristic* is defined as:

$$LCC = 100 \ln^{-1}(n \ln 2)$$

For the example, $LCC = 93\%$. For $LCC = 100\%$, learning by experience is not possible and outside influences govern the process. If $LCC < 60\%$ (or so), learning has been expensive, the initial process was very inefficient, or the product was brought to market before the process was fully debugged. Established processing/product schemes have LCC's in the range of 90-95%.

Note again that the analysis is global and assumes that the detailed process analysis is well-known.

Isolated Venture Cost Analysis - Preliminary Items

Simple steady-state cost analyses cannot be used when a *New Business Venture* is considered. A new venture implies staffing and equipping a new, ground-up facility at a site remote from current operations. All projected manufacturing costs are based on production estimates obtained from accurate market research. Thorough market analysis is mandatory for major installations. It is far easier to predict operating expenses, capital costs, and processing costs than either sales or profits. Errors in manufacturing cost projections have much less effect on project profitability than changes in selling price, selling volume, raw material costs, and distribution/transportation costs.

In addition to accurate, detailed market size and price projections, it is necessary to understand fully the impact of two other elements on the proposed business venture: competition from other thermoformers and competition from other processors. Successful business ventures encourage imitators, and this must be included in long-range sales/profits projections. More significant to the early success of the venture is the effect of the potential simultaneous realization of the same (or similar) new product by two (or more) businesses. If the venture has a strong likelihood of this, sales/profit projections must reflect this in lowered expectations. Sales projections are frequently time-dependent, showing market penetration to saturation (maturation) over a finite number of years. This is followed by a decline in sales as new products replace the now-mature one. Profits, on the other hand, should continue to increase throughout the growth and maturation time, as production costs follow down the learning curve. Careful market analysis is needed to determine the time to maturation and the percent penetration at that time. This value (or range in values) is the basis for production cost development.

Manufacturing cost, production cost, and fabricating cost are considered here as identical and interchangeable terms. The cost to produce a sold product can be partitioned several ways. One way is in terms of direct and indirect costs:

$$\text{Production Costs} = \text{Direct Costs} + \text{Indirect Costs}$$

Direct costs are all those elements that are directly related to the production of goods.

$$\text{Direct Costs} = \text{Direct Labor} + \text{Direct Materials} + \text{Other Direct Expenses}$$

As noted earlier, *direct labor* is the cost for those people directly connected or in contact with the product from receipt of raw materials to loading of finished product. Typically, direct laborers are:

$$\text{Direct Labor} = \text{Machine Operators} + \text{Supervisors, Foremen} +$$
$$\text{Materials Handlers} + \text{Finishers} + \text{Inspectors}$$

Direct labor benefits packages may be included in direct labor costs. Inclusion must be so indicated, however.

Direct materials are all those materials that are consumed to produce the final product, and the direct materials cost should include credits for recovery of scrap:

$$\text{Direct Materials Cost} = \text{Incoming Costs} - \text{Returns} + \text{Scrap Recovery Credit}$$

Note that mold costs are *not* direct materials costs. Other direct costs include the cost of power needed to produce the goods, packaging materials costs (if not already included in direct materials costs) and outbound freight charges.

All other costs are indirect costs. These include:

Facility Costs
Indirect Labor/Benefits Costs
Depreciation/Amortization of Facilities
Mold/Mold Repair Costs
Repairs/Maintenance Costs
Expendable Supplies
Rental/Royalties Costs
Utility Costs (except Direct Costs)
Security/Cafeteria/Stockroom Costs
And so on.

Production costs can also be partitioned into those costs that are proportional to production rate and those that are not:

$$\text{Production costs} = \text{Variable Costs} + \text{Fixed Costs} + \text{Semivariable Costs}$$

A *fixed cost* is independent of production rate. Fixed costs are generally:

Insurance
Property Taxes
Plant Management
Engineering Personnel
Laboratory Personnel
Maintenance Supervision
Plant Security
Maintenance Shops (Toolroom, Mold Repair Room)
Stockroom
Depreciation of Facility
Depreciation of Ancillary Machinery,
    Lab Equipment, Computers, Electrical
    Equipment
Depreciation and Maintenance of
    Cafeteria, Roads, Parking Lots,
    Sewers, Fences
Fire Protection Costs/Fees
Accounting
Purchasing
Quality Control (all aspects)
Traffic Dispatching

Variable costs are those that are in direct proportion to the production rate. These costs include:

Raw Material
Operating Labor
Materials Handling
Royalties and Rentals
Supervision
Operating Supplies

Semivariable costs are those that increase with increasing production rate but not necessarily in direct proportion. Examples include:

Depreciation of Equipment
Maintenance
Repair and Replacement
Mold Costs
Utilities
Outbound Freight (to some extent)

Although there are general accounting software programs available for most office computers, there are none for detailed determination of projected production costs for new thermoforming business ventures. Several aspects of such projections should be kept in mind when developing such schemes. Some of the concepts that follow will be used in an example of a projected project cost for a new venture.

As noted, new product production rate is time-dependent. *All* production costs must be clearly accounted for, but *no* production costs should be counted more than once. *Depreciation* is a measure of the falling value of a piece of equipment. Special purpose equipment should be depreciated at faster rates than general purpose equipment. *Mold costs* should not include installation. Care should be taken in accounting for the cost of molds. Occasionally, mold costs are amortized over a fixed number of years (and so become semivariable costs). Or mold costs can be charged against a specific number of sold parts. Current practices set mold costs aside, to be noted in the projected production cost summary. The costs of mold installation and repair are variable costs and are to be included in all projected production cost analyses, however.

Once the need for a new thermoforming business venture has been established, determination of the optimum scheme for fabricating the requisite goods follows. Necessary fabricating equipment is researched. If the new product can be fabricated on already-available equipment, specifications are prepared and quotations requested. If specialized equipment is needed, development laboratories of equipment suppliers are contacted to determine cost and availability. Obvious decisions must be made on the capacity of the equipment, given the needed production rate (after maturation is reached). Oversized equipment may be inefficient and costly on a per unit basis. Undersized equipment may require additional maintenance costs and incremental costs of added shifts to maintain production rate. A table listing all capital cost items (and installation costs) should be made at this point.

When the proposed processing scheme has been accepted and the requisite equipment lists approved, production cost analyses follow. In the analysis that follows, the purchase price of the equipment is assumed to be known. Further, it is assumed that part design is (relatively) complete and so the unit material cost is known.

Typically, a production layout schematic is prepared showing equipment location and floor space, warehouse space, and so on (Figure 8.5). The process can then be "walked through and timed" and manpower allocated. With this information and estimates of other indirect costs, a quick product cost study (similar to the "steady-state" example above) should be made to ensure that the project is still economically feasible. Expected manufacturing efficiencies must be carefully thought out and included in the study.

In addition to standard material and labor costs, other elements must be included in the projected production cost. *Depreciation* and *profit* are two. Depreciation should be thought of as a tax-free portion of the difference between income and expenditure. The *average annual depreciation* is obtained by dividing some measure of the net cost of an item of fixed capital by its useful life. There are several ways of *discounting* the item:

> Straight-Line Depreciation
> Declining-Balance
> Double-Declining-Balance
> Sum-of-Years Digits
> Sinking-Fund

These methods are compared in standard economics texts (4, 5). Consider the simple straight-line depreciation. If F is the fixed value of the item, S is its scrap value, and N its useful life, then the average annual depreciation, D (for any year) is given as:

$$D = (F - S)/N$$

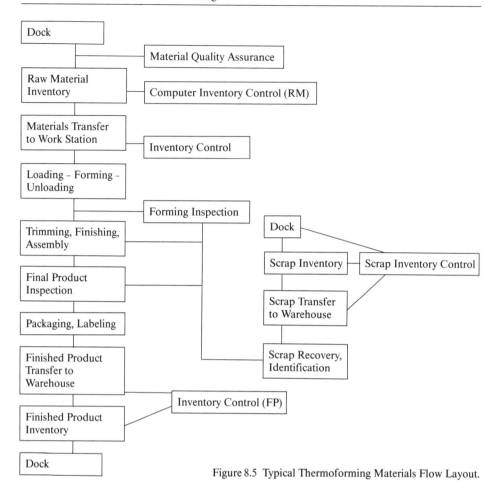

Figure 8.5 Typical Thermoforming Materials Flow Layout.

The *book value* (BV) after n years is:

$$BV = F - nD$$

For a $100,000 item with a $10,000 scrap value after ten years, the annual depreciation is D = $9,000 and the book value after 5 years is BV = $55,000. Now consider the sum-of-years digits depreciation, D:

$$D = [2(N - n + 1)/N(N + 1)] (F - S)$$

The item book value after n years is:

$$BV = 2[(1 + 2 + \ldots + (N - n))/N(N + 1)](F - S) + S$$

The annual depreciation and book value at the nth year for the item in the prior example are given in Table 8.11.

It is assumed that for an isolated venture, external financial sources must be sought. The *in-*

TABLE 8.11 ANNUAL DEPRECIATION AND BOOK VALUE OF THERMOFORM EQUIPMENT (Sum-of-Years Digits)
(Capital Cost = $ 100 000 Scrap Value = $ 10 000 Useful Life = 10 Years)

Year	Annual Depreciation, $	Book Value, $
0	18 000	100 000
1	16 360	83 640
2	14 730	68 910
3	13 100	57 450
4	11 450	49 270
5	9 820	34 550
6	8 180	26 360
7	6 550	19 820
8	4 910	14 910
9	3 300	11 640
10	1 640	10 000

terest on borrowed monies is the inducement offered to the lender to make the risk acceptable. Interest rates vary but are usually greater than the prevailing prime lending rate. The *capitalized cost of equipment* (FK) should include the interest on borrowed money. This is given as:

$$FK = [F - S/(1+i)^M][(1+i)^M/(1+i)^{M-1}]$$

where i is the interest rate fraction and M is the number of payment years. For the example, if $i = 0.15$ and $M = 8$, $FK = \$143,700$. Thus, $\$143,700 - \$100,000 = \$43,700$ is the cost of money for this item and is an indirect cost to be charged against production costs over the $M = 8$ year period.

When a business is begun, monies must be set aside in two general areas: working capital and start-up capital. *Start-up capital* are the financial resources needed to meet immediate costs, and are in reality a portion of the working capital costs. Some of these costs might be:

Initial interest on borrowed monies for:
    Site Evaluation
    Site Preparation
    Building Construction
Building Permits/Operating Licenses
Equipment Installation
Equipment Start-Up Costs, including Labor
Personnel Living Expenses
Initial Payment on Materials
Contingency Fees/Expenses
Utility Deposits
And so on

Working capital is the amount of money needed to meet day-to-day operating expenses (Table 8.12). Initially, nearly all working capital is start-up capital. Within a few months of established production, start-up costs should be small when compared with net costs for materials and accounts (Figure 8.6).

Projected production costs ultimately focus on *profit*. For a business to succeed a reasonable fraction of the product selling price must be returned as profit. Two types of profitabili-

TABLE 8.12 WORKING CAPITAL COSTS

Inventories
   Raw Materials
   Intermediate Materials (Warehoused)
   Ancillary Materials (Purchased Components, Packaging)
   Finished Product (Unpacked, Shipment-Ready)

Start-up Costs
   Payrolls
   Supplies
   Raw Materials
   Utility Deposits

Money
   Emergency Funds
   (Accounts Receivables – Accounts Payable) Monies

Running Costs
   Inventory Control
   Warehousing
   Transportation
   Insurance Deposits
   Taxes (Prepayments only)

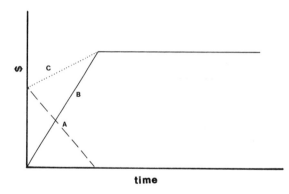

Figure 8.6 Working Capital Costs – Schematic. Abscissa: Time, yrs. Ordinate: Annual Cost. A: Start-Up Costs. B: Non-Start-Up Costs. C: Working Capital. (Figure redrawn, adapted from (5), used with expressed written permission of McGraw-Hill Book Co., Inc., in accordance with copyright protection laws.)

ty are considered here: rate-of-return and discounted-cash-flow. *Rate-of-return* is a traditional method:

$$\text{Fractional Rate-of-Return} = \frac{\text{Annual Profit}}{\text{Invested Capital}}$$

Unfortunately, there are several ways of defining profit and invested capital. Profit could be net annual profit before or after taxes or annual cash income before or after taxes. Capital can be the original invested capital, depreciated investment, current investment, or time-averaged investment. If the fractional rate of return, i, is based on the initial cash investment (F) and the net annual profit after taxes (PAT), it can be written as:

$$i = PAT/F$$

The net annual cash income after taxes (CIAT) is the sum of the net annual profit after taxes and the average annual depreciation (D):

$$CIAT = PAT + D$$

D is obtained from depreciation formulae, such as the sum-of-years digits method used in the example above. The effect of depreciation on rate-of-return is shown in Figure 8.7 (5). Rate-of-return methods have been refined to include more carefully calculated items such as land value appreciation and initial start-up costs. Similarly, there are other traditional techniques as *payback period*, the time needed for net cash flow to recoup original fixed capital costs. Typically, all these techniques lack flexibility to account for the time-dependent nature of new ventures.

Figure 8.7 Rate-of-Return for Sum-of-Years Digits Depreciation. t: Time, yrs. r: Rate-of-Return, %. i: Interest rate of return, based on net annual profit after taxes. f: Depreciation rate. P: Gross rate of return, ratio of net annual cash income to total capital cost. P = i + f. See (5) for additional details. (Figure redrawn, adapted from (5), used with expressed written permission of McGraw-Hill Book Co., Inc., in accordance with copyright protection laws.)

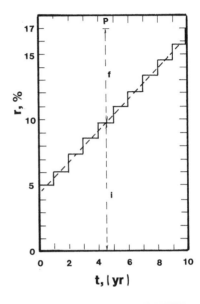

Figure 8.8 Example of Time-Dependent Annual Discounted Cash Flow. DCF: Discounted Cash Flow. t: Time, yr. i: Discounted Cash-Flow Rate-of-Return. See (5) for additional details. (Figure redrawn, adapted with expressed written permission of McGraw-Hill Book Co., Inc., in accordance with copyright protection laws.)

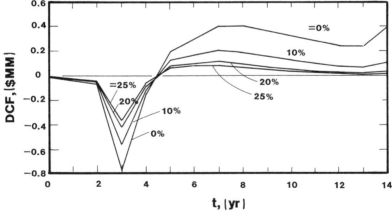

Profitability should be a quantification of the attractiveness of taking a risk. *Discounted cash-flow rate-of-return (i)* and *net present worth (NPW)* are two such quantifying methods. Cash-flow (CF) is essentially the transient money supply. It can be shown that cash-flow value is much greater at the beginning of a project than when the project is fully established. Initially, cash-flow is negative. Start-up costs are not counterbalanced by incoming sales receipts. Eventually, start-up costs drop to zero, working capital costs stabilize, and incoming monies exceed expenditures, producing a positive cash-flow (Figure 8.8 (5)). *Cumulative cash-flow* (CCF) is the sum of unit time cash-flows. The break-even point is the number of years required to recoup the invested money. The present value P of a future sum of money f is given as:

$$P = fd = f/(1+i)^n$$

where d is the discount factor, i is (now) the *discounted cash-flow rate-of-return*, and n is the number of years. The discounted cash-flow rate-of-return (i) is also known as the *profitability index* (PI) or the *true rate-of-return*. If CF is the annual cash-flow, the annual *discounted cash-flow* DCF is given as:

$$DCF = CF/(1+i)^n$$

Net present worth (NPW) is the sum of the annual discounted cash-flows to the year n:

$$NPW = \sum_{}^{n} DCF_n$$

To obtain a suitable value for i, (the discounted cash-flow rate-of-return), the net present worth is assumed to go to zero at some year, N, say:

$$NPW = CF_0/(1+i)^0 + CF_1/(1+i)^1 + CF_2/(1+i)^2 + \\ \ldots + C_{FN}/(1+i)^N = 0$$

Since i is implicit, it is obtained by iteration, graphical means or table interpolation. The effective use of NPW and i in making sound venture decisions depends upon the accuracy of annual cash-flow estimates.

Several points are worth noting here. First, depreciation is not considered as a separate expense. It is instead deducted from the annual cash-flow prior to computing the net present worth. The discounted cash-flow rate-of-return (i) represents the fraction of money returned on the investment *plus* sufficient funds to repay the original investment, interest on borrowed monies, taxes and expenses. A made-up example (Tables 8.13 and 8.14) illustrates the

TABLE 8.13 NET PRESENT WORTH (NPW) AND DISCOUNTED CASH-FLOW RATE-OF-RETURN (i) (Assumptions for Example)

(F) Capital Equipment Cost (One-Time):	$1 000 000
(S) Scrap Value:	-0-
(N) Process NPW = 0 in 10 years	
(WC) Working Capital Cost:	160 000
(L) Cost of Land:	40 000
(K = F + WC + L) Total Capital Cost:	1 200 000
(D) Annual S.L. Depreciation: D = (F–S)/N	100 000
(E) Annual Expenses = $100 000 + n × $10 000	
($) Annual Sales:	
Year 0– 1	-0-
Year 2	$1500 M
Year 3– 4	$1000 M
Year 5– 7	$ 800 M
Year 8–10	$ 400 M

TABLE 8.14 NET PRESENT WORTH – AN EXAMPLE

Year	$, Sales, M$	E, Expenses, M$	$-E=I Income, M$	D, Depreciation, M$	I-D=TI Taxable Income, M$	T=(TI)t Tax (50%) M$	(K=F+WC+L) Total Capital Cost, M$	(TI-T-K) (CF) Cash Flow M$	DCF=(CF)d* Discounted Cash Flow, M$ i=10%	i=15%	NPW, Net Present Worth, M$ i=10%	i=15%
0	0	0	0	0	0	0	1200	-1200	-1200	-1200	-1200	-1200
1	0	110	-110	100	-210	0	0	-210	-191	-183	-1391	-1383
2	1500	120	1380	100	1280	640	0	640	528	484	-863	-899
3	1000	130	870	100	770	385	0	385	298	253	-565	-646
4	1000	140	860	100	760	380	0	380	260	217	-305	-429
5	800	150	550	100	450	225	0	225	140	119	-165	-317
6	800	160	540	100	440	220	0	220	124	95	-41	-222
7	800	170	530	100	430	215	0	215	110	81	69	-141
8	400	180	220	100	120	60	0	60	28	20	97	-121
9	400	190	210	100	110	55	0	55	23	16	120	-105
10	400	200	200	100	100	50	-200	250	97	62	217	-43
	7100	1550	5550	1000	4550	2330	1000					

* Discount factor, d, given in Table 8.23.

interactions of cash-flow (CF), net present worth (NPW), and discounted cash-flow rate-of-return (i). As seen, to achieve a zero value for net present worth (NPW) at 10 years, the discounted cash-flow rate-of-return must be $i = 14.2\%$. Created values for annual sales and expenses are used here. The break-even point (where actual costs are recouped) occurs shortly after year 5.

The *payback period (PBP)* can now be defined in terms of the discounted cash-flow rate-of-return (i). Simply, it represents the ratio of capital expenditures to cash flow. For a single capital investment (F) and an annual cash-flow (CF), the payback period is:

$$PBP = F/CF$$

If the net present worth (NPW) to the nth year is given as:

$$NPW = F - CF(d') = F - CF \sum (1+i)^{-n}$$

then, $PBP = d'$. If $n = \infty$, $PBP = (1/i)_{max}$. For example, if the payback period is 5 years, the maximum discounted cash-flow rate-of-return is $i = 20\%$.

The equations presented so far assume zero inflation. If a general average *inflation* (I) is included, net present worth (NPW) is defined as:

$$NPW = CF_0 + \sum^{n} CF_n/[(1+i)^n (1+I)^n]$$

The effect on discounted cash-flow rate-of-return (i) is to generate a new rate of return, called the *effective discounted cash-flow rate-of-return (ie)*:

$$ie = (1+i)/(1+I) - 1$$

For example, if $i = 20\%$ with an inflation rate of $I = 10\%$, the effective value of i (ie) would be only 9.1%. Other terms are reduced in similar manners.

New Venture Economics Applied to Thermoforming

The previous discussion and examples served to introduce certain important general accounting terms. Application to a new thermoforming business venture is best shown by example. Consider a new business venture to produce crystallizing PET dinner trays for the convertible oven convenience food market (6). From development efforts, the following production elements have been defined:

Part Dimension: $203 \times 254 \times 19$ mm (dp)   [$8 \times 10 \times \frac{3}{4}$ in (dp)]

Finished Part Average
   Wall Thickness: 0.75 mm   [0.030 in]
   Draw Ratio: 1.34
   Initial Sheet Thickness: 1.0 mm   [0.040 in]
   On-Mold Cycle Time: 12 s

After careful evaluation, engineering selects a special purpose, roll fed thermoformer with rapid-response high-temperature quartz heaters, sheet temperature monitoring and feed-back control, but with (near) standard die-cut equipment. Part layout on its platen yields 4 trays per cycle with 50% of the sheet being web, to be recycled or sold as reclaim. The fixed capital cost for the unit is $400M (Table 8.15) and the total one-time capital costs, including building and land, are estimated to be $1300 M.* The unit selected by engineering has a maximum production rate of:

$$\text{MPR} = (24.365)(\text{h/yr}) \times (\text{unit/cycle}) \times (\text{cycle/h})$$

$$= 10.5 \, \text{MM units/yr*}$$

Through careful discussions with prospective customers, an estimate of the selling price can be determined. This should be ascertained very early in the venture analysis to determine if the effort is worth pursuing. If the selling price is unknown, an early estimate can be made from the rules-of-thumb given above. In this study, marketing estimates maximum sales of 4 MM units/yr at a selling price of $1.20/unit. They estimate that sales will build to this level in 2 years and plan on discontinuing the product after 5 years. Price elasticity allows sales of 6 MM units/yr at a selling price of $1.00/unit. One shift (2000 h/yr) can produce a maximum of 2.4 MM units/yr. Thus, a 3-shift operation (no weekends) is indicated.

TABLE 8.15 FIXED CAPITAL AND MOLD COSTS THERMOFORMED CPET TRAY

A. Fixed Capital Costs

Item	Capital Cost, M$	Scrap Value, M$	5 Yr SL Depreciation M$	Instaltion, M$
Thermoformer-Rollfed	280			27
Trim Station (Web Rollup)	47			8
Web Regrind	12			–
Ancillary Equipment (Mold Heaters, Warehouse Equipment)	21			–
Contingency	40			5
	400	0	80	40
Building: 40000 ft^2 @ $ 20/ft^2 (including Heated Warehouse)	800	400	80	–
Land: 4 acres @ $ 125000 (Fully Improved)	100	100	0	–
Total Capital Cost, M$:	1300	500	160	40

B. Mold Costs:
   Steel Molds, 4-Cavity, Channeled for Oil Heat
   Unit Cost: $ 2500
   Lifetime: 1 MM Units
   Contingency: 20%
   To Produce 2 MM Good Parts: $3.175 \times 1.2 = 3.81 \, (=4) \times \$ 2500 = 10 \, \text{M\$}$
   To Produce 4 MM Good Parts: $6.35 \times 1.2 = 7.6 \, (=8) \times \$ 2500 = 20 \, \text{M\$}$

* "M" equals 1000 here. "MM" equals 1,000,000. "M" in technical units equals 1,000,000.

TABLE 8.16 SHEET MATERIAL COST THERMOFORMED CPET TRAY
Sheet Material Cost: $ 2/kg [$ 0.90/lb]
Sheet Contains 10% New Regrind
Scrap Value of Regrind: $ 0.45/kg [$ 0.20/lb]   PET sp. gr. = 1.37 g/cm^3.
Material Used in Single Tray:
    $20.3 \times 25.4 \times 0.1 = 51.6$ cm^3 $[8 \times 10 \times 0.04/32.1$ in$^3]$

	51.6 cm^3 × 1.37	= 70.6 g	[3.1 × 62.4 × 1.37/1728 = 0.156 lb]
	Web = 50% Sheet	= 70.6	[= 0.156]
Total Single Tray Wt.		= 141.2 g	[= 0.311 lb]

Code	Item	2 MM Trays/yr		4 MM Trays/yr	
Nl	Actual Number of Trays Needed, = No/(0.9 × 0.7)	3.175		6.35	
MT	Material Used, Mkg [Mlb] Nl × wt.	448	[987]	895	[1975]
Mt	Material Sold as Trays, Nox(wt), Mkg [Mlb]	141	[311]	282	[620]
R	Material Reclaimed, (MT − Mt), Mkg [Mlb]	307	[676]	613	[1355]
F'	Fraction Recovered in New Sheet, MT × 0.1, Mkg [Mlb]	45	[99]	90	[198]
S'	Amount Sold as Scrap (R − F'), Mkg [Mlb]	262	[577]	523	[1157]
VS	Scrap Value, M$	118	[115]*	235	[231]*
G	Gross Material Cost, M$	896	[888]*	1790	[1778]*
MC	Net Material Cost, M$ (G − VS)	778	[773]*	1555	[1547]*
	Value Continued to Table 8.17	775		1550	

*Round-Off Error in Part Weight

Purchasing has selected a special-purpose controlled-crystallizing PET sheet at $1.54/kg [$0.70/lb] and can have it converted to sheet at $0.45/kg [$0.20/lb]. Only 10% new regrind can be used, however. The rest is to be sold at $0.45/kg [$0.20/lb]. Material costs are given in Table 8.16. Management has found capital investment monies at 10%, a (semi)skilled labor force at an average wage of $6/h, plus $2/h benefits package, and no shift differential. Only one-half the labor force is needed the first year. Management would like NPW = 0 in five years. Therefore capital equipment is to be straight-line depreciated over 5 years. The building and equipment scrap values are shown in Table 8.15. The land does not decrease in value. (For this example only.) Molds are expected to last 1 MM units and cost $2500 each (Table 8.15). Engineering estimates that the special purpose machine may be functional only 70% of the clock operating time. They expect good parts 90% of the functional time. Thus, three shifts (6000 h/yr) could produce:

$$\text{Good units/yr} = 6000 \ (\text{h/yr}) \times 4 \times (5 \times 60) \times 0.9 \times 0.7 = 4.5 \ \text{MM}$$

Each shift requires 2 machine operators, 1 materials handler, one supervisor and one QC/inspector as direct labor. One maintenance man, one shipping clerk, one mold man and one handyman are needed each shift as indirect labor. Part-time shop secretarial help is also expected. Power company costs are estimated to be $3 per machine operating hour (Table 8.17).

Management has also determined property taxes to be $30,000/yr or 2.3% of fixed capital cost. (The range is usually 1.5 to 3%.) Insurance is $15,000/yr or 1.2% of the fixed capital cost. (The range is typically 1 to 2%.)

TABLE 8.17 MANUFACTURING COSTS THERMOFORMED CPET TRAY

Costs	Year 1	Year 2–5
Direct Manufacturing Costs:		
Raw Materials (Table 8.16), M$:	775	1550
Operating Labor (Table 8.18), M$:	96	180
Utilities, M$:	8	16
Maintenance (Table 8.18), M$:		
Labor	32	48
Supplies	32	48
	943	1842
Indirect Manufacturing Costs, (Excluding SAR, Taxes):		
Labor (Table 8.18), M$:	126	182
Benefits (All Labor) (Table 8.18), M$:	76	124
Operating Supplies/Expenses, M$:	60	90
Molds (Table 8.15), M$:	10	20
	272	416
SAR (Table 8.19), M$:	194	238
Property Taxes, MS:	30	30
Insurance, M$:	15	15
	239	283
Total Manufacturing Costs, M$:	1454	2541
Working Capital Costs (Table 8.20), M$:	515	1029
Start-Up Costs (Table 8.21), M$:	307	–
Operating Expenses, M$:	2276	3570

TABLE 8.18 LABOR COSTS THERMOFORMED CPET TRAY

Item	Year 1	Year 2–5
Number of Good Trays Needed, MM	2	4
Min. Number Hours to Produce Good Trays	1667	3333
Actual Number Hours to Produce Good Trays (Operating Hours)	2646	5291
Number Shifts at 2000 h/shift yr.	1.3	2.7
Assumed No Shifts	1*	3
Total Labor (DL = 5/shift)	8*	15
Min. DL Cost at $ 6/h, M$ (Op. hrs) × $ 6/h × 5	79	159
DL Cost Based on Shifts, M$	96	180
Maintenance Labor (Total)	2	3
Maintenance Cost at $ 8/h, M$	32	48
Maintenance Supplies (= Maintenance Cost), M$	32	48
Additional Indirect Labor (Total)		
Foreman	2	3
Mold Shop	2	3
Shipping Clerk	2	2
Shop Secretary	1	2
Handyman	2	3
	9	13
Indirect Labor Cost at $ 7/h, M$	126	182
Total Labor Force	19	31
Benefits at $ 2/h (All Labor), M$	76	124

* One Shift + Overtime

TABLE 8.19 SALES, ADMINISTRATION, RESEARCH (SAR) COSTS THERMO-FORMED CPET TRAY

Item	Year 1	Year 2-5
Administration (Plant Manager), M$	60	60
Operations Manager, M$	–	35
Sales/Marketing, M$	35	35
Purchasing, M$	25	25
Tech Service/Engineer, M$	35	35
	155	190
Benefits (25%)	39	48
Total SAR	194	238

TABLE 8.20 WORKING CAPITAL COSTS (EXCLUDING START-UP COSTS) THERMOFORMED CPET TRAY

Item	Year 1	Year 2-5
Net Accounts (Receivables – Payables), 10% Annual Product Value (3X Material Cost), M$	233	465
(Net) Raw Materials Inventories, 30 Days, M$	65	129
Finished Product Inventories, 30 Days, at 3X Material Cost, M$	194	388
	492	982
Contingencies (20% Net Accounts)	23	47
Working Capital Costs, M$	515	1029

TABLE 8.21 START-UP COSTS – FIRST YEAR ONLY THERMOFORMED CPET TRAY

Item	Cost, M$
Installation Costs (Table 8.15)	40
Permits, Utilities Deposits	2
Outside Equipment Rental/Start-up	20
Personnel On-Site Living Expenses, Personnel Hiring Costs	25
Initital Payment on Raw Materials	120
Interest on Start-Up Monies	80
Contingency Fees/Expenses	20
Total Start-Up Expenses, M$	307

With the various elements of the production in mind, total manufacturing costs can be obtained (Table 8.17). Operating expenses are given here as the sum of total manufacturing costs, start-up costs and working capital costs. If the selling price is unknown, a net present worth table can be constructed with a range in values, for several values of (i), the discounted cash-flow rate-of-return. Unit selling prices of $1.25 and $1.15 bracket the proposed unit selling price of $1.20 (Table 8.22). The PI = i for a unit selling price of $1.25 is i = 28%. At $1.15, the interpolation gives i = 13.6%, and for $1.20, i is expected to be about 21% (Figure 8.9). The effect of price elasticity on projected sales can be illustrated by repeating the above

TABLE 8.22 NET PRESENT WORTH (NPW) – DISCOUNTED CASH-FLOW RATE-OF-RETURN (1) THERMOFORMED CPET TRAT

A. 4 MM Units/Yr Selling at $ 1.25/Unit

Year	Sales M$	Expenses M$	Income M$	Depreciation, M$	Taxable Income, M$	50% Tax M$	Total Cap. Cost, M$	Cash Flow, M$	Discounted Cash-Flow* i=10%	20%	30%	NPW i=10%	20%	30%
0	0	0	0	0	0	0	-1300	-1300	-1300	-1300	-1300	-1300	-1300	-1300
1	2500	2276	224	160	64	32	0	32	29	27	25	-1271	-1273	-1275
2	5000	3570	1430	160	1270	635	0	635	525	469	376	-746	-804	-899
3	5000	3570	1430	160	1270	635	0	635	477	368	289	-269	-436	-610
4	5000	3570	1430	160	1270	635	0	635	434	306	222	165	-130	-388
5	5000	3570	1430	160	1270	635	500	1135	705	456	305	870	326	83

B. 4 MM Units/Yr Selling at $ 1.15/Unit

Year	Sales M$	Expenses M$	Income M$	Depreciation, M$	Taxable Income, M$	50% Tax M$	Total Cap. Cost, M$	Cash Flow, M$	Discounted Cash-Flow* i=10%	20%	30%	NPW i=10%	20%	30%
0	0	0	0	0	0	0	-1300	-1300	-1300	-1300	x	-1300	-1300	x
1	2300	2276	24	160	-136	0	0	-136	-124	-113	x	-1424	-1413	x
2	4600	3570	1030	160	870	435	0	435	359	321	x	-1065	-1092	x
3	4600	3570	1030	160	870	435	0	435	327	252	x	-738	-840	x
4	4600	3570	1030	160	870	435	0	435	297	210	x	-441	-630	x
5	4600	3570	1030	160	870	435	500	935	581	376	x	140	-254	x

C. 6 MM Units/Yr Selling at $ 1.10/Unit

Year	Sales M$	Expenses M$	Income M$	Depreciation, M$	Taxable Income, M$	50% Tax M$	Total Cap. Cost, M$	Cash Flow, M$	Discounted Cash-Flow* i=10%	20%	30%	NPW i=10%	20%	30%
0	0	0	0	0	0	0	-1300	-1300	-1300	-1300	-1300	-1300	-1300	-1300
1	3300	2903	397	160	237	118	0	119	108	99	92	-1192	-1201	-1208
2	6600	4553	2047	160	1887	943	0	944	780	697	559	-412	-504	-649
3	6600	4553	2047	160	1887	943	0	944	709	547	430	297	43	-219
4	6600	4553	2047	160	1887	943	0	944	645	455	330	942	498	111
5	6600	4553	2047	160	1887	943	500	1444	897	580	388	1839	1078	499

D. 6 MM Units/Yr Selling at $ 1.00/Unit

Year	Sales M$	Expenses M$	Income M$	Depreciation, M$	Taxable Income, M$	50% Tax M$	Total Cap. Cost, M$	Cash Flow, M$	Discounted Cash-Flow* i=10%	20%	30%	NPW i=10%	20%	30%
0	0	0	0	0	0	0	-1300	-1300	-1300	-1300	-1300	-1300	-1300	-1300
1	3000	2903	97	160	-63	0	0	-63	-57	-52	-48	-1357	-1352	-1348
2	6000	4553	1447	160	1287	643	0	644	532	475	381	-825	-877	-967
3	6000	4553	1447	160	1287	643	0	644	484	373	293	-341	-504	-674
4	6000	4553	1447	160	1287	643	0	644	440	310	225	99	-194	-449
5	6000	4553	1447	160	1287	643	500	1144	710	460	308	809	266	141

* Values for Discount Factor given in Table 8.23.   x: not calculated.

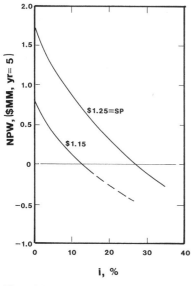

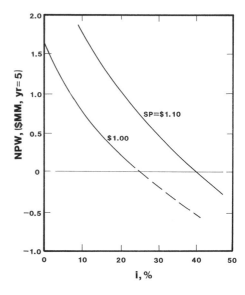

Figure 8.9 Net Present Worth for Thermoform Molding 4 MM CPET Trays. NPW: Net Present Worth, $MM, at Year 5. i: Discounted Cash-Flow Rate of Return (PI = Profitability Index). SP: Selling Price. Top Curve: $1.25. Bottom Curve: $1.15.

Figure 8.10 Net Present Worth for Thermoform Molding 6 MM CPET Trays. NPW: Net Present Worth, $MM, at Year 5. i: Discounted Cash-Flow Rate of Return (PI = Profitability Index). SP: Selling Price. Top Curve: $1.10. Bottom Curve: $1.00.

analyses at 6 MM units/yr. Variable costs are approximately proportional to production throughput. Fixed costs are constant. Thus expenses do not increase in direct proportion to throughput rate. For purposes of this example (only), assume expenses to increase in proportion to throughput rate to a power b:

$$Exp = A \, (unit)^b \qquad 0 < b < 1$$

For b = 0, the operation is controlled entirely by fixed costs. For b = 1, the operation is entirely driven by variable costs. b = 0.6 is an established scale-up power factor for many pro-

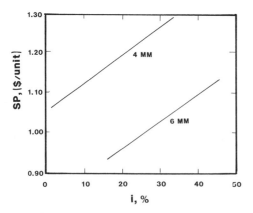

Figure 8.11 Selling Price-Profit for Thermoform Molding CPET Trays. SP: Selling Price, $/Unit. i: Discounted cash-flow rate of return, %. Curve 4: 4 MM Trays. Curve 6: 6 MM Trays.

TABLE 8.23 DISCOUNT FACTOR $d = (1+i)^{-n}$

Year	$i=0$	$=10\%$	$=15\%$	$=20\%$	$=30\%$	$=40\%$
0	1.00	1.000	1.000	1.000	1.000	1.000
1	1.00	0.909	0.870	0.833	0.769	0.714
2	1.00	0.826	0.756	0.738	0.592	0.510
3	1.00	0.751	0.658	0.579	0.455	0.364
4	1.00	0.683	0.572	0.482	0.350	0.260
5	1.00	0.621	0.497	0.402	0.269	0.186
6	1.00	0.564	0.432	0.335	0.207	0.133
7	1.00	0.513	0.376	0.279	0.159	0.0949
8	1.00	0.467	0.327	0.233	0.123	0.0678
9	1.00	0.424	0.284	0.194	0.0943	0.0484
10	1.00	0.386	0.247	0.162	0.0725	0.0346

CUMULATIVE DISCOUNT FACTOR

$i=$	Year 1-4	Year 1-9
0%	4.00	9.00
10	3.169	5.758
15	2.856	4.772
20	2.632	4.075
30	2.166	3.018
40	1.848	2.378

cesses (7). For a 50% increase in production rate, expenses are expected to increase 27.5%. This scale-up is used to estimate expenses and discounted cash-flow rate-of-return (i) for 6 MM annual units at $1.10 and $1.00 (Table 8.22 and Figure 8.10). If management agrees to a given value for i, the selling price can be used at *any* production rate (up to the real capacity of the equipment). For example, if $i = 20\%$ is acceptable, the unit selling price at 4 MM units/yr would be about $1.20. At 6 MM, it would be about $0.96. By (intelligent) interpolation, the unit price at 5 MM and $i = 20\%$ should be about $1.02–$1.05 (Figure 8.11).

Once the basic elements of the process are well understood, a simple computer program can be written to provide more accurate, rapid, and complete price/capacity/expense profiles. This program can then be used to develop other business scenarios and compare such effects as overtime pay versus additional shift addition, and so on.

Entrepreneurial Risk

Many new ventures are proposed by *entrepreneurs*. Venture capitalists frequently require that entrepreneurial projects pay a *risk factor*, in excess of the discounted cash-flow rate-of-return. Since working capital and (for the most part) costs for buildings and grounds can be (in theory) fully recovered, the added risk factor should be applied only to those costs for items that are lost by premature project termination or liquidation. If CAC is the cost of allocated capital and RR is the risk rate, the minimum acceptable rate (MAR) is:

$$MAR = CAC + RR$$

This can be viewed in terms of the discounted cash-flow rate-of-return (i) as:

$$1 + i = (1 + BIR)(1 + MAR)$$

Again, i is the net return on invested capital, given as:

> i, Net Return = Gross Return − Payback of Capital − Interest on Borrowed Capital − Taxes − Other Expenses

(i) is then the entrepreneurial return for *managing* the capital used in the venture. BIR is the best risk-free interest rate (from banks or bonds or treasury notes), and MAR is now the *entrepreneurial risk factor*. In the PET tray example, if i = 20% and the best risk-free interest rate, BIR = 10%, the entrepreneurial risk factor is MAR = 9.1%. Consider $100,000 deposited in a bank at 10%. Borrow half at 15% and add a 50% corporate tax. The risk-free income is:

$$[\$100,000 \times 0.1 - (0.5)(\$100,000) \times 0.15](1 - 0.5) = \$1250$$

or BIR = $1250/$100,000 = 0.0125. The same money invested in a project with an after-tax return, i = 10% produces an entrepreneurial risk factor of 8.6% or $8600 on the $100,000 investment. If the entrepreneur had invested his own money in the venture, he would have achieved an after-tax return of (0.1)(1 − 0.5) = 5% on $50,000 or $2500 on $100,000. Thus by *managing* the venture, the entrepreneur obtains an effective tax-free income of $8600 − $2500 = $6100 on his $100,000 effort.

The Incremental Operation

An incremental expansion usually includes addition of a new, dedicated process to an existing plant operation to produce a new product (Table 8.1). If the new process/product is very similar to the existing operation, costs can be projected from existing business costs. On the other hand, if the new process/product is substantially different from current products, a new business venture plan should be proposed. In this case, certain costs such as start-up costs and stand-alone ancillary facilities costs (land, cafeteria, parking lots) can be reduced or eliminated. If a modified new venture plan is used, most incremental operating costs are usually much better documented than those for isolated ventures. The information collection procedures are essentially the same, however (Table 8.24). Emphasis should now be on determination of the feasibility of expansion at an existing location. In addition to physical site location, there are legitimate concerns of adequate space for materials handling, loading dock, parking, toilets, traffic control, office space, cafeteria space, and so on. The adequacy of sewers, power, HVAC, and other utilities must also be assessed. If the new process/product is technically more advanced than current systems, the availability of a trainable labor supply must be assessed as well. The efficiency of in-plant materials distribution is an important factor in siting any addition. Intrinsically inefficient schemes may require entire plant rehabilitation and this cost *must* be included in the cost analysis.

The proposed equipment for many incremental systems may be similar (or identical) to existing equipment and so initial process efficiencies may be relatively high. For modest incremental systems developments, the financial burden can be underwritten by the existing business. If this is done, management must prudently avoid rate-of-return comparisons between the proposed incremental operation and the current business. The financial status of

TABLE 8.24 INFORMATION COLLECTION PROCEDURE INCREMENTAL OPERA-
TION

1. Determine Market Size, Share, Elasticity
2. Determine Characteristics of Product (Material, Design Parameters)
3. Determine Cycle Times, Scrap Level
4. Material Specifications, Regrind Useage, Material Costs
5. Development of Process/Equipment, Cost, Delivery
6. Assessment of Current Warehouse/Dock/Parking/Office Space Utilization
7. Labor Requirements
8. Power Requirements
9. Cost of Plant Addition/Refurbishing
10. Management Consideration of Incremental SAR

all efforts, including new efforts, should *always* be assessed against the best available risk-free ventures (and *not* against continuing in-house operations).

An example of an incremental operation illustrates those elements of an isolated venture that can be altered to fit. Consider the addition of a camper top production line to an operation currently producing shower stalls, soaking tubs and wading pools (3). Current ancillary real property is assumed adequate, but a 3700 m^2 [40,000 ft^2] cement block building is needed for the production equipment. The thermoformer and trimming equipment are identical to existing equipment (except with improved processing controls). The PMMA/ABS coextruded sheet is to be backed with sprayed-up fiberglass-reinforced polyester resin (FRP), a process new to the corporation. Start-up is assumed to be instantaneous (after equipment delivery and installation). Start-up costs are expected to increase the working capital costs by only 10% the first year. Working capital costs are considered to be twice the net accounts (receivables minus payables). From experience, the net accounts run about 30% of the annual raw material costs (Tables 8.25 to 8.27).

Six good camper tops an hour are to be produced on a two-shift operation ($6 \times 2000 \times 2 = 24,000$ units/yr). Production efficiency is expected to be 95%. Shift labor is estimated at 20 direct (including maintenance) and 20 indirect, each at $7/h and $2/h benefits. The unit cost of producing a camper top is $429.63 the first year and $421.63 every year thereafter. Assume the unit cost is constant at $425. All 24,000 can be sold at $475 each. A discounted cash-flow rate-of-return i = 24.8% is achieved if NPW = 0 in 5 years and i = 37.1% if NPW = 0 in 10 years (Table 8.28).

TABLE 8.25 FIXED CAPITAL COST THERMOFORMED CAMPER TOP
(Equipment Has Zero Value After Depreciation)

Item	Capital Cost, M$	SL Depreciation, M$		Salvage M$
		5 yr	10 yr	
Shuttle Thermoformer-Two-Station	270			
FRP Spray-Up Equipment	130			
Ovens, Saws	80			
Ancillary Equipment	60			
Contingency	60			
	600	120	60	-0-
Building: 40000 ft^2 × $20/ft^2	800	160	120	400
	1400	200	100	400

TABLE 8.26 THERMOFORMED SHEET MATERIAL COST CAMPER TOP

Part Dimensions: $1270 \times 2540 \times 508$ mm (dp.) [$50 \times 100 \times 20$ in (dp)]

Part Thickness: PMMA/ABS   2.03 mm   [0.080 in]

              FRP   4.5 mm   [0.175 in]

Draw Ratio:

$$\frac{((1270 \times 2540) + 2 \times (1270 \times 508) + 2 \times (2540 \times 508))}{(1270 \times 2540)} = 2.2$$

Initial Thermoplastic Sheet Thickness: 4.5 mm   [0.175 in]

Part Weight:

PMMA/ABS:	1.2 (sp.gr.) $\times 127 \times 254 \times 0.45$	= 17.4 kg	[38.0 1b]
FRP:	1.2 (sp.gr.) $\times 2.2 \times 127 \times 254 \times 0.45$	= 38.3 kg	[84.3 1b]
	Unit Weight	= 55.7 kg	[122.3 1b]

Scrap (Zero Scrap Value):

PMMA/ABS:	(40%)	17.4×0.4	= 7.0 kg	[15.0 1b]
FRP:	(30%)	38.3×0.3	= 11.5 kg	[25.3 1b]
		Scrap Weight	= 18.5 kg	[40.3 kg]

Total Weight of Material:

PMMA/ABS:	= 24.4 kg	[53.0 1b]
FRP:	= 49.8 kg	[109.6 1b]
	Total Weight	= 74.2 kg	[162.6 1b]

Sheet Material Cost:

PMMA/ABS	($ 4/kg)	$24.4 \times \$ 4$	= $ 97.60
FRP:	($ 1.10/kg)	$49.8 \times \$ 1.10$	= $ 54.78
	Cost		= $ 152.38

Material Cost per Good Unit (Assumes All Hardware Recoverable):

            $ 152.38/0.95   = $ 160.40

Ancillary Materials Cost:

   Aluminum Trim, Metal Rails,

   Window Assemblies, Hardware,

   Decoration/Decals (Purchased):   = $ 96.00

Shipping Crate: = $ 10.00

   Product Material Cost: = $ 266.40

TABLE 8.27 MANUFACTURING COSTS THERMOFORMED CAMPER TOP

Item	Year 1	Year 2+
Direct Manufacturing Costs, M$:		
Raw Materials	6394	6394
Labor (inc. Maintenance)	560	560
Utilities	20	20
Other Direct Costs	100	100
	7074	7074
Indirect Manufacturing Costs, M$:		
Labor	560	560
Benefits (All Labor)	320	320
Operating Supplies/Expenses	120	120
Molds	5	5
	1005	1005

(continued on page 255)

TABLE 8.27 MANUFACTURING COSTS THERMOFORMED CAMPER TOP

Item	Year 1	Year 2+
Incremental SAR (10% Labor)	112	112
Incremental Property Taxes, Insurance	10	10
Total Manufacturing Costs, M$:	8 201	8 201
Working Capital, M$:	1918	1918
Start-Up Costs, M$:	192	
Expenses, M$:	10 311	10 119
Expenses, $/Good Unit:	$ 429.63	$ 421.63

TABLE 8.28 NET PRESENT WORTH THERMOFORMED CAMPER TOP INCREMENTAL PRODUCT STUDY

A. 5 Year SL Depreciation

Year	Sales M$	Expenses* M$	Income M$	Deprec-tion, M$	Taxable Income, M$	50% Tax M$	Total Cap. Cost, M$	Cash Flow M$
0	0	0	0	0	0	0	− 1400	− 1400
1–4	11 400	10 200	1200	200	1000	500	0	500
5	11 400	10 200	1200	200	1000	500	400	900

(NPW) Net Present Worth, M$ = 743 (i = 10%)
278 (i = 20%)
− 75 (i = 30%)

NPW = 0 (i = 27.9%)

B. 10 Year SL Depreciation

0	0	0	0	0	0	0	− 1400	− 1400
1–9	11 400	10 200	1200	100	1100	550	0	550
10	11 400	10 200	1200	100	1100	550	400	950

(NPW) Net Present Worth, M$ = 995 (i = 20%)
= 329 (i = 30%)
= − 59 (i = 40%)

NPW = 0 (i = 38.5%)

* Start-Up Expenses Averaged Over Total Project Cost

Comparative Process Economics

Thermoforming is a competitive technology. In thin gage, it competes with paper, paperboard, paper pulp, aluminum and roll-sheet steel and with plastics extrusion, stretch-blow molding and injection-blow molding. In heavy gage, it competes with plastics rotational molding, injection molding, blow molding, fiberglass-reinforced polyester resin (FRP) spray-up and lay-up, sheet molding compounds (SMC) and bulk molding compounds (BMC), and sheet metal forming and die casting. In certain areas, such as equipment cabinets, boxes, and containers, thermoforming competes directly with injection molding, blow molding and rotational molding. The comparative characteristics of these processes are giv-

TABLE 8.29 GENERAL CHARACTERISTICS OF COMPARATIVE PLASTICS PRO-
CESSES (From (3), by Permission of Marcel Dekker, Inc)

Characteristics	Thermo-forming	Injection Molding	Blow Molding	Rotational Molding
Resin Form	Sheet	Pellets	Pellets	Powder
Variety of Material	Good	Excellent	Very Good	Fair
Material Cost	Price Includes Extrusion to Sheet	Standard	Standard	Price Includes Grinding
Types of Materials	Low Rubber Content	All	Somewhat Restricted	Very Restricted
Scrap Reuse	Economically Required	Immediate	Immediate	No Thermal Sensitive Materials
Color	Colored Sheet	Concentrates	Concentrates	Dry Blend
Processibility of Thermally Sensitive Materials	Controllable	Moderate	Difficult	Very Difficult
Thermoset Materials	SMC, PUR, foams	Difficult	Not Feasible	Possible
Variety of Mold Materials	Very Many	Very Limited	Very Limited	Many
Cost of Molds	Lowest	Highest	High	Moderate to High
Mold Maker Reliability	Fair	Excellent	Fair to Good	Poor to Fair
Mold Closure	Rim Clamp	Butt	Butt	Tongue/Groove
Nonferrous Tooling	Excellent	Limited	Limited	Good
Method of Hold	Mechanical Vacuum	Hydraulic Mechanical	Mechanical	Mechanical
Thermal Cycling	Gentle	Moderate	Moderate	Severe
Major Trial/Error Problems	Corner Draw-down	Gating/Weld Lines	Pinchoff/wall uniformity	Wall Uniformity
Cooling Method	Air Jets	Mold Core	Mold Core/Air	Water Quench
Part Release	Air	Ejector Pins	Push Pins/Air	Manual/Air
Life of Molds, 1000 Parts	10-100	1000-100000	100-1000	10
Operating Pressure, atm	$-1-5$	100-1000	5-50	0
Operating Temperature, C	RT-200	150-300	100-250	200-350
Controlling Portion of Cycle	Heating/Cooling	Cooling	Blowing	Heating
Skill of Operator	Low	Moderate	High	Low
Man/Machine Interaction	Normally High	Nil	Low	Very High
Filling Methods	Manual/Semi-automatic	Automatic	Automatic	Manual
Part Removal	Manual/Semi-automatic	Automatic	Automatic	Manual

(continued on page 257)

TABLE 8.29 GENERAL CHARACTERISTICS OF COMPARATIVE PLASTICS PRO-
CESSES (From (3), by Permission of Marcel Dekker, Inc)

Characteristics	Thermo-forming	Injection Molding	Blow Molding	Rotational Molding
Part Wall Uniformity	Fair to good	Excellent	Good to Very Good	Fair
Flash	Highest	Low	Moderate to High	Fair
Inserts	Questionable	Feasible/ Costly	Questionable	Feasible
Material Orientation	Biaxially Oriented	Oriented	Uniaxially/ Biaxially Oriented	Unoriented
Stress Retention	High	Highest	High	Little
Method of Controlling Distortion, Warp	Heating	Pressure	Cooling	Air/Water Cooling
Method of Forming Closed Part	Welding/Two-Sheet Forming	Welding	Intrinsic	Intrinsic
Primary Mechanical Part Failure	Thin Corners	Weld Line	Thin Side Walls	Poor Tensile Strength
Surface Finish	Excellent	Excellent	Very Good	Good

en in Table 8.29 (3). Generally, when compared with these processes, thermoforming is characterized as having higher raw material costs and scrap losses and lower equipment and mold costs.

Two decades ago, a major study (8) compared conversion costs for fabricating a $300 \times 300 \times 300 \times 3.2$ mm [$12 \times 12 \times 12 \times 0.125$ in] five-sided box of LDPE. Four processes were compared – thermoforming, injection molding, blow molding and rotational molding. Thermoforming was most economical for the production of relatively few units, owing to its low capital and mold costs. Injection molding was most economical at high production rates owing to lower material and labor costs. Although the absolute values are outdated, the analysis can be repeated using typical machine hour costs (Tables 8.30 through 8.33) and the scale factors from the earlier study, developed here as power-law. The machine hour costs are assumed to be applicable at 0.1 MM units/yr. Process cycle times, scrap percentages, and processing efficiencies are estimated from typical processing texts (3, 9), as are mold, material and finishing costs. The comparative processing costs indicate that thermoforming and rotational molding manufacturing costs are lowest at low volume and (2–up) blow molding is most economical at high volume (Table 8.34 and Figure 8.12). Material cost is a significant factor in the unit price sensitivity of both injection molding and blow molding. The high machine hour cost scale factor for thermoforming (from the earlier analysis (8)) is the primary cause for its relatively flat unit price curve. This may be a reflection of the 1960's intensive labor burden on thermoforming. Nevertheless, even at a more-modern machine hour cost scale factor, the inherently higher raw material cost eventually would eliminate thermoforming as a competitive process (see dashed line in Figure 8.12 for $n = 0.5$). It should be noted that the part analyzed (a 5 draw ratio cube from 16 mm [0.625 in] sheet) is not an ideal part for thermoforming. A similar analysis comparing thermoforming and injection molding manufacturing costs for, say, thin-wall drink cups would be expected to show lower thermoforming costs at any production rate.

TABLE 8.30 PLASTIC PROCESS SCALE FACTORS [From A. D. Little – See (8)]
Cost, $ = A (Units, 1000 s)^n

Process	Mfg. Cost n	Mold Cost n	Mat'l Cost n	A*
Thermoforming	0.89 (0.50)	0.41	− 0.14	3.925
Injection Molding	0.53	0.45	− 0.40	8.202
Blow Molding	0.45	0.22	− 0.51	14.45
Rotational Molding	0.34	0.73	− 0.11	2.689

* Values based on 1985 materials costs.

TABLE 8.31 TYPICAL MACHINE HOUR COSTS PLASTICS PROCESSING – 1985
[Updated and Supplemented from Graf (2)]

Process	Range, $/h	Average, $/h
Compression Molding (< 200 T)	45– 80	50
Injection Molding (< 150 T)	60–110	75
Extrusion (3-in Extruder)	20– 40	35
Rotational Molding (Rotary)	20– 60	30
Thermoforming (Shuttle)	30– 65	40
Blow Molding (Extrusion – Gallon Bottle)	50– 70	55

TABLE 8.32 MACHINE HOUR COSTS FOR COMPARATIVE PROCESS ANALYSIS
FIVE-SIDED BOX (For 100 000 Units)

Process	Cycle Time, Min	Parts/h	Total h, 100% Efficiency	Overall* Efficiency %	Actual H	Machine Hour Cost, $/h	Total Machine Hour Cost, M$
TF (2-up)	7	17	5880	85	6920	40	277
IM (1-up)	3	20	5000	90	5560	75	417
BM (1-up)	4	15	6670	85	7850	55	432
RM (2-up)	10	12	8330	75	11110	30	333

* Combined machine/labor efficiency.

TABLE 8.33 MATERIAL COSTS COMPARATIVE PLASTICS PROCESSES FIVE
SIDED BOX (Part weighs 1.36 kg [3 lb])

Process	Scrap, %	Gross Mat'l Wt, kg [lb]	Mat'l Form	Mat'l Cost $/kg [$/lb]*	M$**
TF	25%	1.70 [3.75]	Sheet	1.21 [0.55]	206
IM	8%	1.47 [3.24]	Pellets	0.88 [0.40]	130
BM	15%	1.57 [3.45]	Pellets	0.88 [0.40]	138
RM	20%***	1.64 [3.60]	Powder	1.00 [0.45]	162

*   Includes scrap recovery value.
**   For 100 000 units.
***Includes center section of 2-up forming.

TABLE 8.34 COMPARATIVE PROCESS COSTS – FIVE SIDED BOX
$300 \times 300 \times 300 \times 3,2$ mm [$12 \times 12 \times 12 \times 0.125$ in]

Process	Machine Hour Cost, M$, per 1000 Units			Material Cost, M$, * 1000 Units			Finishing Costs, M$, 1000 Units			Mold Cost, M$, 1000 Units			Total Mfg Cost, 1000 Units, M$ ($/Unit)		
	100	300	1000	100	300	1000	100	300	1000	100	300	1000	100	300	1000
TF	277	736	2150	206	530	1492	17	33	68	12	19	31	512/5.12	1318/4.39	3471/3.74
IM	417	746	1413	130	251	518	–	–	–	50	82	141	597/5.97	1079/3.59	2072/2.07
BM	432	708	1218	138	236	426	33	64	131	25	32	42	628/6.28	1040/3.46	1817/1.82
RM	333	484	729	162	431	1258	33	64	131	10	22	54	538/5.38	1001/3.33	2172/2.17
TF-Modern	277	480	876	206	530	1492	17	33	68	12	19	31	512/5.12	1062/3.54	2467/2.47

* See Table 8.33

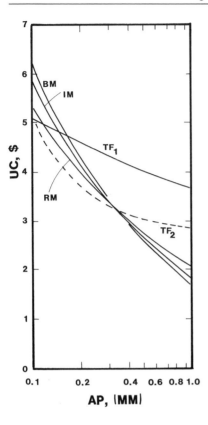

Figure 8.12 Comparative Process Costs. Five-Sided Box, $300 \times 300 \times 300 \times 3.2$ mm [$12 \times 12 \times 12 \times$ 0.125 in]. AP: Annual Production (MM Units). UC: Unit Cost, $/Unit. BM: Blow Molding. IM: Injection Molding. RM: Rotational Molding. TF1: Thermoforming, $n = 0.89$. TF2: Thermoforming, $n = 0.50$. See (8) for additional details.

References

1. A Typical Standard is *Procurement and Supply Form SP-101*, Chrysler Corporation, P.O. Box 2866, Detroit MI 48288.
2. G.L. Graf, Jr., "Applied Economics", in E. Baer, Ed., *Engineering Design for Plastics*, Reinhold, 1964, pg. 1146.
3. J.L. Throne, *Plastics Process Engineering*, Marcel Dekker, 1979, pp. 850–859.
4. W.D. Baasel, *Preliminary Chemical Engineering Plant Design*, Elsevier, 1976, Chapter 1. See also, F.A. Holland, F.A. Watson and J.K. Wilkinson, *Introduction to Process Economics*, John Wiley & Sons, 1983.
5. F.A. Holland, F.A. Watson, and J.M. Wilkinson, "Process Economics", in R.H. Perry, D.W. Green, and J.O. Maloney, Eds., *Perry's Chemical Engineers' Handbook*, 6th Ed., McGraw-Hill, 1984, Section 25.
6. J.L. Throne, "Thermoforming Crystallizing PET", SPE Tech. Papers *27*, 1981, pg. 598.
7. H.E. Mills, "Costs of Process Equipment", in H. Popper, Ed., *Modern Cost-Engineering Techniques*, McGraw-Hill, 1967, pg. 111.
8. A.D. Little, Boston MA, 1966. This report was detailed in J.L. Throne, *Plastics Process Engineering*, Marcel Dekker, 1979, pp. 853–854.
9. Z. Tadmor, C.G. Gogos, *Principles of Polymer Processing*, John Wiley & Sons, 1979, pp. 11–22.

Appendix A

Typical Conversion Factors Used in Thermoforming
(US Customary to European Customary Metric)

European Metric	Multiply by	to Get US Units	Multiply by	To Get European Metric
kg_f	$\times 0.454$	$= lb_f$	$\times 2.2$	$= kg_f$
Newton (N)	$\times 0.225$	$= lb_f$	$\times 4.448$	$=$ Newton (N)
cm/s	$\times 118.1$	$= ft/h$	$\times 0.00847$	$=$ cm/s
cm^2/s	$\times 3.875$	$= ft^2/h$	$\times 0.258$	$= cm^2/s$
g/cm^3	$\times 62.4$	$= lb_m/ft^3$	$\times 0.016$	$= g/cm^3$
l/min	$\times 0.0353$	$= ft^3/min$ (CFM)	$\times 28.32$	$=$ l/min
atm	$\times 14.696$	$= lb_f/in^2$ (psi)	$\times 0.068$	$=$ atm
Pascals (Pa)	$\times 1.45 \times 10^{-4}$	$= lb_f/in^2$ (psi)	$\times 6895$	$=$ Pascal
MN/m^2	$\times 145$	$= lb_f/in^2$ (psi)	$\times 6.895 \times 10^{-3}$	$= MN/m^2$
kW	$\times 3413$	$=$ Btu/h	$\times 2.93 \times 10^{-4}$	$=$ kW
kW/m^2	$\times 317.1$	$= Btu/ft^2$ h	$\times 3.154 \times 10^{-3}$	$= kW/m^2$
W/cm^2	$\times 3171$	$= Btu/ft^2$ h	$\times 3.154 \times 10^{-4}$	$= W/cm^2$
cal/cm^2 s	$\times 13277$	$= Btu/ft^2$ h	$\times 7.54 \times 10^{-5}$	$= cal/cm^2$ s
cal/g °C	$\times 1.00$	$=$ Btu/lb °F	$\times 1.00$	$=$ cal/g °C
W s/kg °C	$\times 2.39 \times 10^{-4}$	$=$ Btu/lb °F	$\times 4184$	$=$ W s/kg °C
J/m	$\times 0.01875$	$=$ ft-lb/in	$\times 53.34$	$=$ J/m
J/m^2	$\times 4.755 \times 10^{-4}$	$=$ ft-lb/in^2	$\times 2103$	$= J/m^2$
kg/m s	$\times 2415$	$=$ lb/ft h	$\times 4.14 \times 10^{-4}$	$=$ kg/m s
$kW/m^2 \mu$ m	$\times 317.4$	$= Btu/ft^2$ h µm	$\times 3.151 \times 10^{-3}$	$= kW/m^2$ µm
kW/m °C	$\times 528$	$=$ Btu/ft h °F	$\times 1.71 \times 10^{-3}$	$=$ kW/m °C
W/cm °C	$\times 57.79$	$=$ Btu/ft h °F	$\times 0.0173$	$=$ W/cm °C
cal/s cm °C	$\times 241.9$	$=$ Btu/ft h °F	$\times 4.134 \times 10^{-3}$	$=$ cal/s cm °C
cal/s cm °C	$\times 2903$	$=$ Btu in/ft h °F	$\times 3.445 \times 10^{-4}$	$=$ cal/s cm °C
cal/s cm^2 °C	$\times 7376$	$= Btu/ft^2$ h °F	$\times 1.356 \times 10^{-4}$	$=$ cal/s cm^2 °C
W/cm^2 °C	$\times 1761$	$= Btu/ft^2$ h °F	$\times 5.68 \times 10^{-4}$	$= W/cm^2$ °C
kW/m^2 °C	$\times 176.1$	$= Btu/ft^2$ h °F	$\times 5.68 \times 10^{-3}$	$= kW/m^2$ °C
Pa s	$\times 1.45 \times 10^{-4}$	$= lb_f$ s/in^2	$\times 6895$	$=$ Pa s

Other Notation
$M = 1 \times 10^6$ except $M = 1 \times 10^3$ for tonnage and for US$
$k = 1 \times 10^3$
$\mu m = 1 \times 10^{-6}$
$G = 1 \times 10^9$

Appendix B

List of Symbols
(TX.XX is Table Number. FX.XX is Figure Number.)

Symbol	Definition	Page
a	Coefficient in energy equation	69
a	Absorptivity	74
a	Time constant of heater	84
a	Coefficient in equilibration expression	92
a	Absorptance	92
a	Disk radius	110
a	Crack length	140
a	Part dimension	194
a	Sheet radius	208
a	Cone radius	217
a	Geometric factor	T7.12
a	Rate of crack propagation	141
A	Area perpendicular to energy direction	68
A	Preexponential term	115
A	Mold surface area	121
A	Melting fluid film parameter	146
A	Cross-sectional contact area of the mold	168
A	Geometric constant	212
A	Exponent in expenses equation	250
A_c	Area of cap	199
A_t	Material property	141
A'	Cross-sectional area	197
b	Coefficient in equilibration expression	91
b	Sheet width	115
b	Sheet thickness	135
b	Part dimension	194
b	Plug radius	208
b	Geometric factor	T7.12
b	Coefficient in expenses equation	250
b_c	Chip width	F5.10
b'	Sheet width – 1 sag band	116
b''	Sheet width – 2 sag bands	116
B	Wheel thickness	137
B	Bulk modulus	138
B	Melting solid film parameter	146
B	Geometric constant	212
B	Locus of tangent points, plug assist	F7.20
Bi	Biot Number, ratio of convection to conduction resistance at sheet surface	88
BIR	Built-in risk	252
BV	Book value	238
c	Coefficient in equilibration expression	92
c	Frictional coefficient, kinetic	168
c	Part dimension	194
c	Geometric factor	T7.12
c_p	Heat capacity at constant pressure	52
C	Cumulative conductance of vacuum system	32

ie	Effective discounted cash-flow rate of return	244
I	Gross income	T8.14
I	Average inflation rate	244
IR	Infrared	57
J	Creep compliance	105
J_0	Initial creep compliance	106
k	Thermal conductivity	55
k	Coolant thermal conductivity	127
k	Correction factor, corner draw-down	T7.12
k_m	Thermal conductivity of mold material	127
K	Avrami coefficient	45
K	Heater proportionality factor	81
K	Cost of first unit	233
K	Total capital cost	T8.14
K_c	Fracture toughness	140
L	Pipe length	33
L	Sheet half-thickness	66
L	Length of aluminum plate	76
L	Length of coolant channel	127
L	Sheet thickness	123
L	Local element	210
Le	Equivalent length for elbows, constrictions	33
LCC	Learning curve characteristic	234
m	Mass of aluminum plate	76
m	Strain-hardening factor	101
m	Exponent in strain-hardening model	102
m	Material property	141
m	Plastic melting rate	146
M	Gas molecular weight	33
M	Number of payment years	239
M_i	Molecular weight of polymer chain of length i	43
M_r	Mechanical property of regrind	63
M_m	Mechanical property of mixture	63
M_n	Number-average molecular weight	43
M_0	Virgin material property	61
M_{pN}	Material property after N passes	61
$M_{p\infty}$	Material property after infinite passes	62
M_w	Weight-average molecular weight	43
MAR	Minimum acceptable risk	251
MC	Machine hour cost	229
[MD]	Machine direction	227
MPR	Maximum production rate	245
MW	Molecular weight	44
MWD	Molecular weight distribution	44
n	Number of constrictions in equivalent pipe diameters	33
n	Number of polymer chains	43
n	Avrami exponent	46
n	Wavenumber	F2.10
n	Index of refraction	92
n	Exponent in strain-hardening model	102
n	Number of teeth on drill	150
n	Power-law coefficient	F7.27
n	Slope of learning curve	233
n	Number of years	238
N	Number of recycle passes	61
N	Normal force acting on membrane	118
N	Number of coolant channels in parallel	127
N	Fraction of cycle time devoted to part removal and indexing	131

$R_{plastic}$	Conduction resistance through plastic	121
R_t	Ratio, center-to-center distance	
	between tubes to tube diameter	F3.11
R_{total}	Total heat transfer resistance	121
Ra	Areal draw ratio	191
Ra_1	Areal draw ratio for cylinder with	
	bottom corner radius	194
Ra*	Reduced areal draw ratio $(=Ra-1)$	191
Ra'	Partial areal draw ratio	192
Ra''	Partial areal draw ratio	192
Re	Reynolds Number	126
RL	Linear draw ratio	194
RL_2	Partial linear draw ratio into corner	195
RL_3	Partial linear draw ratio into corner	195
RL_m	Partial linear draw ratio into corner	195
RL*	Reduced linear draw ratio $(=RL-1)$	154
RL'	Partial linear draw ratio	194
RL''	Partial linear draw ratio	194
RR	Risk rate	251
RT	Room temperature (usually 25 C, 77 F)	65
s	Distance along cone side	110
s	Part height	191
S	Shape factor, conduction	127
S	Drill feed speed	150
S	Stress concentration factor	F7.28
S	Geometric factor	T7.12
S	Scrap value	237
S_f	Cut surface roughness	137
S_0	Evacuation speed	32
S_p	Evacuation speed of vacuum pump	32
SI	Geometric factor	T7.12
SAR	Sales, administration, research	228
SWB	Salaries, wages, benefits	228
t	Transmission coefficient	F2.10
t	Time	45
t	Transmittance	92
t	Thickness of aluminum plate	76
t	Sheet thickness	121
t_a	Average sheet thickness	191
t_{avg}	Average sheet thickness	121
t_c	Sheet thickness in corner	206
t_F	Time to failure, creep rupture	F2.6
t_0	Wavelength-specific transmittance at polymer surface	92
$t_{1/2}$	Half-time for crystallization	F2.4
t*	Thickness when sheet contacts mold surface	200
t'	Thickness in partial, stepped draw-down	203
t_I	Thickness in first step	T7.12
t_{II}	Thickness in second step	T7.12
T	Gas temperature	33
T	Sheet strength	197
T_a	Average sheet temperature	122
T_a*	Time-average sheet temperature	131
T_f	Forming temperature	65
T_f	Equilibrated forming temperature	120
T_g	Glass transition temperature	44
T_h	Heater temperature	76
T_i	Initial sheet temperature	122
T_m	Melting temperature	47

α	Sheet angle during plug penetration	208
β	Angle of membrane above horizontal	118
β	Crack geometry factor	141
β	Vent hole safety factor	167
β	Sheet angle in forming, cone angle	199
γ	Relief angle	F5.10
γ	Surface energy	140
δ	Height above horizontal	110
δ	Air gap	125
δ	Depth of penetration	130
δ	Inflation height	206
δ	Plug penetration depth	208
δl	Differential meridonal length	F4.15
Δ	Factor proportional to ratio of second to first normal stress difference	106
ΔK	Stress intensity factor range	141
ΔP	Pressure drop	32
ΔT	Temperature difference	68
Δx	Differential thickness	68
Δε	Differential change in elongation	114
Δη	Volumetric change by dilatometry	45
$\Delta\eta_\infty$	Volumetric change after infinite time	45
ε	Elongation or strain	F2.7
ε	Emissivity	74
ε	True strain (deformation per unit length)	101
ε_b	Elongation at burst	114
ε_f	True strain at fracture	102
ε_h	Emissivity of heater	76
ε_i	Strain in direction i	101
ε_s	Emissivity of sheet	76
ε_1	Source emissivity	83
ε_2	Sink emissivity	83
$\dot{\varepsilon}$	Rate of strain (deformation rate)	107
$\dot{\varepsilon}_0$	Initial strain rate	106
η	Machinability of plastic	137
η_e	Fluid elongational viscosity	101
η_{Newt}	Newtonian shear viscosity	101
η_0	Zero-shear shear viscosity	107
η_{Trout}	Trouton elongational viscosity	101
θ	Pump-down time	32
θ	Point tooth angle	150
θ_b	Time to burst	114
θ_{draft}	Draft angle	149
θ_r	Time to recover vacuum tank pressure	33
θ_t	Total cycle time	33
θ_1	Fluid relaxation or retardation time	105
θ^*	Time for penetration to depth, δ	130
λ	Wavelength	F2.10
λ	Stress relaxation time	149
λ_h	Extension ratio in sheet thickness direction	110
λ_i	Extension ratio in direction i	107
λ_l	Extension ratio in direction parallel sheet surface	110
λ_{max}	Wavelength at maximum black body energy emission	69
λ_θ	Extension ratio in θ direction	110
μ	Beer's law absorption coefficient	92
μ	Absorption coefficient	F3.19
μ	Newtonian shear viscosity	105
μ	Coolant viscosity	116

ν	Poisson's ratio	101
ξ	Radiant heater efficiency	84
ξ_0	Initial radiant heater efficiency	84
ρ	Gas density	33
ρ	Plastic density	68
ρ	Density of aluminum plate	76
ρ	Coolant density	126
σ	Stress	F2.7
σ	Applied stress	101
σ	Stefan-Boltzmann constant	72
σ_i	Stress in direction i	101
σ_0	Initial stress	101
τ	Tensile strength	168
φ	Fraction of uncrystallized material	45
φ	Cut-off angle	136
φ(T)	Material, design parameter	97
ψ	Material parameter	118
∂_-/∂_-	Partial derivative	68
I	First invariant of Cauchy strain tensor	107
II	Second invariant of Cauchy strain tensor	107
III	Third invariant of Cauchy strain tensor	107
$	Sales	T8.14

Appendix C

Glossary of Thermoforming Terms
(Number in parens refers to page of first reference)

Asperities	Microscopic surface roughness. (125)
Amorphous Polymers	Polymers that exhibit no melting points. (18)
Absorptance	That fraction of radiant energy that is retained by the sheet. (92)
Biaxial Deformation	Stretching in two directions. (preface)
Billow	Prestretching sheet by inflation with air pressure. (24)
Biot Number	A dimensionless ratio of internal to external heat transfer, $Bi = hL/k$. (87)
Black Body	A body that emits the maximum amount of radiant energy at a given wavelength. (71)
Blend	Physical mixing of two or more polymers. (49)
Book Value	Depreciated value of a machine. (238)
Bursting Time	Time to burst a membrane, being biaxially inflated under a known differential pressure. (114)
Cauchy Strain	Tensor functions of the extent of deformation. (107)
Chill Mark	A surface blemish on a formed part. (190)
Computer-Aided Design (CAD)	Computer design of part wall thickness using geometry or FEM. (213)
Computer-Aided Engineering (CAE)	Computer control of the thermoforming process. (214)
Conduction	Energy transfer by direct solid contact. (67)
Convection	Energy transfer by moving, flowing fluids. (20)
Constrained Deformation	Sheet stretching with a portion in contact with the mold. (98)
Copolymer	Polymer with two sets of monomers, such as HIPS. (49)
Creep Compliance	A function related to retardation time. (105)
Crystalline Polymers	Polymers that exhibit melting points. (18)
Cut Sheet	Usually, heavy gage sheet, fed one at a time to rotary or shuttle thermoformers. (18)
Deformation	Stretching. (97)
Depth of Draw	Also known as draw ratio. (21)
Discounted Cash-Flow Rate-of-Return	Profitability index or true rate-of-return. (240)
Draw Ratio	A gross measure of the extent of sheet stretching. (21)
Draw Ratio	A measure of the area or thickness of the sheet after being formed into a mold to that before. (175)
Effective Discounted Cash-Flow Rate-of-Return	The discounted cash-flow rate-of-return adjusted for inflation. (244)
Elastic Liquid	A material that has both fluid and solid characteristics. (105)
Enthalpy	A thermodynamic measure of the intrinsic heat content of a material. (66)
Entrepreneurial Risk Factor	The additional cost of a speculative venture. (251)
Equilibration	Allowing a sheet to reach uniform temperature after the heating source is removed. (91)
Eversion	Transfer of a bubble shape from above a horizontal plane to below. (206)
Finite Element Method (FEM)	A computer technique for predicting how a sheet of plastic deforms under load. (210)
Fourier Number	A dimensionless time, $Fo = \alpha\theta/L^2$. (88)

Fracture Toughness	A measure of the stress intensity at a crack tip needed to propagate a sustained fracture. (140)
Free Surface	The sheet surface *not* in contact with the mold surface. (preface)
Galerkin Weighted Residual Method	A common numerical method for including boundaries in FEM problems. (211)
Gels	Hard resinous particles in sheet. (224)
Glass Transition Temperature	The temperature (range) above which a brittle (tough) polymer becomes rubbery. (44)
Global Cost	Overall cost of a business. (226)
Grey Body	A body emitting a fixed fraction of the maximum amount of energy, regardless of the wavelength. (74)
Grey Body Correction Factor	In net radiant energy interchange, the factor that accounts for energy interchange that is lower than black body interchange. (76)
Heat Flux	The energy incident on a surface element per unit time (W/in^2) $[Btu/ft^2 \cdot h]$. (68)
Heat Transfer Coefficient	A measure of the effectiveness of energy transport between a flowing fluid and the solid surface. A.k.a. *convection* heat transfer coefficient. (68)
Heavy-Gage	Commonly, sheet having thickness greater than 1.5 mm [0.060 in]. (18)
Homopolymer	Polymer with a single set of monomers, such as PS. (49)
Hot Creep Test	Application of a constant uniaxial load to a tensile strip of plastic that has been heated above its glass transition temperature. (100)
Index	To move a sheet forward a fixed length. (35)
In-Situ Trimming	In rollfed technology, trimming that takes place while the formed sheet is still on the mold surface. (34)
Kirksite	A zinc-based alloy used in prototype or short-run tooling. (165)
Learning Curve	The cost to produce a given part as a function of the number of parts produced. (233)
Lumped-Parameter Model	An approximate mathematical heat transfer model that assumes no thermal gradient across the plastic sheet. (76)
Machine Hour Cost	The cost require to run a machine for one hour, all labor and overhead costs included. (228)
Material Allocation	The theory that material on a given spot on a plastic sheet will *always* appear at a given location on the final part. (215)
Maxwell Fluid	A model fluid comprised of elastic springs and viscous dashpots in series. (105)
Melt Temperature	The temperature (range) above which a crystalline polymer changes from a rubbery solid to a viscoelastic liquid. (44)
Mode III Antiplane Pure Shear	A term describing the nature of nibbling or shear cutting in part trimming. (133)
Mooney Rubbery Solid	A material that follows a simple linear form for the strain energy function. (108)
Newtonian Viscosity	A measure of the linear resistance of a molecularly simple fluid to applied shear. (101)
Node	Junction or intersection, used in Finite Difference Equations or FEM. (211)
NonNewtonian Viscosity	A measure of the resistance of a molecularly complex fluid such as a polymer to applied shear. (101)
Nusselt Number	A dimensionless ratio of convection to conduction heat transfer for flowing fluids. (146)
Orientation	The amount of residual or frozen-in stretch in a plastic sheet (usually in a given direction). (222)
Pattern Heating	The practice of selectively applying gauze or tissue to a sheet (usually heavy-gage) to achieve uniform heating rates. (85)
Peclet Number	A dimensionless product of Reynolds Number and Prandtl Number. (146)

$\varphi(T)$	A material design parameter, related to the rate of change of strain energy with the first principal invariant of the Cauchy strain tensor. (100)
Pin Chains	Chains used to accurately feed rollfed sheet. (30)
Plug	A mechanical device used to aid in sheet stretching prior to total contact with mold. (171)
Poisson's Ratio	A measure of the volumetric change in material while undergoing nonuniform deformation. (101)
Prandtl Number	A dimensionless ratio of fluid physical properties. (146)
Pressure Forming	Commonly, differential pressure in excess of 2 atm [30 psi]. (21)
Price Elasticity	The effect of quantity on unit selling price. (250)
Pseudo-Convection Heat Transfer Coefficient	A measure of the effectiveness of radiant energy interchange between heat source and sink. A.k.a., *radiation* heat transfer coefficient. (69)
Radiation	Electromagnetic energy transfer *or* interchange. (20)
Rate of Return	Ratio of annual profit to invested capital. (240)
Reflectance	The fraction of radiant energy that is reflected at the surface of a sheet. (92)
Replication	Faithful imaging of the mold surface by the hot formed sheet. (97)
Retardation Time	A measure of the ratio of viscous to solid characteristics in a polymer. (105)
Reynolds Number	A dimensionless ratio of inertial to viscous forces, for flowing fluids. (126)
Rollfed	Thin-gage sheet, fed continuously into thermoformer. (18)
Sag Bands	In continuous-sheet thermoformers, metal support bands that run the length of the oven to help minimize sheet sag. (116)
Set Temperature	The temperature below which a part can be removed from the mold without (appreciable) distortion. (52)
Soaking Time	Equilibration time. (91)
Sonic Velocity	The speed of sound, for air exiting a mold cavity through vent holes. (167)
Steady-State	Income equals outgo, with no accumulation. (220)
Stefan-Boltzmann Constant	$(=0.5674 \times 10^{-10} \, kW/m^2 \cdot C^4)$ or $[=0.1714 \times 10^{-8} \, Btu/ft^2 \cdot h \cdot R^4]$. (72)
Strain	Polymer static response to applied stress. (51)
Strain Energy Function	In solid mechanics, the amount of energy that occurs when a polymer is extended under stress. (107)
Strain Rate	The slope of the elongation-time curve. (99)
Stress	Externally applied load per projected area of material. (51)
Surge Tank	The tank between the vacuum pump and the mold, to allow (near-)uniform differential applied pressure to be applied during forming. (189)
Syntactic Foam	A mixture of sintered inorganic foam spheres and plastic (foam) matrix, used in plugs. (171)
Terpolymer	Polymer with three sets of monomers, such as ABS. (49)
Thermal Diffusivity	Used as a material property measure of the rate of energy transmission, $\alpha = k/\rho c_p$. (55)
Thermoplastics	Two-dimensional organic molecules. (39)
Thermosets	Three-dimensional organic molecules. (39)
Thin-Gage	Commonly, sheet thickness less than 0.25 mm [0.010 in]. (18)
Transmittance	The fraction of energy that is transmitted through a polymer sheet. (92)
Trim	That portion of sheet that is not part of the final product. (31)
Trouton Viscosity	A measure of the resistance of a fluid to applied uniaxial stress. (101)
Unconstrained Deformation	Free-form sheet stretching without mold contact. (98)
Uniaxial Deformation	Stretching in one dimension. (Preface)

View Factor	A measure of the fraction of radiant interchange that occurs between primary sources and sinks. (76)
Virgin	Unprocessed. (221)
Watt Density	Heater output (rating). (77)
Wavelength	A measure of the nature of incident electromagnetic radiation. Ultraviolet: 0 to 0.38 μm. Visible: 0.38 to 0.70 μm. Infrared: 0.7 to 3 μm. Far infrared: 3 to 20 μm. (72)
Wavenumber	Reciprocal of wavelength in radiation. (57)
Web	During draw-down, a fold of plastic sheet that cannot be stretched flat against a mold surface. (189)
Yield Point	The polymer stress/strain level below which plastic recovers elastically. (51)
Young's Modulus	The initial stress per unit strain of a polymer under uniaxial tensile load. (99)

Author Index

(TX.XX is Table Number. FX.XX is Figure Number)

T. Alfrey, Jr.	44, 62, 105, 117
R. Allard	113, 117, 211, 212, 216, F7.23
S. Anthony, Jr.	21, 36
R. C. Armstrong	101, 102, 116, F4.6, F4.7
W. D. Baasel	233, 237, 260
E. Baer	149, 154, 225, 260, T8.3, T8.4
S. Bahadur	101, 117, T4.2
M. Bakker	6, 8, 15, 36, F1.1, T1.2
R. L. Baldwin	49, 62
G. Beall	8, 18, 21, 23, 36, 191, 194, 215
W. P. Benjamin	158, 160, 161, 163, 173, T6.4
C. J. Benning	198, 216
N. M. Bikales	48, 62, 63, 142, 147, 154
R. B. Bird	101, 102, 116, F4.6, F4.7
F. Brinken	50, 62, 77, 95, F3.8
A. I. Brown	95, F3.11, F3.13, T3.7
P. F. Bruins	6, 13, 15, 16, 17, 36, 101, 102, 112, 117, F1.1, F4.3, T1.2, T1.3, T4.8
J. A. Brydson	46, 51, 62, 105, 117
R. M. Caddell	154, F5.14
C. M. Campbell	216, T7.1
R. C. Campbell	212, 216
J. F. Carley	105, 110, 117, 191, 215, T4.6
C. Chaney	157, 173, T6.3
H. Chang	168, 174, 197, 215
J. M. Charrier	113, 117, 211, 212, 216, F7.23
E. S. Childs	15, 16, 17, 36, F1.1, T1.2, T1.3
J. Coates	54, 63
R. J. Crawford	191, 200, 202, 203, 216, F7.15
R. A. Daane	168, 174, 197, 215
J. M. Dealy	113, 117
R. D. Deanin	42, 62, F2.3, F2.5, T2.4
R. G. Dempsey	35, 37
R. E. Dempsey	46, 62
C. D. Denson	98, 101, 113, 115, 116, F4.12, F4.14, T4.1
J. H. DuBois	13, 36, T1.1
G. L. F. Ehlers	149, 154
L. Erwin	101, 117
S. E. Farnham	14, 36
J. Frados	39, 62, 69, 95, 151, 154, 208, 209, 216
J. Franey	92, 93, 95
R. E. Fruzzetti	35, 37
J. M. Funt	101, 105, 107, 109, 117, T4.5, T4.6
R. J. Gallo	101, 113, 116
D. S. Garrett	212, 216, F7.25
R. J. Gartland	35, 37
W. L. Gheen	191, 196, 215
A. Ghosh	113, 117, 211, 212, 216, F7.23
C. G. Gogos	54, 63, 101, 116, 149, 154, 257, 260
H. Gonzolez	101, 117
T. R. Goodman	130, 154
G. L. Graf, Jr.	225, 260, T8.4, T8.31
D. W. Green	242, 260, F8.7, F8.8
O. M. Griffin	146, 154
R. G. Griskey	54, 62, T2.6

Subject Index

(T. X is Table Number, F. X is Figure Number, A. X is Appendix Number)

Biography

James L. Throne is an Engineering Consultant specializing in advanced plastics processing and technology transfer. He has a BS (Honors) degree from Case Institute of Technology and MChE and PhD degrees in chemical engineering from University of Delaware. He has taught plastics processing at Ohio University and University of Wisconsin (Milwaukee) and has worked in processing research at duPont, American Standard, Beloit Corporation and recently as Research Associate, Plastic Products Division, Amoco Chemicals Corporation. He has coauthored nearly 200 papers in plastics processing and is the author of *Plastics Process Engineering,* Marcel Dekker, 1979. He is Fellow of the Plastics and Rubber Institute and the Society of Plastics Engineers and a member of Society of Rheology and Polymer Processing Society. He is a Professional Member of the Society of Plastics Industry.